Grade K NCTM Focal Points Alignment

Math Triumphs, Grade K provides the prerequisite concepts and skills necessary for success with the Grade K NCTM Focal Points. Horizontal alignment ensures successful transitions between *Math Connects* and *Math Triumphs.*

Preparation for NCTM Grade K Focal Points	*Math Triumphs,* Grade K	Targeted Prerequisite Skills and Concepts	Preparation for *Math Connects,* Grade K
Focal Point 1 Number and Operations *Math Triumphs* Section 1	**Chapter 1** Represent Whole Numbers	Count verbally to 10.	Chapter 2 Chapter 4 Chapter 6 Chapter 8
		Count structured arrangements of objects to 10.	
	Chapter 2 Compare and Order Whole Numbers	Make accurate comparisons via counting, but only when objects are about the same size and groups are small.	Chapter 2 Chapter 4 Chapter 6 Chapter 8
	Chapter 3 Introduction to Addition	Find sums for joining sets up to sums of 9 by counting with objects.	Chapter 11
	Chapter 4 Introduction to Subtraction	Find differences for separating sets with subtrahends up to 9 by counting with all objects.	Chapter 12
Focal Point 2 Geometry *Math Triumphs* Section 2	**Chapter 5** Two-Dimensional Figures	Recognize and name the basic shapes, such as circle, square, triangle, and rectangle.	Chapter 10
	Chapter 6 Three-Dimensional Figures	Relate plane and solid figures.	Chapter 10
	Chapter 7 Space and Position	Describe the relative position of objects using appropriate vocabulary terms.	Chapter 3 Chapter 10
		Recognize and identify a shape after a simple turn or translation.	
Focal Point 3 Measurement *Math Triumphs* Section 3	**Chapter 8** Sort Objects by Attributes	Identify objects and sets of objects by amount, size, shape, or color.	Chapter 1 Chapter 5
	Chapter 9 Order Objects by Attributes	Identify objects by size, shape, or color.	Chapter 1 Chapter 7
	Chapter 10 Patterns	Identify and duplicate a simple pattern.	Chapter 3 Chapter 9

For a complete correlation to the NCTM Curriculum Focal Points, go to www.macmillanmh.com and select **Math,** then **Teacher View.** The complete Curriculum Focal Points may be viewed at www.nctm.org/focalpoints.

NCTM Focal Points

NCTM Focal Points	Preparation in *Math Triumphs*, Grade K
Number and Operations and **Algebra** (GK-FP1) **Representing, comparing, and ordering whole numbers and joining and separating sets** Children use numbers, including written numerals, to represent quantities and to solve quantitative problems, such as counting objects in a set, creating a set with a given number of objects, comparing and ordering sets or numerals by using both cardinal and ordinal meanings, and modeling simple joining and separating situations with objects. They choose, combine, and apply effective strategies for answering quantitative questions, including quickly recognizing the number in a small set, counting and producing sets of given sizes, counting the number in combined sets, and counting backward.	**Chapter 1: Represent Whole Numbers** **Chapter 2: Compare and Order Whole Numbers** **Chapter 3: Introduction to Addition** **Chapter 4: Introduction to Subtraction**
Geometry (GK-FP2) **Describing shapes and space** Children interpret the physical world with geometric ideas (e.g., shape, orientation, spatial relations) and describe it with corresponding vocabulary. They identify, name, and describe a variety of shapes, such as squares, triangles, circles, rectangles, (regular) hexagons, and (isosceles) trapezoids presented in a variety of ways (e.g., with different sizes or orientations), as well as such three-dimensional shapes as spheres, cubes, and cylinders. They use basic shapes and spatial reasoning to model objects in their environment and to construct more complex shapes.	**Chapter 5: Two-Dimensional Figures** **Chapter 6: Three-Dimensional Figures** **Chapter 7: Space and Position**
Measurement (GK-FP3) **Ordering objects by measurable attributes** Children use measurable attributes, such as length or weight, to solve problems by comparing and ordering objects. They compare the lengths of two objects both directly (by comparing them with each other) and indirectly (by comparing both with a third object), and they order several objects according to length.	**Chapter 8: Sort Objects by Attributes** **Chapter 9: Order Objects by Attributes** **Chapter 10: Patterns**

Focal Points Connections

Focal Points Connections	Preparation in *Math Triumphs*, Grade K
Data Analysis (GK-FP4C) Children sort objects and use one or more attributes to solve problems. For example, they might sort solids that roll easily from those that do not. Or they might collect data and use counting to answer such questions as, "What is our favorite snack?". They re-sort objects by using new attributes (e.g., after sorting solids according to which ones roll, they might re-sort the solids according to which ones stack easily).	**Chapter 2: Compare and Order Whole Numbers** **Chapter 8: Sort Objects by Attributes** **Chapter 9: Order Objects by Attributes**
Geometry (GK-FP5C) Children integrate their understandings of geometry, measurement, and number. For example, they understand, discuss, and create simple navigational directions (e.g., "Walk forward 10 steps, turn right, and walk forward 5 steps").	**Chapter 4: Introduction to Subtraction** **Chapter 5: Two-Dimensional Figures** **Chapter 6: Three-Dimensional Figures** **Chapter 7: Space and Position** **Chapter 10: Patterns**
Algebra (GK-FP6C) Children identify, duplicate, and extend simple number patterns and sequential and growing patterns (e.g., patterns made with shapes) as preparation for creating rules that describe relationships.	**Chapter 2: Compare and Order Whole Numbers** **Chapter 10: Patterns**

For a complete correlation to the NCTM Curriculum Focal Points, go to www.macmillanmh.com and select **Math,** then **Teacher View.** The complete Curriculum Focal Points may be viewed at www.nctm.org/focalpoints.

TEACHER EDITION

Macmillan/McGraw-Hill • Glencoe

K

Math
Triumphs

What is *Math Triumphs*?

- Intensive intervention for students two more years behind grade level.

- Prerequisite Grade K concepts and skill that prepare students for the Grade K NCTM Focal Points.

- Horizontal alignment with Macmillan/McGraw-Hill's *Math Connec* a balanced basal program.

The *McGraw·Hill* Companies

 Macmillan/McGraw-Hill

Send all inquires to:
Macmillan/McGraw-Hill
8787 Orion Place
Columbus, OH 43240-4027

Teacher Edition
ISBN: 978-0-07-888216-6
MHID: 0-07-888216-8

Student Study Guide, Book 1
ISBN: 978-0-07-888193-0
MHID: 0-07-888193-5

Printed in the United States of America.

3 4 5 6 7 8 9 10 055/006 14 13 12 11 10 09

Math Triumphs

Preparation for **Focal Points and Connections**
See front cover folder for key.

Authors and Consultants

CONSULTING AUTHORS

Frances Basich Whitney
Project Director, Mathematics K–12
Santa Cruz County Office of Education
Capitola, California

Kathleen M. Brown
Math Curriculum Staff Developer
Washington Middle School
Long Beach, California

Dixie Dawson
Math Curriculum Leader
Long Beach Unified
Long Beach, California

Philip Gonsalves
Mathematics Coordinator
Alameda County Office of Education
Hayward, California

Robyn Silbey
Math Specialist
Montgomery County Public Schools
Gaithersburg, Maryland

Kathy Vielhaber
Mathematics Consultant
St. Louis, Missouri

CONTRIBUTING AUTHORS

Viken Hovsepian
Professor of Mathematics
Rio Hondo College
Whittier, California

FOLDABLES Study Organizer **Dinah Zike**
Educational Consultant
Dinah-Might Activities, Inc.
San Antonio, Texas

CONSULTANTS

Assessment

Donna M. Kopenski, Ed.D.
Math Coordinator K–5
City Heights Educational Collaborative
San Diego, California

Instructional Planning and Support

Beatrice Luchin
Mathematics Consultant
League City, Texas

ELL Support and Vocabulary

ReLeah Cossett Lent
Author/Educational Consultant
Alford, Florida

Reviewers

Each person reviewed at least two chapters of the Student Study Guide, providing feedback and suggestions for improving the effectiveness of the mathematics instruction.

Dana M. Addis
Teacher Leader
Dearborn Public Schools
Dearborn, MI

Renee M. Blanchard
Elementary Math Facilitator
Erie School District
Erie, PA

Jeanette Collins Cantrell
5th and 6th Grade Math Teacher
W. R. Castle Memorial Elementary
Wittensville, KY

Helen L. Cheek
K-5 Math Specialist
Durham Public Schools
Durham, NC

Mercy Cosper
1st Grade Teacher
Pershing Park Elementary
Killeen, TX

Bonnie H. Ennis
Math Coordinator
Wicomico County Public Schools
Salisbury, MD

Sheila A. Evans
Instructional Support Teacher - Math
Glenmount Elementary/Middle School
Baltimore, MD

Lisa B. Golub
Curriculum Resource Teacher
Millennia Elementary
Orlando, FL

Donna Hagan
Program Specialist - Special Programs
  Department
Weatherford ISD
Weatherford, TX

Russell Hinson
Teacher
Belleview Elementary
Rock Hill, SC

Tania Shepherd Holbrook
Teacher
Central Elementary School
Paintsville, KY

Stephanie J. Howard
3rd Grade Teacher
Preston Smith Elementary
Lubbock, TX

Rhonda T. Inskeep
Math Support Teacher
Stevens Forest Elementary School
Columbia, MD

Albert Gregory Knights
Teacher/4th Grade/Math Lead Teacher
Cornelius Elementary
Houston, TX

Barbara Langley
Math/Science Coach
Poinciana Elementary School
Kissimmee, FL

David Ennis McBroom
Math/Science Facilitator
John Motley Morehead Elementary
Charlotte, NC

Jan Mercer, MA; NBCT
K-5 Math Lab Facilitator
Meadow Woods Elementary
Orlando, FL

Rosalind R. Mohamed
Instructional Support Teacher - Math
Furley Elementary School
Baltimore, MD

Patricia Penafiel
Teacher
Phyllis Miller Elementary
Miami, FL

Lindsey R. Petlak
2nd Grade Instructor
Prairieview Elementary School
Hainesville, IL

Lana A. Prichard
District Math Resource Teacher K-8
Lawrence Co. School District
Louisa, KY

Stacy L. Riggle
3rd Grade Spanish Magnet Teacher
Phillips Elementary
Pittsburgh, PA

Wendy Scheleur
5th Grade Teacher
Piney Orchard Elementary
Odenton, MD

Stacey L. Shapiro
Teacher
Zilker Elementary
Austin, TX

Kim Wilkerson Smith
4th Grade Teacher
Casey Elementary School
Austin, TX

Wyolonda M. Smith, NBCT
4th Grade Teacher
Pilot Elementary School
Greensboro, NC

Kristen M. Stone
3rd Grade Teacher
Tanglewood Elementary
Lumberton, NC

Jamie M. Williams
Math Specialist
New York Mills Union Free School District
New York Mills, NY

Teacher Handbook

Mathematics Teacher Handbook

Table of Contents

Welcome to Macmillan/McGraw-Hill Mathematics

Concepts • Skills • Problem Solving

The only true vertically aligned PreK–12 Mathematics Curriculum

Math Connects offers three dimensions of vertical alignment.

❶ Content Design

Vertical content alignment is a process that ensures you and your students experience an articulated, coherent sequence of content from grade level to grade level. This provides you with the assurance that content is introduced, reinforced, and assessed at appropriate times in the series, eliminating gaps and unnecessary duplication. You are able to target your instruction to student needs because you are not teaching content intended to be covered later or that students have previously mastered.

❷ Instructional Design

Our strong vertical alignment in instructional approach from PreKindergarten through Algebra 2 provides a smooth transition for students from elementary to middle school to high school. Our common vocabulary, technology, manipulatives, lesson planning, and Data-Driven Decision Making reduce the confusion students often encounter when transitioning between grade levels without this built-in articulation.

❸ Visual Design

The student pages of ***Math Connects*** have a consistent visual design from grade to grade. This aids students' transition from elementary school to middle school and from middle school to Algebra 1. Students are more likely to succeed when they are already familiar with how to navigate student pages.

TIER 3 — Intensive Intervention

PreK–2   3–5

TIER 1 — Daily Intervention
TIER 2 — Strategic Intervention

5 Keys to Success

① Backmapping

According to College Board research, about 80% of students who successfully complete Algebra 1 and Geometry by 10th grade attend and succeed in college. (Changing the Odds: Factors Increasing Access to College, 1990) **Math Connects** was conceived and developed by backmapping with the final result in mind—student success in Algebra 1 and beyond.

② Balanced, In-Depth Content

Math Connects was developed to specifically target the skills and topics that give students the most difficulty, such as Problem Solving, in each grade span.

Grades K–2	Grades 3–5
1. Problem Solving	1. Problem Solving
2. Money	2. Fractions
3. Time	3. Measurement
4. Measurement	4. Decimals
5. Fractions	5. Time
6. Computation	6. Algebra
Grades 6–8	**Grades 9–12**
1. Fractions	1. Problem Solving
2. Problem Solving	2. Fractions
3. Measurement	3. Algebra
4. Algebra	4. Geometry
5. Computation	5. Computation
	6. Probability

– K–12 Math Market Analysis Survey, Open Book Publishing, 2006

③ Ongoing Assessment

Math Connects includes diagnostic, formative, and summative assessment; data-driven instruction; intervention options; and performance tracking, as well as remediation, acceleration, and enrichment tools throughout the program.

④ Intervention and Differentiated Instruction

A three-tiered Response To Intervention (RTI) is provided.

TIER 1 Daily Intervention Reteach masters and Alternative Strategy suggestions address concepts from a different modality or learning style.

TIER 2 Strategic Intervention Teachers can use the myriad of intervention tips and ancillary materials, such as the Strategic Intervention Guide (1–5) and Study Guide and Intervention (6–8).

TIER 3 Intensive Intervention For students who are two or more years below grade level, **Math Triumphs** provides step-by-step instruction, vocabulary support, and data-driven decision making to help students succeed.

⑤ Professional Development

Math Connects includes many opportunities for teacher professional development. Additional learning opportunities in various formats—video, online, and on-site instruction—are fully aligned and articulated from Kindergarten through Algebra 2.

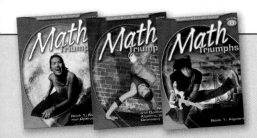

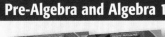

6–8　　　Pre-Algebra and Algebra 1　　　Geometry and Algebra 2

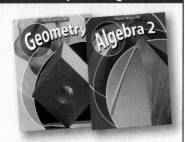

Implementing Intensive Intervention

Data-Driven Intensive Intervention

Ongoing assessment aids the teacher in student placement, progress monitoring, and exit.

Instructional Design

❶ Diagnose and Prescribe
- Course Placement Test
- Online Readiness Quiz
- Chapter Preview
- Chapter Pretest
- Book Pretest

❷ Teach and Practice
- Student Study Guide
- Teacher Edition Strategies
- Vocabulary Cards
- Manipulatives

❸ Advance and Exit
- Assessment Masters
- Chapter Test
- Book Test

Classroom Implementation

Teacher prepares individual or group intervention plan(s).

Teacher modifies instruction based on results of formative assessments.

Test success indicates that a student can progress to another *Math Triumphs* chapter (if needed) or exit the intervention program.

Alignment to NCTM Focal Points

Foundational Skills for Pre-Kindergarten

Preparation for

NCTM Focal Points for Kindergarten*

Macmillan/McGraw-Hill • Glencoe

Math Triumphs

Beginning Skills and Concepts

Focal Point 1 Number and Operations

Focal Point 2 Geometry

Focal Point 3 Measurement

*See front cover folder for key and complete NCTM Focal Points.

Program Organization

Planning for Success

Each *Math Triumphs* chapter in the Teacher Edition begins with important tools to assist teachers in their instructional planning including:

- Chapter-at-a-Glance
- Content-at-a-Glance
- Chapter Assessment Manager
- Chapter Resource Manager
- Chapter Notes

Chapter Overview

Chapter-at-a-Glance allows teachers to preview the lessons and objectives covered in the chapter.

Content-at-a-Glance provides a graphic organizer to enable teachers to see connections between mathematics concepts, skills, and vocabulary covered throughout the chapter.

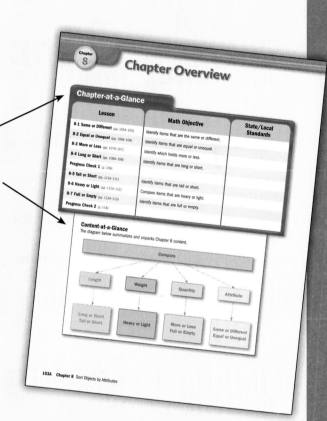

The **Home Connection** letter provides information and activities for each chapter.

Real-World Applications encourages the use of real-world applications of mathematical concepts, skills, and vocabulary covered throughout the chapter.

Key Vocabulary gives the definition and visual examples of the important math vocabulary in the chapter.

Four-Step Teaching Plan

A clear instructional format organizes teachers' instruction as they **Introduce** and **Teach** lessons, and enables students to **Practice** and **Assess** what they have learned.

Key Concept

The Key Concept presents foundational skills and concepts covered in the lesson. Teacher-directed whole-class activities are provided for instruction.

Using Manipulatives

Every lesson includes a hands-on activity using common mathematical classroom manipulatives. These activities provide a concrete, tactile learning opportunity to model the concept.

Additional Strategies

Intervention Strategy and **English Learner Strategy** features provide additional alternative teaching activities for various types of learners. These strategies are linked to the content in the lesson and provide opportunities for assessment.

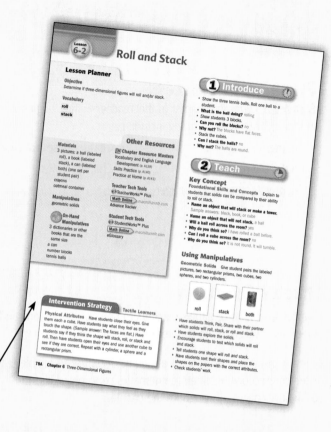

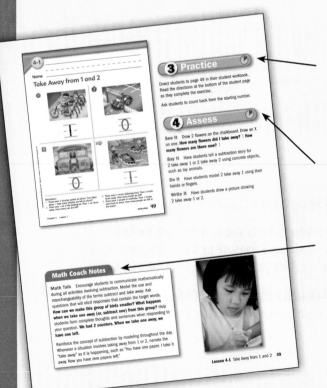

Practice

Additional assistance and suggestions are provided for teachers as they guide students through the practice exercises on the Student Study Guide pages.

Assess

Options for various approaches to assessment are provided for each lesson using the See It, Say It, Do It, Write It strategies.

Math Coach Notes

Important mathematical content, instructional, and classroom management issues are presented in the Math Coach Notes.

Balance

The **Student Study Guide** helps provide a balanced approach to mathematics learning by offering them the opportunity to:

- develop pictorial and abstract concept knowledge;
- investigate concepts and build their conceptual understanding; and
- review, learn, and practice basic computational and procedural skills.

Study Guide Practice

Practice exercises for every lesson provide opportunities to reinforce lesson concepts and skills. They can be used as formative assessment to monitor progress and guide your instruction.

Replay pages allow students to apply their mathematical knowledge in different and engaging ways.

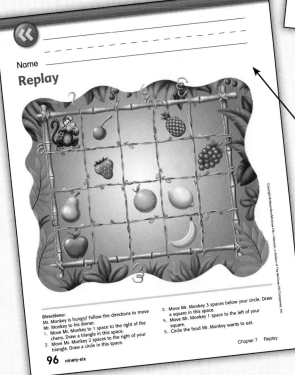

Comprehensive Assessment System

Data-Driven Decision Making

Math Triumphs offers frequent and meaningful assessment of student progress within the curriculum structure and teacher support materials.

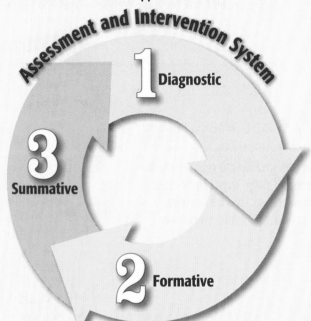

Assessment and Intervention System

1 Diagnostic

2 Formative

3 Summative

1 Diagnostic

Initial Assessment Assess students' knowledge **at the beginning of the year** with the *Diagnostic and Placement Tests*.

Entry–Level Assessment Assess students' prior knowledge **at the beginning of a chapter** with one of the following options.

Student Study Guide
• Get Ready

Teacher Edition
• Vocabulary Preview

Print Resources
• Assessment Masters, Chapter Pretest

Technology Resources
ExamView®
Assessment Suite

Math Online > Online Readiness Quiz

Advance

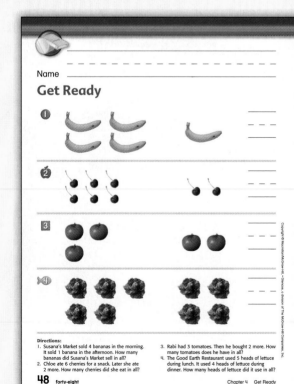

Name

Get Ready

Directions:
1. Susana's Market sold 4 bananas in the morning. It sold 1 banana in the afternoon. How many bananas did Susana's Market sell in all?
2. Chloe ate 6 cherries for a snack. Later she ate 2 more. How many cherries did she eat in all?
3. Rabi had 3 tomatoes. Then he bought 2 more. How many tomatoes does he have in all?
4. The Good Earth Restaurant used 5 heads of lettuce during lunch. It used 4 heads of lettuce during dinner. How many heads of lettuce did it use in all?

48 forty-eight

Chapter 4 Get Ready

Formative

Progress Monitoring Determine if students are progressing adequately as you teach each lesson. Use the assessments to differentiate lesson instruction and practice.

Student Study Guide
- Progress Check
- Study Guide
- Foldables®

Teacher Edition
- Intervention Strategy
- See It, Say It, Do It, Write It
- Data-Driven Decision Making

Print Resources
- Assessment Masters
- Chapter Resource Masters

Technology Resources
ExamView® Assessment Suite

Advance TRACKER

Math Online > My Math Zone

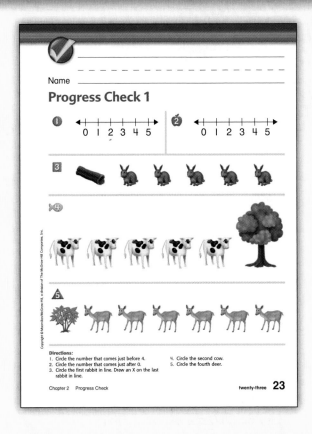

Summative

Summative Evaluation Assess student success in learning the concepts in each chapter.

Student Study Guide
- Chapter Test
- Foldables®

Teacher Edition
- Data-Driven Decision Making

Print Resources
- Assessment Masters
- Chapter Resource Masters

Technology Resources
ExamView® Assessment Suite

Math Online >

Advance TRACKER

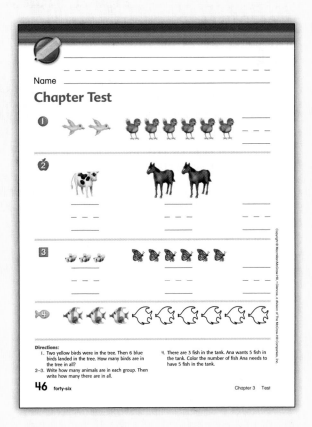

PreK-12 Data-Driven Professional Development

McGraw-Hill Professional Development (MHPD) provides a comprehensive plan for mathematics that is fully aligned and articulated with *Math Connects K–8* and the *Glencoe Mathematics* high school series.

Professional Development Needs	Online Courses	DVD Workshops	Video Library	Teach-Use-Succeed	Ready-Access Math
Has immediate classroom application	✓	✓	✓	✓	✓
Builds content knowledge	✓	✓			✓
Promotes best teaching practices		✓	✓		
Supports new and experienced teachers	✓	✓	✓	✓	✓
Allows customization of courses	✓	✓			✓
Can be self-paced	✓	✓		✓	✓
Adaptable for various timeframes	✓	✓	✓		✓
Is grade-level specific			✓	✓	✓
Promotes a learning community	✓	✓			✓
Provides vertically-aligned content	✓	✓	✓		✓
Helps with RTI (Response to Intervention), Tiers 1–3	✓	✓	✓		✓

Use students' mathematics achievement data to help develop a targeted Professional Development Plan.

Accredited Online Courses

(available for purchase)

- Watch video clips of math classrooms.
- Complete interactive exercises.
- Develop electronic portfolios.
- Complete each 3- to 5-hour online module one segment at a time.
- Earn university credit (additional tuition).

DVD Workshops

- Watch video clips of classroom mathematics lessons and commentaries by leading educators.
- Complete lessons and activities.

MHPD Online

- Access this online Professional Development resource for K–12 educators.
- Link to relevant Web sites.
- Download grade-level student resources.

Video Library Math Online ▷

- Access hundreds of K–12 video clips.
- See clips that illustrate mathematics content and instructional strategies.
- Watch demonstrations or commentaries.

Teach-Use-Succeed Textbook Implementation Modules

- Watch an experienced teacher demonstrate the *Math Connects* K–8 Student Editions, Teacher Editions, and program ancillaries—Online or DVD.

Ready-Access Math, Personalized Professional Development

- Access training materials for nearly 300 lessons.
- Create a customized sequence of professional development sessions.
- Deliver 45–60 minute after-school professional development sessions.

Contents

CHAPTER 1 · Represent Whole Numbers

Preparation for Focal Points and Connections
See front cover folder for key.

Contents

Contents

Contents

Introduction to Subtraction

Preparation for
Focal Points
and Connections
See front cover folder
for key.

Contents

CHAPTER 5 Two-Dimensional Figures

Preparation for Focal Points and Connections
See front cover folder for key.

Contents

Contents

Preparation for Focal Points and Connections
See front cover folder for key.

Contents

Full   Empty

CHAPTER 9 Order Objects by Attributes

Contents

CHAPTER 10 Patterns

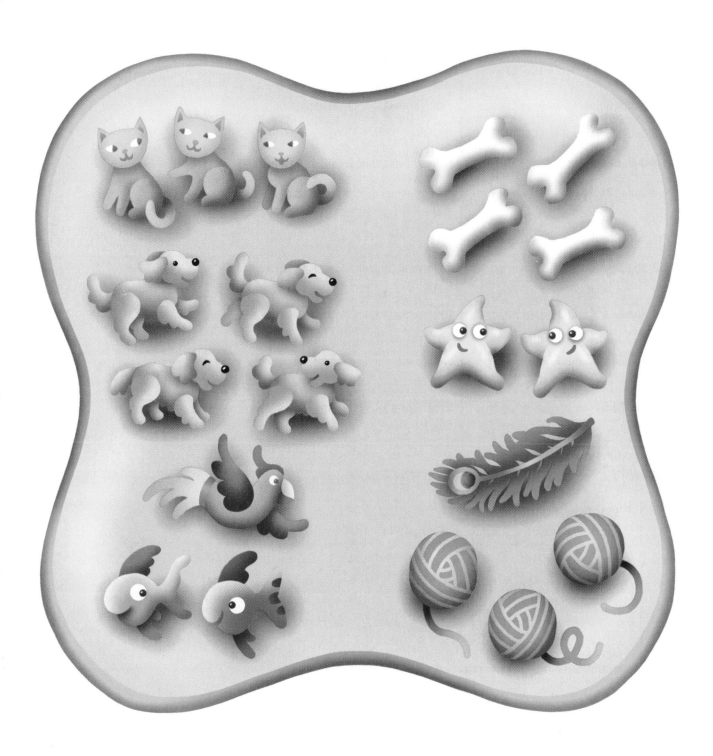

Chapter Overview

Chapter-at-a-Glance

Lesson	Math Objective	State/Local Standards
1-1 Count Objects 0 to 5 (pp. 3A–3)	Count from 0 to 5 by using objects.	
1-2 Count Objects 6 to 10 (pp. 4A–4)	Count from 6 to 10 by using objects.	
1-3 Count Forward (pp. 5A–5)	Count forward from 0 to 5 using a number line.	
1-4 Count Backward (pp. 6A–6)	Count backward from 5 to 0 using a number line.	
Progress Check 1 (p. 7)		
1-5 Numbers 0 and 1 (pp. 9A–9)	Write, represent, and identify the numbers 0 and 1.	
1-6 Numbers 2 and 3 (pp. 10A–10)	Write, represent, and identify the numbers 2 and 3.	
1-7 Numbers 4 and 5 (pp. 11A–11)	Write, represent, and identify the numbers 4 and 5.	
1-8 Numbers 6 to 10 (pp. 12A–12)	Write, represent, and identify the numbers 6 to 10.	
Progress Check 2 (p. 13)		

Content-at-a-Glance

The diagram below summarizes and unpacks Chapter 1 content.

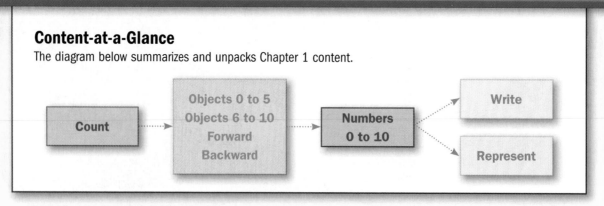

Chapter Assessment Manager

Diagnostic   Diagnose students' readiness.

	Student Study Guide/ Teacher Edition	Assessment Masters	Technology
Intensive Intervention Placement Test		1–4	ExamView® Assessment Suite
Section Pretest (Chapters 1–4)		6–7	ExamView® Assessment Suite
Chapter 1 Pretest		9–10	ExamView® Assessment Suite
Get Ready	SSG 2		Math Online macmillanmh.com StudentWorks™ Plus

Formative   Identify students' misconceptions of content knowledge.

	Student Study Guide/ Teacher Edition	Assessment Masters	Technology
Progress Checks	SSG 7, 13		Math Online macmillanmh.com StudentWorks™ Plus
Vocabulary Review	TE 15		Math Online macmillanmh.com
Lesson Assessments			ExamView® Assessment Suite

Summative   Determine student success in learning the concepts in the lesson, chapter, or section.

	Student Study Guide/ Teacher Edition	Assessment Masters	Technology
Chapter 1 Test	SSG 16	12–13	ExamView® Assessment Suite
Alternative Assessment	TE 16	17–18	ExamView® Assessment Suite
See It, Say It, Do It, Write It	TE 3, 4, 5, 6, 9, 10, 11, 12		
Section Test (Chapters 1–4)		39–40	ExamView® Assessment Suite

Backmapping and Vertical Alignment McGraw-Hill's *Math Triumphs* intervention program was conceived and developed with the final result in mind: student success in grade-level mathematics, including Algebra 1 and beyond. The authors, using the **NCTM Focal Points and Focal Connections** as their guide, developed this brand-new series by backmapping from grade-level and Algebra 1 concepts, and vertically aligning the topics so that they build upon prior skills and concepts and serve as a foundation for future topics.

	Lesson 1-1	**Lesson 1-2**	**Lesson 1-3**	**Lesson 1-4**
Concept	Count Objects 0 to 5	Count Objects 6 to 10	Count Forward	Count Backward
Objective	Count from 0 to 5 by using objects.	Count from 6 to 10 by using objects.	Count forward from 0 to 5 using a number line.	Count backward from 5 to 0 using a number line.
Math Vocabulary	five three four two one zero	eight six nine ten seven	forward number line	backward
Lesson Resources	**Materials** • 5 apples in basket or bag • small paper cups • beans • paper clips • pennies **Manipulatives** • connecting cubes **Other Resources** CRM Vocabulary and English Language Development CRM Skills Practice CRM Practice at Home	**Materials** • classroom-safe balls • note cards with 6–10 geometric shapes • buttons • straws • chalk • pencils • pennies **Manipulatives** • connecting cubes • two-color counters **Other Resources** CRM Vocabulary and English Language Development CRM Skills Practice CRM Practice at Home	**Materials** • beans • picture number line 0–5 • number lines with 6 tick marks • small stickers • paper clips • pennies **Manipulatives** • two-color counters **Other Resources** CRM Vocabulary and English Language Development CRM Skills Practice CRM Practice at Home	**Materials** • poster board • self-stick notes • pennies • paper clips **Manipulatives** • two-color counters • connecting cubes **Other Resources** CRM Vocabulary and English Language Development CRM Skills Practice CRM Practice at Home
Technology	Math Online macmillanmh.com StudentWorks™ Plus ⊙ ExamView® Assessment Suite	Math Online macmillanmh.com StudentWorks™ Plus ⊙ ExamView® Assessment Suite	Math Online macmillanmh.com StudentWorks™ Plus ⊙ ExamView® Assessment Suite	Math Online macmillanmh.com StudentWorks™ Plus ⊙ ExamView® Assessment Suite

Lesson 1-5	Lesson 1-6	Lesson 1-7	Lesson 1-8	
Numbers 0 and 1	Numbers 2 and 3	Numbers 4 and 5	Numbers 6 to 10	**Concept**
Write, represent, and identify the numbers 0 and 1.	Write, represent, and identify the numbers 2 and 3.	Write, represent, and identify the numbers 4 and 5.	Write, represent, and identify the numbers 6 through 10.	**Objective**
one zero	three two	five four group	set	**Math Vocabulary**
Materials • 1 book • 1 crayon • 1 piece of chalk • cardboard shapes: rectangles, squares, triangles, circles	**Materials** • sheets of paper with dotted 2s and 3s for tracing • 3 balls • number 2 and 3 cut out of velvet • paper clips • crayons • pencils • number cards 2 and 3	**Materials** • number cards 4, 5 • patty or tracing paper • puffy or glitter glue • poster board • crayons • pencils • buttons • beans	**Materials** • picture number line with 11 tick marks • number cards 6–10 • patty or tracing paper • paper clips • sets of 6 to 10 objects	**Lesson Resources**
Manipulatives • attribute blocks: circles, rectangles, squares, triangles	**Manipulatives** • connecting cubes	**Manipulatives** • two-color counters	**Manipulatives** • number cubes 6–10 • two-color counters • connecting cubes	
Other Resources **CRM** Vocabulary and English Language Development **CRM** Skills Practice **CRM** Practice at Home	**Other Resources** **CRM** Vocabulary and English Language Development **CRM** Skills Practice **CRM** Practice at Home	**Other Resources** **CRM** Vocabulary and English Language Development **CRM** Skills Practice **CRM** Practice at Home	**Other Resources** **CRM** Vocabulary and English Language Development **CRM** Skills Practice **CRM** Practice at Home	
Math Online macmillanmh.com StudentWorks™ Plus 💿 ExamView® Assessment Suite	**Math Online** macmillanmh.com StudentWorks™ Plus 💿 ExamView® Assessment Suite	**Math Online** macmillanmh.com StudentWorks™ Plus 💿 ExamView® Assessment Suite	**Math Online** macmillanmh.com StudentWorks™ Plus 💿 ExamView® Assessment Suite	**Technology**

Chapter Notes

Home Connection

- Read the Home Connection letter with students and have them write their name in the space below.
- Read and explain the activity under Help at Home. If time allows, complete a portion of the activity so students can introduce the activity to a parent or other caregiver.

Real-World Applications

- Ask five students to stand at the front of the class.
- Assign each student a number, from one to five, and have them stand in order.
- Direct the class to begin counting from one to five. Tell the students to raise their arms high as their number is called.
- Once the class has correctly counted forward, instruct them to count backward from five to one. Again, direct the students to raise their arms as their number is called.
- Divide students into small groups, where they can practice counting from one to five. Monitor their progress.

Math Online

Visit macmillanmh.com for ongoing support of chapter content and instruction, including:
- Online Games
- Concepts in Motion

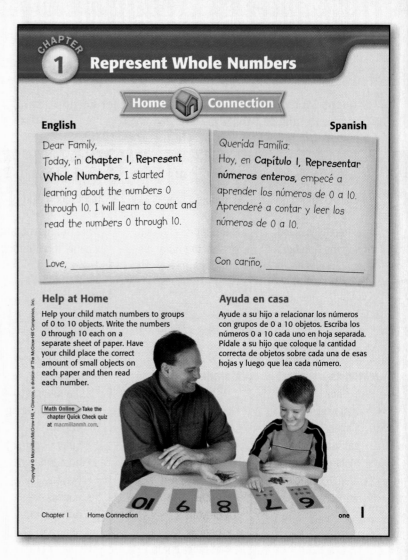

CHAPTER 1 Represent Whole Numbers

Home Connection

English | **Spanish**

Dear Family,
Today, in **Chapter 1, Represent Whole Numbers**, I started learning about the numbers 0 through 10. I will learn to count and read the numbers 0 through 10.

Love, _____

Querida Familia:
Hoy, en **Capítulo 1, Representar números enteros**, empecé a aprender los números de 0 a 10. Aprenderé a contar y leer los números de 0 a 10.

Con cariño, _____

Help at Home
Help your child match numbers to groups of 0 to 10 objects. Write the numbers 0 through 10 each on a separate sheet of paper. Have your child place the correct amount of small objects on each paper and then read each number.

Math Online Take the chapter Quick Check quiz at macmillanmh.com.

Ayuda en casa
Ayude a su hijo a relacionar los números con grupos de 0 a 10 objetos. Escriba los números 0 a 10 cada uno en hoja separada. Pídale a su hijo que coloque la cantidad correcta de objetos sobre cada una de esas hojas y luego que lea cada número.

Chapter 1   Home Connection   **one** 1

Key Vocabulary

Find interactive definitions in 13 languages in the **eGlossary** at macmillanmh.com.

English   Español *Introduce the most important vocabulary terms from Chapter 1.*

backward   hacia atrás
toward the rear; back-to-front (p. 6A)

forward   hacia adelante
toward the front; front-to-back (p. 5A)

number line   linea de números
a line with number labels (p. 5A)

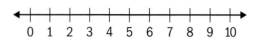

0 1 2 3 4 5 6 7 8 9 10

zero 0   cero 0
the number zero equals none or nothing (p. 3A)

Name _____

Get Ready

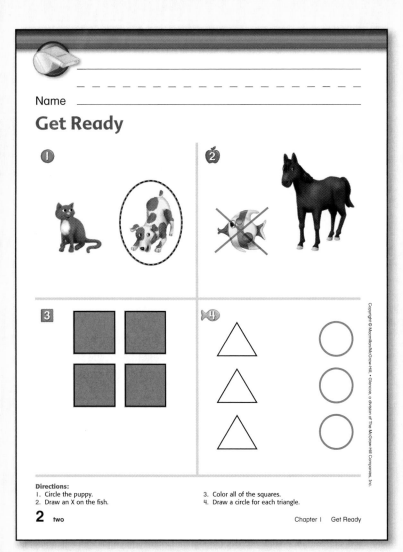

Directions:
1. Circle the puppy.
2. Draw an X on the fish.
3. Color all of the squares.
4. Draw a circle for each triangle.

 **Dinah Zike's Foldables**

Guide students through the directions on p. A1 in the Chapter Resource Masters to create their own Foldable graphic organizer for use with this chapter.

Vocabulary Preview

- Before students begin the chapter, have them make a word wall of important terms throughout the chapter. Refer to Review on page 15 of this text for chapter vocabulary.
- Have students use the key words as well as additional unfamiliar terms throughout the chapter to complete picture definitions.
- Give students index cards with vocabulary words written on one side. Have students draw a picture on the other side to describe the term, completing one index card for each term.

Get Ready

Diagnostic Assessment

Have students complete Get Ready to assess readiness for the chapter concepts and skills.

You may also assess student readiness with the following resources:

    Assessment Masters: Chapter Pretest (pp. 9–10)

    Math Online
    Online Readiness Quiz at macmillanmh.com

Intervention Strategy

Step 1 Have students identify and count certain classroom objects that number between 1 and 10, for example, clocks, erasers, pencil sharpeners, bookshelves, and so on.

Step 2 Have students draw a representation of each item. If there are two clocks, have them draw two clocks. If objects are too difficult to draw, have students draw a circle or square for every item they count.

McGraw Hill **Professional Development**

Targeted professional development has been articulated throughout **McGraw-Hill's Math Triumphs** intervention program. The **McGraw-Hill Professional Development Video Library** provides short videos that support the **NCTM Focal Points and Focal Connections.** For more information, visit macmillanmh.com.

Model Lessons   Instructional Strategies

Count Objects 0 to 5

Lesson Planner

Objective
Count from 0 to 5 by using objects.

Vocabulary

five	**one**	**two**
four	**three**	**zero**

Materials
5 apples in basket or bag
beans
pennies
small paper cups

Manipulatives
connecting cubes, 5 for
each student

On-Hand Manipulatives
paper clips

Other Resources

CRM Chapter Resource Masters
Vocabulary and English Language
 Development (p. A5)
Skills Practice (p. A6)
Practice at Home (p. A7)

Teacher Tech Tools
TeacherWorks™ Plus
Math Online macmillanmh.com
Advance Tracker

Student Tech Tools
StudentWorks™ Plus
Math Online macmillanmh.com
eGlossary

1 Introduce

Show students an empty basket. Ask students how
many apples are in the basket. 0
- Have students count along with you as you add
  5 apples to the basket, one at a time.

2 Teach

Key Concept

Display 6 paper cups, in a line, containing 0 to 5 beans
in random order. Have students count the beans in
each cup. Then help them arrange the cups in order
from 0 to 5.

Using Manipulatives

Connecting Cubes   Give each student
5 connecting cubes.

- Count to 5 aloud with the class. As you say each
  number, have students move a connecting cube
  into a pile.
- Say a number from 0 to 5. Have students connect
  cubes to show that number. Repeat until students
  have modeled each number at least once.

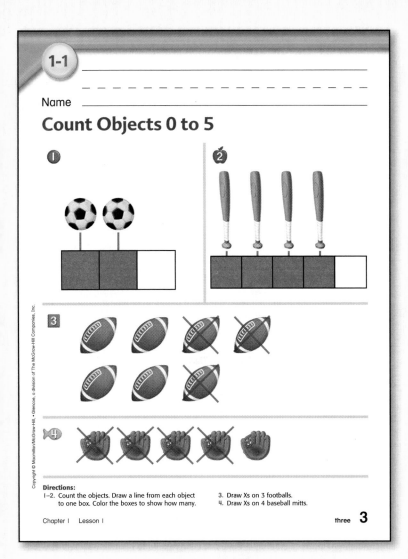

Name _____

Count Objects 0 to 5

Directions:
1–2. Count the objects. Draw a line from each object to one box. Color the boxes to show how many.
3. Draw Xs on 3 footballs.
4. Draw Xs on 4 baseball mitts.

Chapter 1   Lesson 1

three **3**

 **Practice**

Direct students to page 3 of their student workbook. Read the directions at the bottom of the student page as they complete the exercises.

Encourage students to model the number in each picture for each exercise with connecting cubes and count the cubes.

④ Assess

See It   Show students groups of 1, 2, 3, 4, and 5 paper clips, in order. Ask them to identify the group of three paper clips.

Say It   Have students count "0, 1, 2, 3." To help students remember, have them repeat the following rhyme: "Zero, one, two, three, I see a bee!"

Do It   Give students 5 connecting cubes. Have them create a group of 4.

Write It   Say a number from 0 to 5. Have students draw that many circles.

Math Coach Notes

Remembering Zero   To help students remember zero, teach them a rhyme such as, "Zero is the hero and starts the fun for one."

Count Objects 6 to 10

Lesson Planner

Objective
Count from 6 to 10 by using objects.

Vocabulary

eight	seven	ten
nine	six	

Other Resources

Materials
classroom-safe balls, 1 for
each student pair
teacher-prepared note
cards, each showing 6 to
10 geometric shapes

Manipulatives
connecting cubes
two-color counters

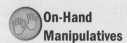 **On-Hand Manipulatives**
buttons
pencils
pennies
straws

CRM Chapter Resource Masters
Vocabulary and English Language
Development (p. A8)
Skills Practice (p. A9)
Practice at Home (p. A10)

Teacher Tech Tools
● TeacherWorks™ Plus
Math Online > macmillanmh.com
Advance Tracker

Student Tech Tools
● StudentWorks™ Plus
Math Online > macmillanmh.com
eGlossary

1 Introduce

Have students sit in a circle on the floor and show them
5 balls, one at a time.
• Count the balls aloud with the students.
• Allow students to work in pairs and roll a ball to
each other, counting with each roll.

2 Teach

Key Concept

Foundational Skills and Concepts Display a
group of 1 to 10 buttons, in order. Have students count
the buttons in each group and say the number for
each group. Then say a number from 1 to 10 and have
students identify the group with that number of buttons.

Using Manipulatives

Connecting Cubes Give each student
10 connecting cubes.

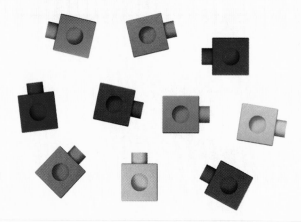

• Count to ten with the class. Have students move a
connecting cube into a pile with each number.
• Say numbers from 6 to 10 and have students
model each number by the correct number of
connecting cubes.
• Once students are able to recognize the numbers by
hearing the word, give them note cards with different
numbers of shapes.
• Have students place one connecting cube on their
card for each shape shown. Have them say the
number of shapes.

Intervention Strategy   Tactile Learners

Counting Objects   Help students to count by having them
pick up groups of objects. Have a station with six straws, eight
pieces of chalk, and ten pencils. Have students pick up the items
in each group and count the items.

Name _____

Count Objects 6 to 10

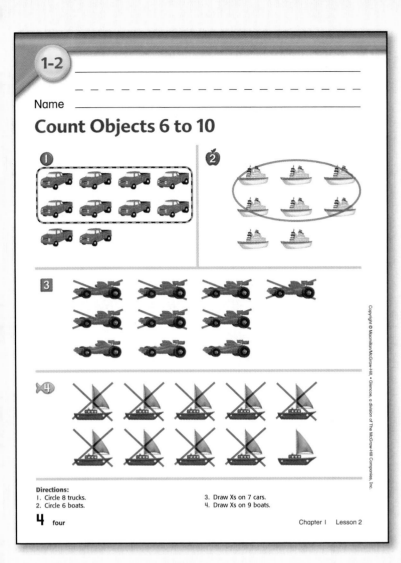

Directions:
1. Circle 8 trucks.
2. Circle 6 boats.
3. Draw Xs on 7 cars.
4. Draw Xs on 9 boats.

4 four

Chapter 1   Lesson 2

---

③ **Practice**

Direct students to page 4 of their student workbook. Read the directions at the bottom of the student page as they complete the exercises.

Have students model the numbers in the pictures with connecting cubes and count the cubes as they work on the exercises.

④ **Assess**

See It   On the board, draw various groups of 1 to 10 circles. Have students identify the group that has 9 circles.

Say It   Have students count aloud from 1 to 10. Allow students to use connecting cubes as they count.

Do It   Give 10 counters to each student. Have them make a group of 7.

Write It   Say "ten." Have students draw 10 circles.

⚠ **Common Error Alert**

Listen, See, Feel   Students may have difficulty recognizing and understanding numbers as presented in different forms. To help students connect the oral, pictorial, and physical objects, make sure to give them time to hear the numbers said as they look at pictures and create models of the numbers.

Count Forward

Lesson Planner

Objective
Count forward from 0 to 5 using a number line.

Vocabulary

forward

number line

Other Resources

Materials
large picture number line
  from 0 to 5
number lines with 6 tick
  marks
small stickers for
  number lines

Manipulatives
two-color counters

 **On-Hand Manipulatives**
beans
paper clips
pennies

CRM Chapter Resource Masters
Vocabulary and English Language
  Development (p. A11)
Skills Practice (p. A12)
Practice at Home (p. A13)

Teacher Tech Tools
TeacherWorks™ Plus
Math Online > macmillanmh.com
Advance Tracker

Student Tech Tools
StudentWorks™ Plus
Math Online > macmillanmh.com
eGlossary

Intervention Strategy   Tactile Learners

Picture Number Lines   Have students make a number line
on a sheet of paper. Tell them to count aloud and put stickers
above the number line to show the different numbers. Then have
students work in pairs and count forward using their number lines.
Make sure each partner agrees on the counting.

---

1 Introduce

Have students work in groups of six and give each
student in the group 0 to 5 beans. Have students
count their beans with their group. Have them count
from 0 to 6 and arrange themselves in order by the
number of their beans.

2 Teach

Key Concept

Foundational Skills and Concepts   Show
students a 0 to 5 picture number line similar to those
on page 5 of the student workbook. Say, "This is a
number line that uses pictures." Have students count
with you as you point to the objects on the number line.
Explain that you are counting *forward* as you count
from 0 to 5.

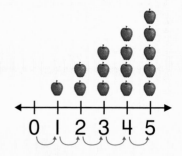

Using Manipulatives

Two-Color Counters   Put students in pairs
and give each pair 15 two-color counters and
3 number lines.

- On the board, draw a large 0 to 5 picture
  number line. Point to the number line.
- **How does the number line show 0?** with a blank
  space
- **How many pictures are next to the blank space?** 1
- Have student pairs put 1 counter above the second
  mark on one of their number lines.
- Have students count forward and put counters above
  the next four places to show the correct numbers. Tell
  students they will use every counter.
- Have each student draw circles on the other number
  lines to show the counters.

1-3

Name _____

Count Forward

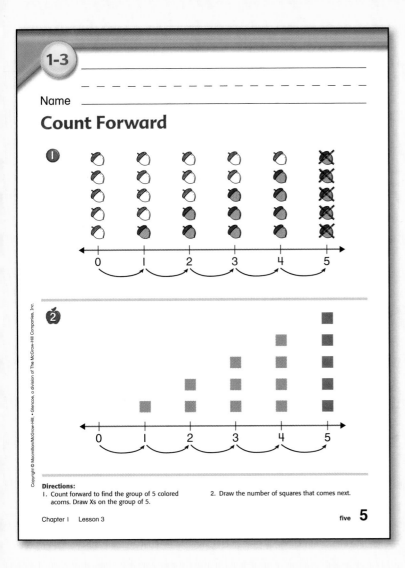

Directions:
1. Count forward to find the group of 5 colored acorns. Draw Xs on the group of 5.

2. Draw the number of squares that comes next.

Chapter 1   Lesson 3

five **5**

③ Practice

Direct students to page 5 of their student workbook. Read the directions at the bottom of the student page as they complete the exercises.

For Exercise 2, help students see that they can draw just one more square than the number on 4.

④ Assess

See It   Show students a picture number line 0 to 5. Have students point to the group that represents 4. Allow students to count each group aloud.

Say It   Have students count forward from 0 to 5. To help them remember, have them recite: "Zero, one, two, three, four, five, bees live in a hive."

Do It   Give students a collection of 15 counters. Have them create a number line by stacking the correct number of counters in order from 0 to 5.

Write It   Draw a number line from 1 to 10 on the board. Have students draw the correct number of objects under each number.

⚠ Common Error Alert

Counting Aloud   Students may have trouble remembering the last number they counted. Encourage students to count aloud as they count forward to help them remember what numbers they have counted.

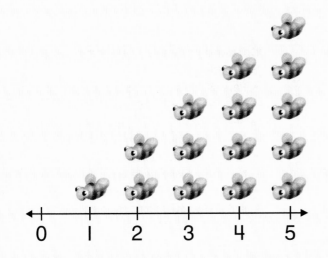

Count Backward

Lesson Planner

Objective

Count backward from 5 to 0 using a number line.

Vocabulary

backward

group

Other Resources

Materials

poster board
self-stick notes

Manipulatives

connecting cubes, 5 for
  each student
two-color counters

 **On-Hand Manipulatives**

paper clips
pennies

CRM **Chapter Resource Masters**

Vocabulary and English Language
  Development (p. A14)
Skills Practice (p. A15)
Practice at Home (p. A16)

Teacher Tech Tools

TeacherWorks™ Plus

Math Online > macmillanmh.com

Advance Tracker

Student Tech Tools

StudentWorks™ Plus

Math Online > macmillanmh.com

eGlossary

1 Introduce

- Give each student 15 two-color counters.
- Have students use their counters to make a 0 to 5 number line.
- Once students have their number line, have them use it to count forward from 0 to 5.

2 Teach

Key Concept

Foundational Skills and Concepts   Draw a 0 to 5 number line on the board. Have the class count aloud as you place 1 to 5 self-stick notes above the numbers on the number line.

- Point to the numbers. Have the class count aloud. Begin by going forward.
- Then lead the class in counting backward from 5 to 0.
- Once students have mastered counting backward, remove the group of three self-stick notes. Have students count backward from 5. Ask them what is missing. 3 notes

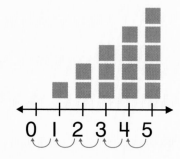

Using Manipulatives

Connecting Cubes   Give each student 5 connecting cubes.

- Have students count forward from 0 to 5 as they make a train with their cubes.
- Have students remove one cube from their train.
- **How many cubes are in your train?** 4
- Have students continue removing cubes and saying how many cubes are in the train.
- Have students repeat until they can count forward and backward without counting the cubes for each number.

English Learner Strategy

Moving Forward and Backward   On the board, draw a number line from 0 to 5. Have a student stand at the board, facing right. Have the student take a step forward (to the right) and say the word *forward*. Then have the student take a step backward (to the left) and say the word *backward*. Explain that "forward" is to the right, while "backward" is to the left. Have the student first point forward on the number line while standing against the number line and then point backward. Model counting forward and backward while the student points to the number line.

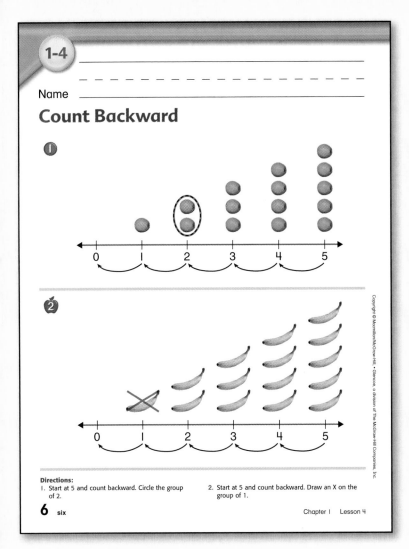

Name

Count Backward

1

2

Directions:
1. Start at 5 and count backward. Circle the group of 2.

2. Start at 5 and count backward. Draw an X on the group of 1.

6 six

Chapter 1 Lesson 4

③ Practice

Direct students to page 6 of their student workbook. Read the directions at the bottom of the student page as they complete the exercises.

To reinforce the concept of numbers, you might have students count the objects above each number.

④ Assess

See It Show a number line with pictures from 0 to 5. Have students count backward from 5 to 0.

Say It Have students recite: "Five, four, three, two, and one, counting back is so much fun!"

Do It Have students make a number line with connecting cubes and count backward from 5 to 0.

Write It Draw a number line with triangles to show 5, 4, and 3. Have students draw the missing triangles for 2 and 1.

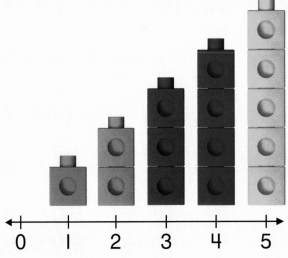

Intervention Strategy   Visual Learners

Picture Number Lines Create a classroom number line from 0 to 5 on a poster board. Ask students to cut out images of 1 to 5 items from a magazine or newspaper. Have students paste the images on the number line in their proper place. When the number line is completed, have students point to the pictures and count backward from 5 to 0.

Lesson 1-4 Count Backward **6**

Progress Check 1

Formative Assessment

Use the Progress Check to assess students' mastery of the previous lessons. Have students review the lesson indicated for the problems they answered incorrectly.

 Common Error Alert

Counting Backward If students are having difficulty with the concept of counting backward, explain that in this concept you start with a large number and end with a smaller number.

Counting backward means you will always end with a smaller number than you started with. For example, if you count backward from 5, the numbers will always be 4, 3, 2, 1, and 0.

Exercise 3 Be sure students understand the concept of shading one for one, or equivalence.

Exercise 4 Be sure students can correctly count backward from 5. If they are having difficulty, have them count the baseballs in each group as they count backward.

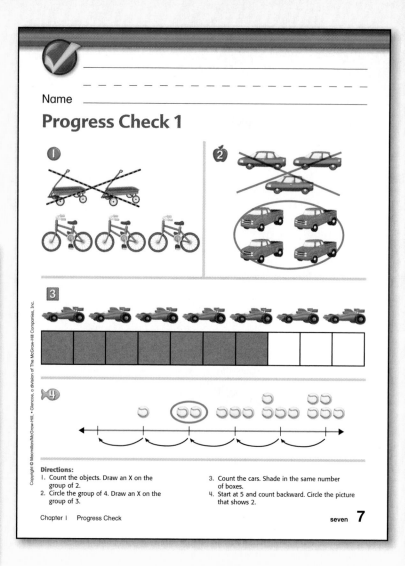

Data-Driven Decision Making

Students missing Exercises . . .	Have trouble with . . .	Should review and practice . . .
1–2	counting from 0 to 5.	TE Lesson 1-1, p. 3 CRM Skills Practice, p. A6
3	counting from 6 to 10.	TE Lesson 1-2, p. 4 CRM Skills Practice, p. A9
4	counting backward using a number line.	TE Lesson 1-4, p. 6 CRM Skills Practice, p. A15

Name _____

Replay

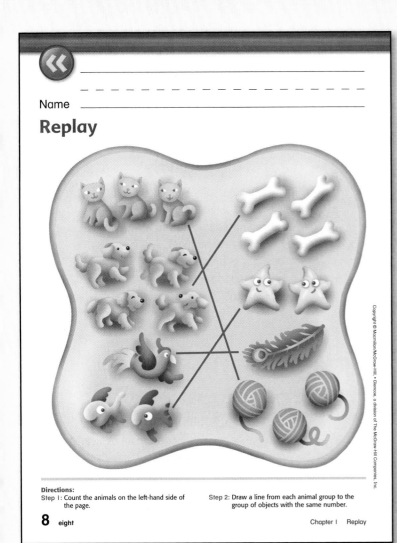

Directions:
Step 1: Count the animals on the left-hand side of the page.

Step 2: Draw a line from each animal group to the group of objects with the same number.

Copyright © Macmillan/McGraw-Hill, Glencoe, a division of The McGraw-Hill Companies, Inc.

8 eight

Chapter 1 Replay

Replay 1

Use the Replay activity to review and reinforce concepts and skills presented in Lessons 1-1, 1-2, 1-3, and 1-4.

Instructions

Explain that students will need to match the animals with the group of items for each item. Have students first count the animals. Then have students count the items on the right side of the page. Once the groups are counted, have students connect the animals to the objects.

Student Technology

Students can use the following technology resources to reinforce chapter content.

StudentWorks™ Plus

Math Online ⟩ macmillanmh.com
- eGames
- eGlossary

Numbers 0 and 1

Lesson Planner

Objective
Write, represent, and identify the numbers 0 and 1.

Vocabulary

one

zero

Other Resources

Materials
1 book
1 crayon
1 piece of chalk

Manipulatives
attribute blocks: circles, rectangles, squares, and triangles

 **On-Hand Manipulatives**
cardboard shapes: rectangles, squares, triangles, circles

CRM Chapter Resource Masters
Vocabulary and English Language Development (p. A17)
Skills Practice (p. A18)
Practice at Home (p. A19)

Teacher Tech Tools
TeacherWorks™ Plus
Math Online ▷ macmillanmh.com
Advance Tracker

Student Tech Tools
StudentWorks™ Plus
Math Online ▷ macmillanmh.com
eGlossary

Intervention Strategy
Kinesthetic Learners

Using Hands Show the number 1 by showing one index finger. Then ball your hand into a fist to demonstrate zero fingers. Have students follow your lead. Say "one" and "zero" aloud, and have students either show one index finger or make a fist.

---

1 Introduce

Warm-up Activity

Give each group of students one rectangle, two squares, and three triangles.
- **How many circles do you have?** zero
- **How many rectangles?** 1
- **How many squares?** 2
- **How many triangles?** 3
- Explain that "zero" means the same as "none."

2 Teach

Key Concept

Foundational Skills and Concepts
- Have students identify classroom objects that are groups of one, such as a door, the teacher's desk, and a clock.
- Write the number "1" on the board. Have students trace the number in the air with their finger.
- **How many pigeons, cows, or pigs are there in the classroom?** zero
- Write the number "0" on the board. Have students trace the number in the air with their finger.

Using Manipulatives

Attribute Blocks Give each student 1 rectangle and 1 circle.

- Hold up a circle.
- **What number does the circle have the same shape as?** zero
- Have students trace their circle on paper.
- Hold up a rectangle so the short side is parallel to the floor and the narrow face is toward the class.
- **What number does the rectangle have the same shape as?** one
- Have students trace the corresponding part of their rectangle on paper.

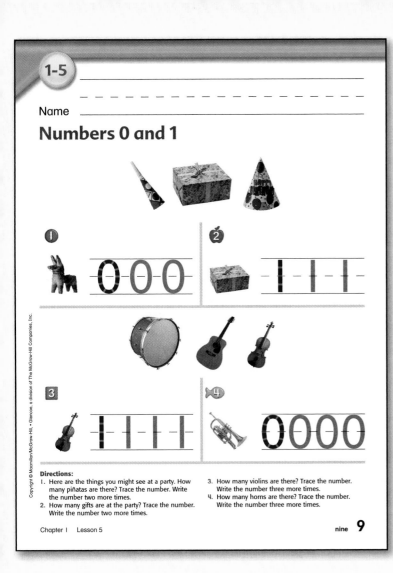

Name

Numbers 0 and 1

Directions:
1. Here are the things you might see at a party. How many piñatas are there? Trace the number. Write the number two more times.
2. How many gifts are at the party? Trace the number. Write the number two more times.
3. How many violins are there? Trace the number. Write the number three more times.
4. How many horns are there? Trace the number. Write the number three more times.

Chapter 1   Lesson 5

nine **9**

③ Practice

Direct students to page 9 of their student workbook. Read the directions at the bottom of the student page as they complete the exercises.

Be sure that students are able to identify the items pictured on the page. You might want to discuss how the various instruments are played.

④ Assess

See It   Show students one book, one crayon, or one piece of chalk. Ask students how many there are. 1 Have them trace the number on their palm.

Say It   Have students show one finger and say: "I can make the number one. Making numbers is so fun!" Have students make a zero with their fingers and say: "Zero is a hero." Have students draw the numbers in the air.

Do It   Have students write "1" on a piece of paper and draw 3 objects in the classroom of which there is only 1. Then have students write "0" on the piece of paper. Ask them to give examples of objects not in the room.

Write It   Have students write the numbers "0" and "1" and draw a picture for each.

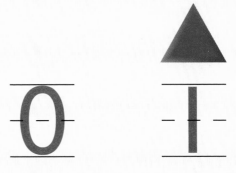

Math Coach Notes

• Tell students that they can remember the number 1 by imagining it to be a person standing up straight.
• Help students understand that there is a difference between the number 0 (zero) and the letter o.

Lesson 1-6

Numbers 2 and 3

Lesson Planner

Objective
Write, represent, and identify the numbers 2 and 3.

Vocabulary

three

two

Other Resources

Materials
3 balls
number cards 2 and 3
numbers 2 and 3 cut out
  of velvet
sheets with dotted 2s and
  3s for tracing

Manipulatives
connecting cubes

 **On-Hand
Manipulatives**
crayons
paper clips
pencils

CRM Chapter Resource Masters
Vocabulary and English Language
  Development (p. A20)
Skills Practice (p. A21)
Practice at Home (p. A22)

Teacher Tech Tools
TeacherWorks™ Plus

Math Online > macmillanmh.com
Advance Tracker

Student Tech Tools
StudentWorks™ Plus

Math Online > macmillanmh.com
eGlossary

1 Introduce

- Give each student one connecting cube.
- **How many cubes do you have?** 1
- Write "1" on the board.
- **How many eggs do you have?** zero or none
- Write "0" on the board.

2 Teach

Key Concept

Foundational Skills and Concepts Give
students sheets with dotted 2s and 3s.
- Show students 2 balls. Have students count them
  aloud. Write "2" on the board. Have students trace a
  2 on their paper.
- Show students 3 balls. Have students count them
  aloud. Write "3" on the board. Have students trace a
  3 on their paper.
- Continue with different objects until students can
  write 2 and 3 on their own.

Using Manipulatives

Connecting Cubes Put students in small groups
and give each group two trains of connecting cubes,
one with 2 cubes and one with 3 cubes, and a velvet
2 and 3.

- Have students put their trains above the correct
  velvet numbers.
- Have students trace the velvet numbers with their
  finger.
- Have students draw the groups of cubes and write
  the numbers beneath their pictures.

Intervention Strategy
Kinesthetic Learners

Clapping Counts Explain the numbers 2 and 3 by creating
rhythms. Clap your hands two or three times. Have students say
the number. If students say the correct number, write it on the
board. Have students trace the numbers on the back of their
hand with their finger. When they have finished, ask the class to
say the number together.

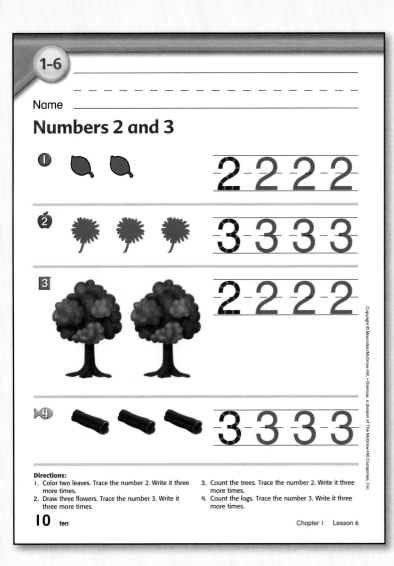

1-6

Name _____

Numbers 2 and 3

1. 🍃 🍃   2 2 2 2

2. 🌻 🌻 🌻   3 3 3 3

3. 🌳 🌳   2 2 2 2

4. 🪵 🪵 🪵   3 3 3 3

Directions:
1. Color two leaves. Trace the number 2. Write it three more times.
2. Draw three flowers. Trace the number 3. Write it three more times.
3. Count the trees. Trace the number 2. Write it three more times.
4. Count the logs. Trace the number 3. Write it three more times.

10 ten

Chapter I   Lesson 6

Direct students to page 10 of their student workbook. Read the directions at the bottom of the student page as they complete the exercises.

To help students write the numbers 2 and 3, show students how to trace each number with their finger before writing the number on their own.

④ **Assess** 🕐

See It   Show 2 crayons and 3 pencils. Have students trace the numbers on a number card with their finger as they say the number aloud.

Say It   Have students trace the numbers on number cards with their finger as they say the following rhyme: "I can write the number three. That's two for you and one for me."

Do It   Have students point to different groups of two and three objects and match the object to the correct number card, then trace the number from the card with their finger.

Write It   Have students write the numbers "2" and "3" and draw a picture for each.

⚠️ **Common Error Alert**

Writing Numbers   Students may have difficulty connecting the written number with the number of objects. Encourage students to draw pictures for the numbers along with the written number.

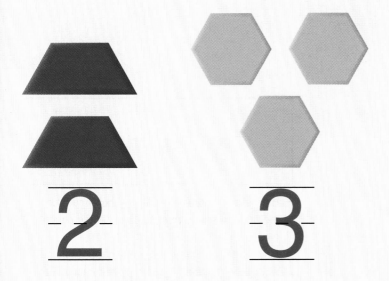

Numbers 4 and 5

Lesson Planner

Objective
Write, represent, and identify the numbers 4 and 5.

Vocabulary

five

four

group

Other Resources

Materials
number cards 4 and 5
patty or tracing paper
poster board
puffy or glitter glue

Manipulatives
two-color counters

 On-Hand Manipulatives
beans
buttons

CRM Chapter Resource Masters
Vocabulary and English Language
Development (p. A23)
Skills Practice (p. A24)
Practice at Home (p. A25)

Teacher Tech Tools
⊙ TeacherWorks™ Plus
Math Online > macmillanmh.com
Advance Tracker

Student Tech Tools
⊙ StudentWorks™ Plus
Math Online > macmillanmh.com
eGlossary

Intervention Strategy
Kinesthetic Learners

Feeling Numbers Use puffy or glitter glue to write the numbers 4 and 5 on poster board so students can feel the numbers. Invite students to trace the numbers with their finger. When they have finished, have them use a pencil to write the numbers on a sheet of paper.

1 Introduce

- Give student pairs 9 two-color counters and number cards 4 and 5.
- Ask students to make groups of four and five counters.
- Have students hold up the 4 card as you say "four" and the 5 card as you say "five."

2 Teach

Key Concept
Foundational Skills and Concepts
- On the board, draw 4 squares, and write "4" next to the squares.
- Have students count the sides on one square and trace the number 4 on the back of their hand with a finger.
- Draw 5 stars, and write "5" next to the stars.
- Have students count the points and trace the number 5 on the back of their hand with a finger.

Using Manipulatives

Two-Color Counters Have pairs use 9 counters and number cards.

- Have students turn 4 counters yellow and 5 counters red and put the number cards under the correct model.
- Encourage students to use patty paper to practice writing the numbers 4 and 5 by first tracing the numbers from the cards.
- Have students draw their counters and write "4" and "5" under the correct pictures.

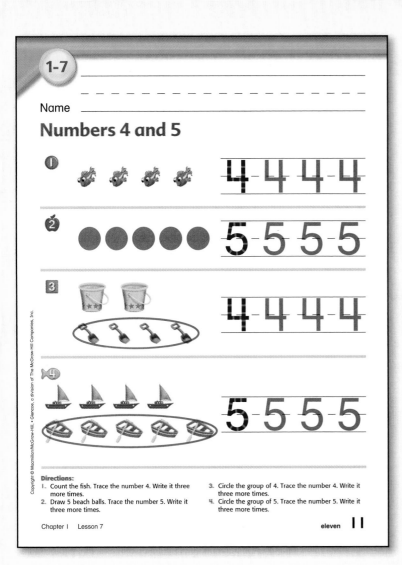

Numbers 4 and 5

Name

① 4 4 4 4

② 5 5 5 5

③ 4 4 4 4

④ 5 5 5 5

Directions:
1. Count the fish. Trace the number 4. Write it three more times.
2. Draw 5 beach balls. Trace the number 5. Write it three more times.
3. Circle the group of 4. Trace the number 4. Write it three more times.
4. Circle the group of 5. Trace the number 5. Write it three more times.

Chapter 1   Lesson 7

eleven   11

③ Practice

Direct students to page 11 of their student workbook. Read the directions at the bottom of the student page as they complete the exercises.

Model how to trace the numbers first with a finger and then with a pencil.

④ Assess

See It   Show students number cards 4 and 5. Have students trace each number with their finger as they say the numbers aloud.

Say It   Have students trace the numbers on their hand with a finger as they say this rhyme: "Every door has sides of four. I've drawn a star with points of five."

Do It   Give students a paper with pictures "4" and a paper with "5." Have students draw or label objects with four and five sides and trace the numbers using patty paper.

Write It   Have students write the numbers "4" and "5" and then draw the correct number of objects for each.

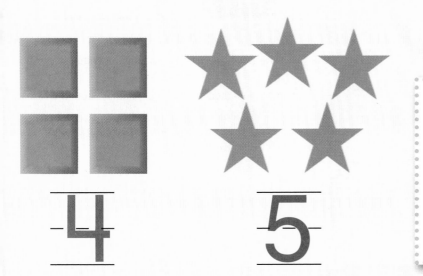

⚠ Common Error Alert

Reversing Numbers   Some students may reverse the numbers 4 and 5. Have students make oversized versions of the numbers "4" and "5" with arrows showing where to start when writing them. Then have students draw arrows in the correct direction from the starting point to the ending point. Students can trace the correct direction with their fingers.

Lesson 1-7 Numbers 4 and 5   **11**

Numbers 6 to 10

Lesson Planner

Objective
Write, represent, and identify the numbers 6 to 10.

Vocabulary
set

Other Resources

Materials
number cards 6 to 10
patty or tracing paper
picture number line with
   number blanks

Manipulatives
connecting cubes
number cubes 6–10
two-color counters

 **On-Hand Manipulatives**
paper clips
set of 6 to 10 objects

CRM Chapter Resource Masters
Vocabulary and English Language
   Development (p. A26)
Skills Practice (p. A27)
Practice at Home (p. A28)

Teacher Tech Tools
TeacherWorks™ Plus
Math Online > macmillanmh.com
Advance Tracker

Student Tech Tools
StudentWorks™ Plus
Math Online > macmillanmh.com
eGlossary

1 Introduce

- On the board, draw six smiley faces, and have students clap once for each smiley face as they count them aloud.
- Then draw another smiley face. Have students start over, clapping from one time to seven times.
- Continue the activity through ten.

2 Teach

Key Concept

Foundational Skills and Concepts   Show students a picture number line with 11 number blanks.
- Explain that a *set* is a group of objects, items, or numbers. Have students count the sets of objects for each number on the number line.
- Write the number for each set below the number line. Have students trace each number on the back of their hand with a finger.

Using Manipulatives

Number Cubes and Number Cards   Give student pairs a number cube, number cards 6 to 10, and patty paper.

- Have one student roll the number cube.
- Have the other student match number from the cube with the number card.
- Have both students trace the number from the card on patty paper.
- Repeat until students have traced all the numbers from 6 to 10.

Intervention Strategy   Linguistic Learners

Using Counters   Give 10 counters to each student. Direct students to count aloud from 1 to 10 as they point to each counter. Write each number on the board, and have students read the number aloud.

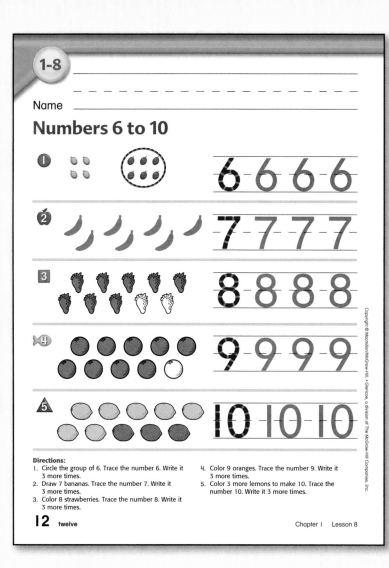

Numbers 6 to 10

Directions:
1. Circle the group of 6. Trace the number 6. Write it 3 more times.
2. Draw 7 bananas. Trace the number 7. Write it 3 more times.
3. Color 8 strawberries. Trace the number 8. Write it 3 more times.
4. Color 9 oranges. Trace the number 9. Write it 3 more times.
5. Color 3 more lemons to make 10. Trace the number 10. Write it 3 more times.

Chapter 1 Lesson 8

③ Practice

Direct students to page 12 of their student workbook. Read the directions at the bottom of the student page as they complete the exercises.

Show students how to practice writing numbers by first tracing the number on the page with a finger and then using their pencils.

④ Assess

See It Show students number cards and a set of 6 to 10 objects. Have them count the objects and find the correct card. Then have students trace the number on the card with a finger.

Say It Have students use a finger to trace each number on a large number line and say "six," "seven," "eight," "nine," and "ten."

Do It Have students match number cards with groups of the same number of connecting cubes and trace the number on the card with a finger.

Write It Have students write the numbers 6 through 10 and draw a picture for each number.

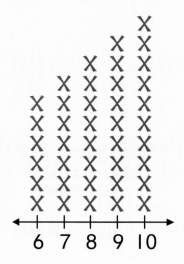

Math Coach Notes

Numbers 6 and 9 Help students remember how to write the numbers 6 and 9 by first asking which is the larger number. 9 Then exaggerate the size of the 9 by drawing a "tall" 9 on the board. Next to the 9, draw a "short" 6 reinforcing the idea that 6 is a smaller number so the circle is lower on the line.

Progress Check 2

Formative Assessment

Use the Progress Check to assess students' mastery of the previous lessons. Have students review the lesson indicated for the problems they answered incorrectly.

 Common Error Alert

Writing Numbers If students are having difficulty distinguishing between particular numbers, explain that many numbers have similar shapes or lines, such as 3 and 8, or 4 and 9. Have students create note cards with one number written on the front and drawings on the back to show the number. Tell students to use the cards to help them learn numbers.

Exercises 1–4 Suggest that students who have difficulty writing numbers practice repeat tracing.

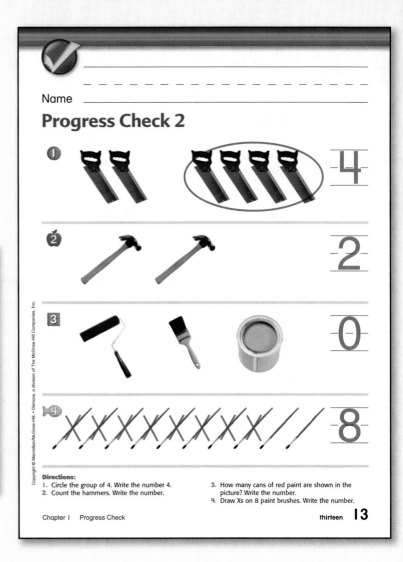

Data-Driven Decision Making

Students missing Exercises . . .	Have trouble with . . .	Should review and practice . . .
1	writing and representing numbers 4 and 5.	TE Lesson 1-7, p. 11 CRM Skills Practice, p. A24
2	writing and representing numbers 2 and 3.	TE Lesson 1-6, p. 10 CRM Skills Practice, p. A21
3	writing and representing numbers 0 and 1.	TE Lesson 1-5, p. 9 CRM Skills Practice, p. A18
4	writing and representing numbers from 6 to 10.	TE Lesson 1-8, p. 12 CRM Skills Practice, p. A27

Name _____

Replay

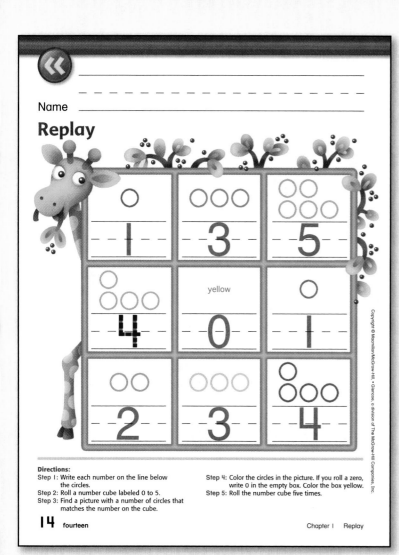

Directions:
Step 1: Write each number on the line below the circles.
Step 2: Roll a number cube labeled 0 to 5.
Step 3: Find a picture with a number of circles that matches the number on the cube.

Step 4: Color the circles in the picture. If you roll a zero, write 0 in the empty box. Color the box yellow.
Step 5: Roll the number cube five times.

Replay 2

Use the Replay activity to review and reinforce concepts and skills presented in Lessons 1-5, 1-6, 1-7, and 1-8.

Instructions

Explain to students that the number cube represents the numbers 0, 1, 2, 3, 4, and 5. Tell students to first roll the cube and then find the same number of circles. They should then write the number on the line and color the pictures. By asking questions, clarify that zero means that students will not see any circles.

Student Technology

Students can use the following technology resources to reinforce chapter content.

🌐 StudentWorks™ Plus

Math Online ⟩ macmillanmh.com

- eGames
- eGlossary

Review

Vocabulary

Before beginning the exercises, review vocabulary introduced in the chapter. Refer to the page numbers to revisit vocabulary activities in the lessons.

backward (p. 6A)	**one** (p. 3A)
eight (p. 4A)	**set** (p. 12A)
five (p. 3A)	**seven** (p. 4A)
forward (p. 5A)	**six** (p. 4A)
four (p. 3A)	**ten** (p. 4A)
group (p. 11A)	**three** (p. 3A)
nine (p. 4A)	**two** (p. 3A)
number line (p. 5A)	**zero** (p. 3A)

Vocabulary Review Strategies

Write the above vocabulary on the board. Call for students to demonstrate each word to the class by acting it out.

Concepts

The exercises in this section are grouped to cover content from most lessons in the chapter.

> **Exercise 1:** Lesson 1-1 (p. 3)
> **Exercise 2:** Lesson 1-3 (p. 5)
> **Exercise 3:** Lessons 1-2, 1-7, 1-8 (pp. 4, 11, and 12)
> **Exercise 4:** Lessons 1-1, 1-6 (pp. 3 and 10)

CRM Find Extra Practice for these concepts in the Practice Worksheets, pages A5–A28.

FOLDABLES® Study Organizer Dinah Zike's Foldables

Have students use the Foldable they created at the beginning of the chapter to review and reinforce the concepts and skills they learned during the chapter. (See Chapter Resource Masters p. A1 for instructions.)

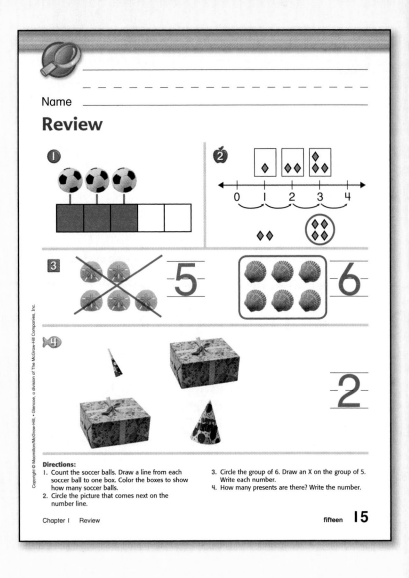

Intervention Strategy — Kinesthetic Learners

Using Counters One alternative method to help students is to provide two-colored counters or connecting cubes to model the numbers and sets in each exercise. Have students write the number that each model represents. Then have them use the models to help complete the exercise.

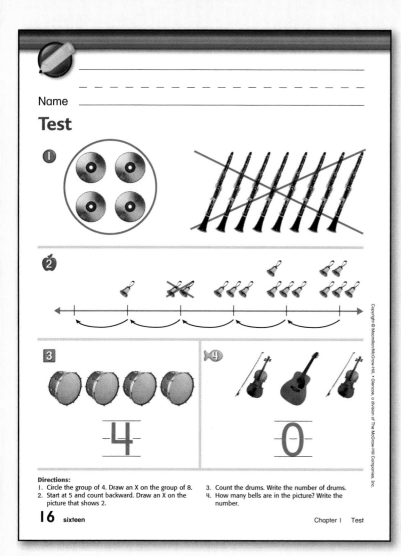

Name _____

Test

①

②

③ ④

Directions:
1. Circle the group of 4. Draw an X on the group of 8.
2. Start at 5 and count backward. Draw an X on the picture that shows 2.
3. Count the drums. Write the number of drums.
4. How many bells are in the picture? Write the number.

16 sixteen

Chapter 1 Test

Test

Chapter Resource Masters

Additional forms of the Chapter 1 Tests are available.

Test Format	Where to Find it
Chapter 1 Test	**Math Online** macmillanmh.com
Blackline Masters	Assessment Masters, pp. 12–13

Alternative Assessment

Number-Line Alternatives If students are having a hard time understanding how to use pictorial number lines, have them create a number line with beans or counters. Give students a piece of paper with a line drawn toward the bottom with numbers 0 to 10 written below the line. Have students glue beans to the paper above each number to create a number line.

ExamView®
Assessment Suite

Customize and create multiple versions of the chapter tests and their answer keys. All of these questions from the chapter tests are available on ExamView® Assessment Suite.

Advance TRACKER

This online assessment tool allows teachers to track student progress with easily accessible, comprehensive reports available for every student. Assess students using any internet-ready computer.

Data-Driven Decision Making

Students missing Exercises . . .	Have trouble with . . .	Should review and practice . . .
1	counting numbers 0 to 10.	**TE** Lessons 1-1 and 1-2, pp. 3 and 4 **CRM** Skills Practice, pp. A6 and A9
2	counting backward on a number line.	**TE** Lesson 1-4, p. 6 **CRM** Skills Practice, p. A15
3	counting and writing numbers 4 and 5.	**TE** Lessons 1-1 and 1-7, pp. 3 and 11 **CRM** Skills Practice, pp. A6 and A24
4	counting and writing numbers 0 and 1.	**TE** Lessons 1-1 and 1-5, pp. 3 and 9 **CRM** Skills Practice, pp. A6 and A18

Chapter Overview

Chapter-at-a-Glance

Lesson	Math Objective	State/Local Standards
2-1 Before and After (pp. 19A–19)	Order whole numbers using the words before and after.	
2-2 First, Next, Last (pp. 20A–20)	Understand the concepts of first, next, and last.	
2-3 Second and Third (pp. 21A–21)	Use ordinal numbers second and third to show position.	
2-4 Fourth and Fifth (pp. 22A–22)	Use ordinal numbers fourth and fifth to show position.	
Progress Check 1 (p. 23)		
2-5 Equal Sets (pp. 25A–25)	Make and identify equal sets of objects.	
2-6 Greater Than and Less Than (pp. 26A–26)	Compare quantities using the terms greater than and less than.	
2-7 Growing Number Patterns (pp. 27A–27)	Identify, duplicate, and extend growing number patterns.	
2-8 More Number Patterns (pp. 28A–28)	Identify, duplicate, and extend descending number patterns.	
Progress Check 2 (p. 29)		

Content-at-a-Glance
The diagram below summarizes and unpacks Chapter 2 content.

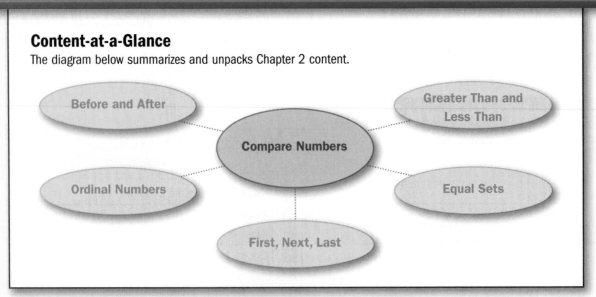

Chapter Assessment Manager

Diagnostic Diagnose students' readiness.

	Student Study Guide/ Teacher Edition	Assessment Masters	Technology
Intensive Intervention Placement Test		1–4	ExamView® Assessment Suite
Section Pretest (Chapters 1–4)		6–7	ExamView® Assessment Suite
Chapter 2 Pretest		19–20	ExamView® Assessment Suite
Get Ready	SSG 18		Math Online > macmillanmh.com StudentWorks™ Plus

Formative Identify students' misconceptions of content knowledge.

	Student Study Guide/ Teacher Edition	Assessment Masters	Technology
Progress Checks	SSG 23, 29		Math Online > macmillanmh.com StudentWorks™ Plus
Vocabulary Review	TE 31		Math Online > macmillanmh.com
Lesson Assessments			ExamView® Assessment Suite

Summative Determine student success in learning the concepts in the lesson, chapter, or section.

	Student Study Guide/ Teacher Edition	Assessment Masters	Technology
Chapter 2 Test	SSG 32	22–23	ExamView® Assessment Suite
Alternative Assessment	TE 32	27–28	ExamView® Assessment Suite
See It, Say It, Do It, Write It	TE 19, 20, 21, 22, 25, 26, 27, 28		
Section Test (Chapters 1–4)		39–40	ExamView® Assessment Suite

Backmapping and Vertical Alignment **McGraw-Hill's** *Math Triumphs* intervention program was conceived and developed with the final result in mind: student success in grade-level mathematics, including Algebra 1 and beyond. The authors, using the **NCTM Focal Points and Focal Connections** as their guide, developed this brand-new series by backmapping from grade-level and Algebra 1 concepts, and vertically aligning the topics so that they build upon prior skills and concepts and serve as a foundation for future topics.

Chapter Resource Manager

	Lesson 2-1	Lesson 2-2	Lesson 2-3	Lesson 2-4
Concept	Before and After	First, Next, Last	Second and Third	Fourth and Fifth
Objective	Order whole numbers using the words before and after.	Understand the concepts of first, next, and last.	Use ordinal numbers second and third to show position.	Use ordinal numbers fourth and fifth to show position.
Math Vocabulary	after before	first last next	first second third	fifth fourth
Lesson Resources	**Materials** • tape • construction paper circles (4–6 colors) • large number cards 0–10 (with numbers and pictures) • number line from 0–10 with pictures and numbers to display • beans or buttons **Manipulatives** • connecting cubes (1 of each color per student) **Other Resources** [CRM] Vocabulary and English Language Development [CRM] Skills Practice [CRM] Practice at Home	**Materials** • paper and pencils • number cards 1–10 (with numbers and pictures) • index cards • beans or buttons **Manipulatives** • connecting cubes (3 per student, red, blue, green) **Other Resources** [CRM] Vocabulary and English Language Development [CRM] Skills Practice [CRM] Practice at Home	**Materials** • 1st, 2nd and 3rd place awards • stuffed animals (3) • crayons **Manipulatives** • pattern blocks **Other Resources** [CRM] Vocabulary and English Language Development [CRM] Skills Practice [CRM] Practice at Home	**Materials** • bag for pattern blocks • cardboard shapes • beans or buttons **Manipulatives** • connecting cubes • pattern blocks **Other Resources** [CRM] Vocabulary and English Language Development [CRM] Skills Practice [CRM] Practice at Home
Technology	**Math Online** macmillanmh.com StudentWorks™ Plus ⊙ ExamView® Assessment Suite	**Math Online** macmillanmh.com StudentWorks™ Plus ⊙ ExamView® Assessment Suite	**Math Online** macmillanmh.com StudentWorks™ Plus ⊙ ExamView® Assessment Suite	**Math Online** macmillanmh.com StudentWorks™ Plus ⊙ ExamView® Assessment Suite

Lesson 2-5	Lesson 2-6	Lesson 2-7	Lesson 2-8	
Equal Sets	Greater Than and Less Than	Growing Number Patterns	More Number Patterns	**Concept**
Make and identify equal sets of objects.	Compare quantities using the terms greater than and less than.	Identify, duplicate, and extend ascending number patterns.	Identify, duplicate, and extend descending number patterns.	**Objective**
equal	equal greater than less than	greater least greatest more growing	fewer most least less	**Math Vocabulary**
Materials • 1" squares of construction paper • index cards • glue • pencils and paper • crayons • cardboard shapes • beans or buttons	**Materials** • bar graph • counting objects (beans, buttons, paper clips, or crayons) • markers	**Materials** • number cards (1–5 numbers and pictures) • counting objects (beans, buttons, paper clips, or crayons)	**Materials** • number cards 1–10 • picture cards with 1–10 objects on each • pencils and paper • counting objects (beans, buttons, paper clips, or crayons) • cardboard shapes	**Lesson Resources**
Manipulatives • pattern blocks • balance scale	**Manipulatives** • two-color counters	**Manipulatives** • connecting cubes	**Manipulatives** • connecting cubes • color tiles	
Other Resources **CRM** Vocabulary and English Language Development **CRM** Skills Practice **CRM** Practice at Home	**Other Resources** **CRM** Vocabulary and English Language Development **CRM** Skills Practice **CRM** Practice at Home	**Other Resources** **CRM** Vocabulary and English Language Development **CRM** Skills Practice **CRM** Practice at Home	**Other Resources** **CRM** Vocabulary and English Language Development **CRM** Skills Practice **CRM** Practice at Home	
Math Online macmillanmh.com StudentWorks™ Plus ⊙ ExamView® Assessment Suite	**Math Online** macmillanmh.com StudentWorks™ Plus ⊙ ExamView® Assessment Suite	**Math Online** macmillanmh.com StudentWorks™ Plus ⊙ ExamView® Assessment Suite	**Math Online** macmillanmh.com StudentWorks™ Plus ⊙ ExamView® Assessment Suite	**Technology**

CHAPTER 2

Chapter Notes

Home Connection

- Read the Home Connection letter with students and have them write their names in the space below.
- Read and explain the activity under Help at Home. If time allows, complete a portion of the activity so students can introduce the activity to a parent or other caregiver.

Real-World Applications

- Arrange students in groups of different sizes (group of one, group of two, group of three, and so on) until all students are in a group.
- Randomly have groups count off the number of students in their group.
- Ask the group with the fewest students to stand. Continue until all groups are standing, in order from fewest to most.
- Ask the group with the fewest students how many students are in their group. Write that number on a large index card for the group to hold. Repeat for each group.
- Have each group tell one more time how many students are in their group.

Math Online

Visit macmillanmh.com for ongoing support of chapter content and instruction, including:
- Online Games
- Concepts in Motion

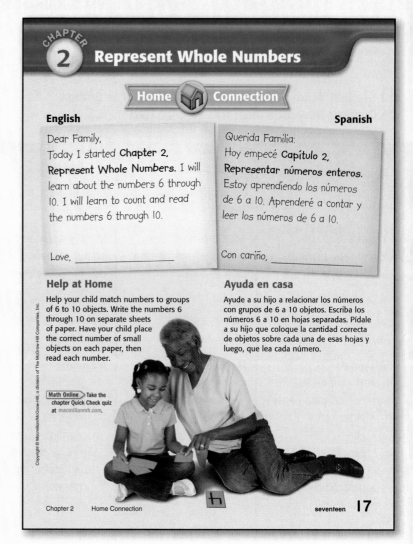

CHAPTER 2 Represent Whole Numbers

Home Connection

English

Dear Family,
Today I started **Chapter 2, Represent Whole Numbers.** I will learn about the numbers 6 through 10. I will learn to count and read the numbers 6 through 10.

Love, _____

Spanish

Querida Familia:
Hoy empecé **Capítulo 2, Representar números enteros.** Estoy aprendiendo los números de 6 a 10. Aprenderé a contar y leer los números de 6 a 10.

Con cariño, _____

Help at Home

Help your child match numbers to groups of 6 to 10 objects. Write the numbers 6 through 10 on separate sheets of paper. Have your child place the correct number of small objects on each paper, then read each number.

Math Online Take the chapter Quick Check quiz at macmillanmh.com.

Ayuda en casa

Ayude a su hijo a relacionar los números con grupos de 6 a 10 objetos. Escriba los números 6 a 10 en hojas separadas. Pídale a su hijo que coloque la cantidad correcta de objetos sobre cada una de esas hojas y luego, que lea cada número.

Chapter 2   Home Connection   **seventeen 17**

Key Vocabulary

Find interactive definitions in 13 languages in the **eGlossary** at macmillanmh.com.

English   Español *Introduce the most important vocabulary terms from Chapter 2.*

equal   igual
having the same number of items or the same value (p. 25A)

first   primero
at the beginning (p. 20A)

greater than   mayor que
7 > 2 (p. 26A)

last   último
at the end (p. 20A)

less than   menor que
4 < 7 (p. 26A)

next   siguiente
coming after, immediately following (p. 20A)

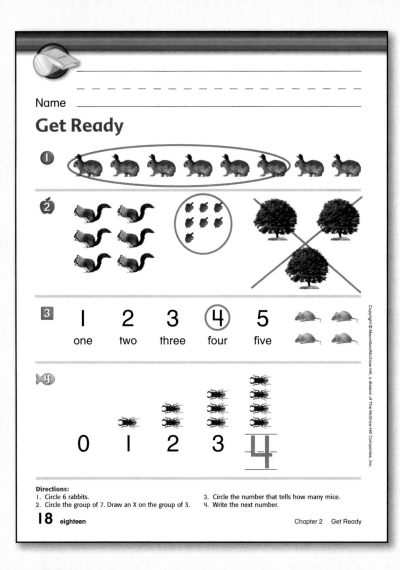

Name _____

Get Ready

① [rabbits]

② [squirrels, apples circled, trees with X]

③

1	2	3	④	5	[mice]
one	two	three	four	five	

④

0   1   2   3   4

Directions:
1. Circle 6 rabbits.
2. Circle the group of 7. Draw an X on the group of 3.
3. Circle the number that tells how many mice.
4. Write the next number.

18 eighteen

Chapter 2   Get Ready

 **Dinah Zike's Foldables**

Guide students through the directions on p. A29 in the Chapter Resource Masters to create their own Foldable graphic organizer for use with this chapter.

Vocabulary Preview

- Before starting the chapter, have students preview the lessons and make a list of all words and terms that are important or unfamiliar.
- Put each word or term on large paper and post throughout the classroom.
- Have students draw pictures or write examples for words as they encounter them in the chapter.

Get Ready

Diagnostic Assessment

Have students complete the Get Ready exercises to assess readiness. Refer to the lessons below for support for prerequisite skills.

Exercises 1–2: Grade K, Chapter 1, Lesson 2 (p. 4)
Exercises 3: Grade K, Chapter 1, Lesson 1 (p. 3)
Exercises 4: Grade K, Chapter 1, Lesson 3 (p. 5)

You may also assess student readiness with:
Assessment Masters: Chapter Pretest (pp. 19–20)

Math Online > macmillanmh.com
Online Readiness Quiz

Intervention Strategy

Step 1 Have students draw and label pictures of family members, including pets.

Step 2 Invite students to share their drawings with the class.

Step 3 Ask questions such as: "Do you have more sisters than brothers?" or "Who is the tallest member of your family?"

McGraw Hill Professional Development

Targeted professional development has been articulated throughout **McGraw-Hill's Math Triumphs** intervention program. The **McGraw-Hill Professional Development Video Library** provides short videos that support the **NCTM Focal Points and Focal Connections.** For more information, visit macmillanmh.com.

Model Lessons   Instructional Strategies

Before and After

Lesson Planner

Objective
Order whole numbers 0 to 10 using the words before and after.

Vocabulary

after

before

Other Resources

Materials
tape
construction paper circles
  (4 to 6 different colors)
number line from 1–10 with
  pictures and numbers to
  display
large number cards (with
  numbers and pictures from
  0–10)

Manipulatives
connecting cubes (1 of each
  color per student)

**On-Hand
Manipulatives**
beans or buttons

CRM Chapter Resource Masters
Vocabulary and English Language
  Development (p. A33)
Skills Practice (p. A34)
Practice at Home (p. A35)

Teacher Tech Tools
TeacherWorks™ Plus
Math Online > macmillanmh.com
Advance Tracker

Student Tech Tools
StudentWorks™ Plus
Math Online > macmillanmh.com
eGlossary

1 Introduce

Give students four to six paper circles. Have students
tape their circles in a row and draw a face on one of
the end circles to make a caterpillar.

Ask students to say the colors of the circles that come
before and after other circles.

2 Teach

Key Concept

Foundational Skills and Concepts   Show
students the number line to reinforce which numbers
come before and after other numbers. Give each
student a number card from 0–10.
- Place a 6 card on the floor.
- **What number comes just after 6?** 7
- Have the student with the 7 card put it just after
  the 6.
- Repeat for the number that comes just before 6.
- Continue until all students have placed their cards
  in the correct order.

Using Manipulatives

Connecting Cubes   Give students connecting
cubes. Have students connect their cubes in order:
red, orange, purple, yellow, green.

- **What color comes just after red?** orange
- **What color comes just before green?** yellow
- **What color comes just before yellow and just after
  orange?** purple
- Have students practice with a partner asking and
  answering their own "before" and "after" questions.

English Learner Strategy

Vocabulary   Ask students to practice lesson vocabulary by
thinking up and saying short sentences in other contexts, such as,
"C comes just before D and just after B," "Before I take off my
socks, I take off my shoes," or "I take off my socks after I take off
my shoes."

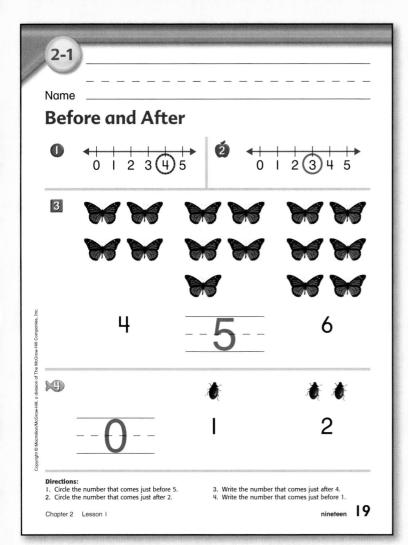

2-1

Name _____

Before and After

① 0 1 2 3 ④ 5   ② 0 1 2 ③ 4 5

③

4   — 5 —   6

④

— 0 —   1   2

Directions:
1. Circle the number that comes just before 5.
2. Circle the number that comes just after 2.
3. Write the number that comes just after 4.
4. Write the number that comes just before 1.

Chapter 2   Lesson 1

nineteen **19**

Direct students to page 19 in their student workbooks. Read the directions at the bottom of the student page as they complete the exercises.

Remind students to count along the number line to help decide which numbers come just before and just after other numbers.

See It   Use a number line. Have students point to and name the number that comes just before or just after five.

Say It   Say and write a number. Have students tell what number comes just before or just after that number.

Do It   Have students use connecting cubes to make a train to find the length that comes just before seven.

Write It   Write "0 1 2 ___ 4 5 ___ 7 8 ___ 10" on the board (leaving space for the missing numbers). Use the terms *before* and *after* to have students fill in the missing numbers. Allow students to use a number line to find the missing numbers.

Math Coach Notes

Understanding Directions   Help students understand that there are many numbers that come before or after any given number. Explain, however, that when we ask, "What number comes after 8?" we are usually talking about the number that comes just after 8.

Lesson 2-2

First, Next, Last

Lesson Planner

Objective
Understand the concepts of first, next, and last.

Vocabulary

first

last

next

Other Resources

Materials
paper
pencils

Manipulatives
connecting cubes (red, blue,
  green, 1 per student)
number cards

On-Hand Manipulatives
beans or buttons
index cards

CRM Chapter Resource Masters
Vocabulary and English Language
  Development (p. A36)
Skills Practice (p. A37)
Practice at Home (p. A38)

Teacher Tech Tools
TeacherWorks™ Plus

Math Online > macmillanmh.com
Advance Tracker

Student Tech Tools
StudentWorks™ Plus

Math Online > macmillanmh.com
eGlossary

1 Introduce

Have students stand to learn a new exercise. Give the following directions:
- First, put your hands on your head.
- Next, put your hands on your hips.
- Last, touch your toes.
- Emphasize the words *first, next,* and *last* as you model the motions.

2 Teach

Key Concept

Foundational Skills and Concepts   Draw a star, a crescent moon, and a heart on the board.
- Point to the star.
- **What did I draw first?** the star
- Repeat for the crescent moon and the heart, using the words *next* and *last*.

Using Manipulatives

Connecting Cubes   Give three different-colored connecting cubes to each student.

- Have students connect the cubes as follows: the first cube is red. The next cube is yellow. The last cube is green.
- Ask students to tell about their cubes, using the words *first, next,* and *last.*
- Repeat the activity as necessary, changing the order of the colors.

Intervention Strategy   Linguistic Learners

Math Stories   Some students may benefit from talking about concepts. Tell students a simple story about getting ready for school, such as "I woke up, got dressed, and ate breakfast." Ask students to say what happened first. Then ask them to tell what happened next and what happened last. Encourage students to tell their own stories using the terms *first, next,* and *last.*

Name _____

First, Next, Last

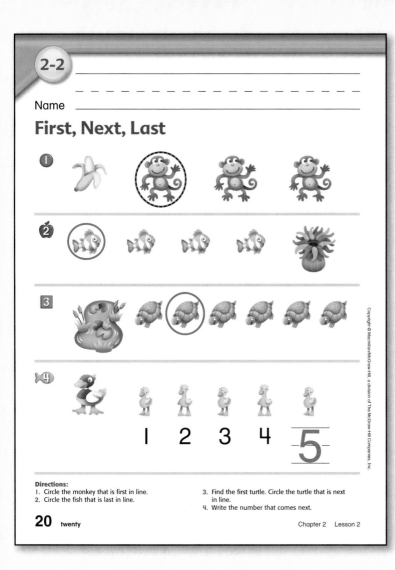

Directions:
1. Circle the monkey that is first in line.
2. Circle the fish that is last in line.
3. Find the first turtle. Circle the turtle that is next in line.
4. Write the number that comes next.

20 twenty

Chapter 2 Lesson 2

Copyright © Macmillan/McGraw-Hill, a division of The McGraw-Hill Companies, Inc.

③ Practice

Direct students to page 20 in their student workbooks. Model how to complete the student page for students. Then, read the directions at the bottom of the student page as they complete the exercises.

Encourage students to draw an arrow above the pictures to help them see the order of pictures. It may help students to draw a star or a dot to mark the first picture in a row.

④ Assess

See It Show students a sequence of actions such as getting paint supplies, painting a picture, and washing the brush. Have students say what was done first, next and last.

Say It Have students tell a story using the words *first, next,* and *last.*

Do It Have students arrange connecting cubes in a given order using the words *first, next,* and *last.*

Write It Draw three shapes or pictures on the board. Have students use the words *first, next,* and *last* to describe the shapes or pictures.

Math Coach Notes

Reinforcing Terms The idea of first, next, and last can be reinforced any time students are lining up for activities. Have students look as they stand in line, and ask: "Who is first? Who is next? Who is last?"

Second and Third

Lesson Planner

Objective
Use ordinal numbers second and third to show position.

Vocabulary
first

second

third

Other Resources

Materials
1st, 2nd, and 3rd place "awards"

stuffed animals (3)

Manipulatives
pattern blocks

 **On-Hand Manipulatives**

assorted colors of crayons

CRM Chapter Resource Masters
Vocabulary and English Language
  Development (p. A39)

Skills Practice (p. A40)

Practice at Home (p. A41)

Teacher Tech Tools
TeacherWorks™ Plus

Math Online ▷ macmillanmh.com

Advance Tracker

Student Tech Tools
StudentWorks™ Plus

Math Online ▷ macmillanmh.com

eGlossary

① Introduce

Show students three stuffed animals and have the class vote for their favorite. Tally the votes and give each animal an award. Explain that the votes put the animals in first, second and third place.

② Teach

Key Concept

Foundational Skills and Concepts   Have three students line up facing the door. Identify who is first, second, and third in line. Explain to students that when we look at pictures or drawings we start from a point of reference, such as an open door, to find first, second, and third.

- Have students rearrange themselves.
- **Now who is first? second? third?**
- Give directions such as: "The second person in line, touch your toes," or "The first person in line, hop on one foot."
- Repeat with other students until everyone has had a chance to be in the line.

Using Manipulatives

Pattern Blocks   Give pairs of students various pattern blocks. Have one student be the designer and the other the tracer.

- Have the designer tell the tracer which color shape to draw first, second, and third to make a pattern by tracing the pattern blocks.
- Have students take turns using *first, second,* and *third* to give and receive directions.

Intervention Strategy
Intrapersonal Learners

Think Aloud   Ask students to draw pictures or arrange pattern blocks or crayons to reflect their understanding of first, second, and third. Allow them to work alone to complete the task. When they are finished, have them show you their work and tell you about it.

Name _____

Second and Third

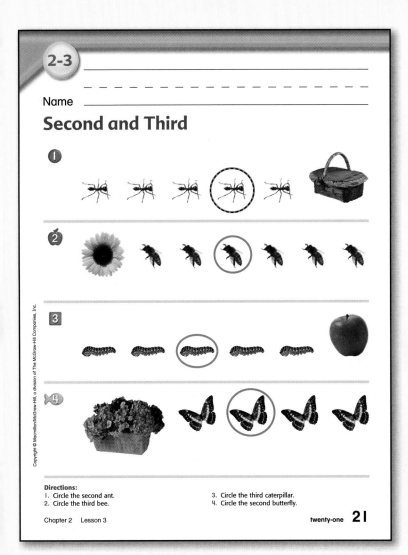

Directions:
1. Circle the second ant.
2. Circle the third bee.
3. Circle the third caterpillar.
4. Circle the second butterfly.

Chapter 2   Lesson 3

twenty-one **21**

③ Practice

Direct students to page 21 in their student workbooks. Read the directions at the bottom of the student page as they complete the exercises.
- Have students put their index fingers on the point of reference.
- To help students understand first, second, and third, have students write the numbers 1, 2, and 3 under the pictures from the point of reference.
- Finally, have students circle the correct pictures.

④ Assess

See It   Draw three shapes or pictures on the board. Have students say which one is first, second, and third.

Say It   Have students say the first, second, and third thing your class does at the beginning of each school day.

Do It   Have students link connecting cubes so the green cube is first, the blue cube is second, and the yellow cube is third.

Write It   Have students draw a picture in which a circle is first, a square is second, and a triangle is third.

Math Coach Notes

Using Terms   Use the words *first, second,* and *third* throughout the day as students perform various activities. For example, "First, we will take our seats. Second, we will get a crayon and paper. Third, we will draw a picture."

Fourth and Fifth

Lesson Planner

Objective
Use ordinal numbers fourth and fifth to show position.

Vocabulary
fifth

fourth

Other Resources

Materials
bag for pattern blocks

Manipulatives
pattern blocks
connecting cubes

 **On-Hand Manipulatives**
cardboard shapes
beans or buttons

CRM Chapter Resource Masters
Vocabulary and English Language
  Development (p. A42)
Skills Practice (p. A43)
Practice at Home (p. A44)

Teacher Tech Tools
TeacherWorks™ Plus
Math Online macmillanmh.com
Advance Tracker

Student Tech Tools
StudentWorks™ Plus
Math Online macmillanmh.com
eGlossary

1 Introduce

- Place pattern blocks in a bag and pull out three blocks, one at a time, and place them in a row.
- Have students say which block you pulled out first, second, and third.
- Invite students to pull out the fourth and fifth blocks.

2 Teach

Key Concept

Foundational Skills and Concepts   Draw a square, star, circle, triangle, and happy face and a number line on the board. Explain to students that the order of pictures is similar to the order on a number line and to start from the left side.

- Have students say which pictures are first, second, and third.
- Explain to students that the next two pictures are the fourth and fifth.
- **What is the fourth picture?** triangle
- **What is the fifth picture?** happy face

Using Manipulatives

Connecting Cubes   Give students five colors of connecting cubes and have students connect them in a given order.

- Say: "The first cube is red. The second cube is yellow. The third cube is purple. The fourth cube is green. The fifth cube is orange."
- Repeat the activity using the colors in different orders.

English Learner Strategy

Word Relationships   Help students make the connection between *fourth* and *four*. Tell students to say "fourth" and "four." Ask students if the words sound similar. Show students a picture with four shapes, have them point to the fourth object, and then have them count the objects. Show them the shape that represents the number four is the fourth in line.

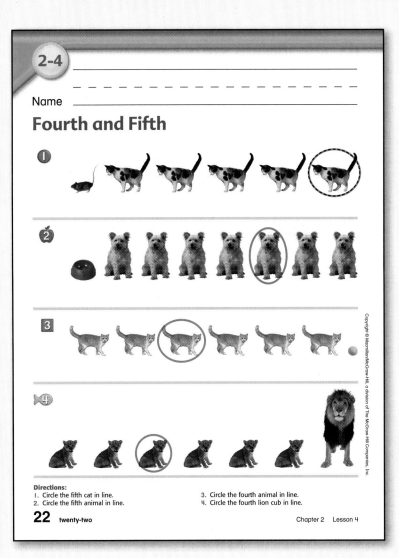

2-4

Name

Fourth and Fifth

Directions:
1. Circle the fifth cat in line.
2. Circle the fifth animal in line.
3. Circle the fourth animal in line.
4. Circle the fourth lion cub in line.

22 twenty-two   Chapter 2   Lesson 4

Copyright © Macmillan/McGraw-Hill, a division of The McGraw-Hill Companies, Inc.

③ Practice

Direct students to page 22 in their student workbooks. Read the directions at the bottom of the student page as they complete the exercises.

Remind students to pay attention to the direction the animals are facing.

④ Assess

See It   Write "a b c d e" on the chalkboard. Have students circle the fourth letter and underline the fifth letter. If students are unable to identify letters, use pictures instead.

Say It   Write "a b c d e" on the chalkboard. Have students say the fourth and fifth letters.

Do It   Have students connect five connecting cubes, making sure that the fourth cube is blue and the fifth cube is yellow.

Write It   Have students draw a row of five shapes in which the fourth shape is a circle and the fifth shape is a square.

⚠ Common Error Alert

It is easy for students to mix up fourth and fifth. When students are completing SE page 22, ask them to read each item aloud when counting the objects.

Intervention Strategy   Tactile Learners

Orientation   Allow students to practice order by using dolls or toy figures. Have them arrange figures from left to right and right to left. Use the edge of a table or a ruler as the "start" line.

Progress Check 1

Formative Assessment

Use the Progress Check to assess students' mastery of the previous lessons. Have students review the lesson indicated for the problems they answered incorrectly.

 Common Error Alert

Ordering Numbers   If students are having difficulty with concepts such as *first*, *second*, *next*, and *last*, help them relate these terms to events in their daily lives. For example, talk with students about what they do *first* when they are getting ready for bed, such as brush their teeth or put on pajamas.

Exercises 1 and 2   Be sure students are able to associate the symbolic representations of numbers with the quantities they represent.

Exercises 3, 4, and 5   Make sure students can correctly identify the beginning of the rows of images based on the information in the picture.

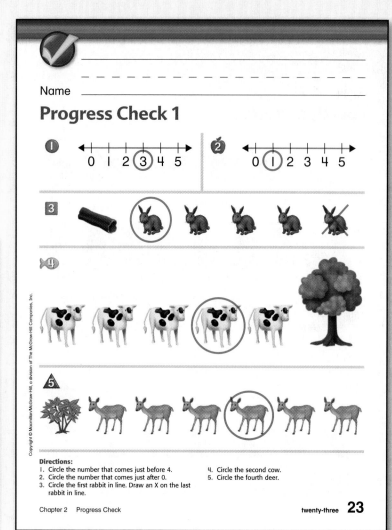

Data-Driven Decision Making

Students missing Exercises . . .	Have trouble with . . .	Should review and practice . . .
1–2	concepts of *before* and *after*.	**TE** Lesson 2-1, p. 19 **CRM** Skills Practice, p. A34
3	concepts of *first*, *next*, and *last*.	**TE** Lesson 2-2, p. 20 **CRM** Skills Practice, p. A37
4	concepts of *second* and *third*.	**TE** Lesson 2-3, p. 21 **CRM** Skills Practice, p. A40
5	concepts of *fourth* and *fifth*.	**TE** Lesson 2-4, p. 22 **CRM** Skills Practice, p. A43

Name _____

Replay

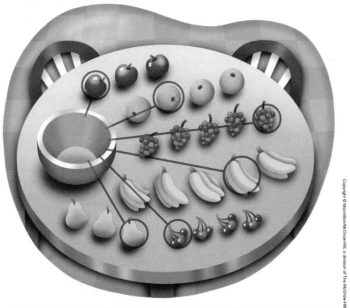

Directions: Help make a fruit salad.
1. Circle the first apple. Draw a line from the first apple to the bowl.
2. Circle the second orange. Draw a line from the second orange to the bowl.
3. Circle the last bunch of grapes. Draw a line to the bowl from this bunch of grapes.
4. Circle the fourth bunch of bananas. Draw a line from the fourth banana to the bowl.
5. Circle the first bunch of cherries. Draw a line to the bowl from this bunch of cherries.
6. Circle the third pear. Draw a line from the third pear to the bowl.

24 twenty-four

Replay

Use the Replay activity to review and reinforce concepts and skills presented in Lessons 2-1, 2-2, 2-3, and 2-4.

Instructions

Remind students that they need a crayon or pencil to complete the exercises.

Student Technology

Students can use the following technology resources to reinforce chapter content.

StudentWorks™ Plus

Math Online ⟩ macmillanmh.com
- eGames
- eGlossary

Equal Sets

Lesson Planner

Objective
Make and identify equal sets of objects.

Vocabulary
equal

Materials
construction paper
  (cut into 1-inch squares,
  5 per student)
large index cards
glue
crayons

Manipulatives
pattern blocks
balance scale

 **On-Hand Manipulatives**
cardboard shapes
beans or buttons

Other Resources

CRM Chapter Resource Masters
Vocabulary and English Language
  Development (p. A45)
Skills Practice (p. A46)
Practice at Home (p. A47)

Teacher Tech Tools
TeacherWorks™ Plus
Math Online > macmillanmh.com
Advance Tracker

Student Tech Tools
StudentWorks™ Plus
Math Online > macmillanmh.com
eGlossary

English Learner Strategy

Using Questions Show students equal groups of objects. Count the objects in each group aloud with the students. Ask simple questions, such as "Are the groups the same?" or "Are the groups equal?" Help students form responses to your questions, using complete sentences, including the words *same* and *equal*. Help students understand that these two words mean the same thing.

1 Introduce

- Place three books in a circle.
- Have two students pick up a book.
- **Is the number of students the same as the number of books?** no
- Have another student pick up a book. Explain how the number of books is the same as or equal to the number of students.

2 Teach

Key Concept

Foundational Skills and Concepts Show students a balance scale and 20 counters. Count aloud and put 10 counters on one side of the scale.
- Explain how the sides of the scale are different and have a different number of counters on each side.
- Count with the class and put 10 counters on the other side of the scale.
- Explain that the sides of the scale are the same height and the number of counters on each side are equal.

Using Manipulatives

Colored Squares Give each student 5 colored squares cut from construction paper and a large index card.

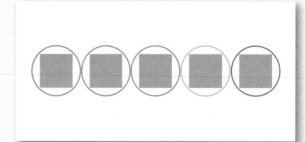

- Have students glue their squares onto an index card in a row.
- **How many squares do you have?** 5
- Have students draw a circle around each square with a different color crayon.
- **How many crayons did you use?** 5
- Discuss how each card has an equal number of squares and circles.

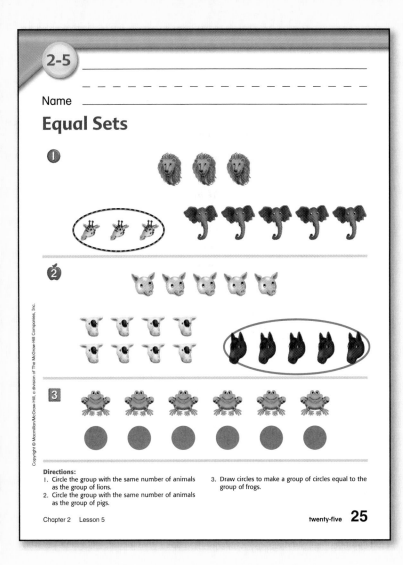

Name

Equal Sets

1

2

3

Directions:

1. Circle the group with the same number of animals as the group of lions.
2. Circle the group with the same number of animals as the group of pigs.
3. Draw circles to make a group of circles equal to the group of frogs.

Chapter 2   Lesson 5

twenty-five **25**

Direct students to page 25 in their student workbooks. Read the directions at the bottom of the student page as they complete the exercises.

Help students to find equal groups by encouraging them to cross out pictures one at a time from each group or by drawing lines between each of the pictures in the groups.

4 Assess

See It   Draw three groups of up to five shapes on the board, with two equal groups. Have students identify the equal groups.

Say It   Show students two equal sets of objects. Have students explain how they know if the sets are equal.

Do It   Clap three times. Have students clap an equal number of times.

Write It   Have students fold a sheet of paper in half and draw a picture of equal sets in each half.

⚠ Common Error Alert

Students may have difficulty with the term *equal*. Remind students that in math *equal* means "the same number of items." To reinforce the idea, have students use two-color counters to compare a pile of five red counters with five yellow counters. Tell students that the two piles of counters are equal because each pile has the same number of counters.

Intervention Strategy   Auditory Learners

Rhythmic Examples   One alternative way to help students understand equal sets is to clap your hands five times and count aloud as you clap. Then ask students to clap the same number of times, counting aloud as they clap. Next, have students clap first, counting as they clap. You clap one more, one less, or the same number of times, and have students tell whether you clapped the same number of times. Repeat as necessary.

Greater Than and Less Than

Lesson Planner

Objective
Use the terms *greater than* or *less than* to compare quantities.

Vocabulary

equal

greater than

less than

Materials
posterboard
red, green, yellow, and blue
  markers

Manipulatives
two-color counters

 **On-Hand
Manipulatives**

counting objects (paper
  clips, crayons, pencils)

Other Resources

CRM **Chapter Resource Masters**
Vocabulary and English Language
  Development (p. A48)
Skills Practice (p. A49)
Practice at Home (p. A50)

Teacher Tech Tools
TeacherWorks™ Plus
Math Online ⟩ macmillanmh.com
Advance Tracker

Student Tech Tools
StudentWorks™ Plus
Math Online ⟩ macmillanmh.com
eGlossary

1 Introduce

Give students six two-color counters and have them
show three yellow and three red.
- **Are the groups equal?** yes
- Have students pair up the colors to show they are
  equal.
- Give students another counter.
- **Are the groups equal now?** no

2 Teach

Key Concept

Foundational Skills and Concepts   Make a
bar graph with students by taking a vote on their
favorite color. Give them the choice of red, yellow, green,
or blue.
- Ask students several questions based on your graph,
  using the vocabulary from the lesson. The following
  questions are examples.
- Which color is liked less than green?
- Which color has a greater number of votes than
  yellow?
- Did any colors have an equal number of votes?
- The questions and answers will depend on the votes
  received in your classroom.

Using Manipulatives

Two-Color Counters   Give each student 10
two-color counters.

- Have students arrange their counters in equal sets of
  yellow and red counters.
- Next, have students turn over one or more of their
  yellow counters and rearrange their rows.
- **Are the sets equal?** no
- **Which color do you have more of?** red
- Say: "The number of red counters is greater than the
  number of yellow counters," and "The number of
  yellow counters is less than the number of red
  counters."
- Repeat turning over more red counters.

English Learner Strategy

Synonyms   Students may need help with the term *less than*.
Tell students that *less than* means "there are fewer items."
Have students compare sets of stickers—seven happy faces
and three stars. Ask students which set has the fewest, and then
have students say, "The number of stars is less than the number
of happy faces."

2-6

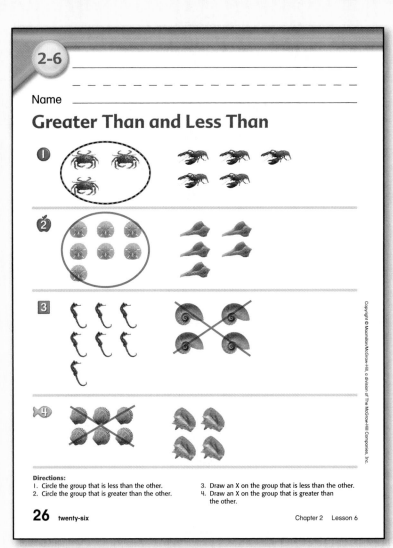

Name _____

Greater Than and Less Than

①

②

③

④

Directions:
1. Circle the group that is less than the other.
2. Circle the group that is greater than the other.
3. Draw an X on the group that is less than the other.
4. Draw an X on the group that is greater than the other.

26 twenty-six

Chapter 2 Lesson 6

3 Practice

Direct students to page 26 in their student workbooks. Read the directions at the bottom of the student page as they complete the exercises.

Have students draw lines to pair up items from each set in Exercises 1 and 2. Then count the items in each set and help students see that the set with objects that are not matched up has more than the other set and is greater than the other set. Do the same to illustrate less than.

4 Assess

See It Show sets of two, five, and eight connecting cubes. While looking at a set of seven cubes, have students say which sets are less than seven.

Say It Show students unequal sets of connecting cubes. Have them explain how they know one set of connecting cubes is greater than the other.

Do It Have students arrange 10 two-color counters into groups so that one group is greater than the other. Then have students explain which is greater than and which is less than.

Write It Give students an index card with five squares. Have students draw a set of circles that is less than five.

⚠️ **Common Error Alert**

Greater and Lesser The words *greater* and *lesser* should be used instead of *larger* and *smaller* when referring to numbers or sets of objects.

Intervention Strategy — Interpersonal Learners

Talk Math Some students learn better when interacting with others. Invite these students to work together to practice identifying greater than, less than, and equal. Give pairs of students connecting cubes in different colors. Ask the pairs to create sets—with the yellow set being greater than the blue set. Have students make the sets and explain which set is less than the other.

Growing Number Patterns

Lesson Planner

Objective
Identify, duplicate, and extend ascending number patterns.

Vocabulary

greater	**least**
greatest	**more**
growing	

Other Resources

Materials
number cards (pictures of objects in rows modeling numbers 1 to 5)

Manipulatives
connecting cubes

 **On-Hand Manipulatives**
counting objects (paper clips, brand-new chalk, or brand-new crayons)

CRM Chapter Resource Masters
Vocabulary and English Language Development (p. A51)
Skills Practice (p. A52)
Practice at Home (p. A53)

Teacher Tech Tools
TeacherWorks™ Plus
Math Online > macmillanmh.com
Advance Tracker

Student Tech Tools
StudentWorks™ Plus
Math Online > macmillanmh.com
eGlossary

English Learner Strategy

Language in Motion Take students to the bottom of a staircase. Tell students that they will start on the first step. Have students explain which step would be next, continuing until they get to the top of the stairs.

---

① Introduce

- Give students cards with different numbers of objects on them.
- Have students work in pairs or groups to arrange their cards from least to greatest.

② Teach

Key Concept

Foundational Skills and Concepts Show students a picture number line from 0 to 5 using sets of shapes.

- Have the students count the number of shapes in each set.
- Write the numbers 0 to 5 below each set of pictures.
- **What do you notice about the number of pictures as we move from left to right?** One more picture is shown each time.
- Explain that the sets become greater.
- **When patterns show sets that become greater, they show growing number patterns.**

Using Manipulatives

Connecting Cubes Give small groups 20 connecting cubes.

- Show students a one-cube train, a two-cube train, and a three-cube train.
- **How many cubes should be in the next train?** 4
- Show me the next train.
- Have groups arrange their sets in ascending order.
- Have all but one member of the group close their eyes while the remaining member removes one or more trains.
- Have group members use number patterns to identify the missing trains.

Name _____

Growing Number Patterns

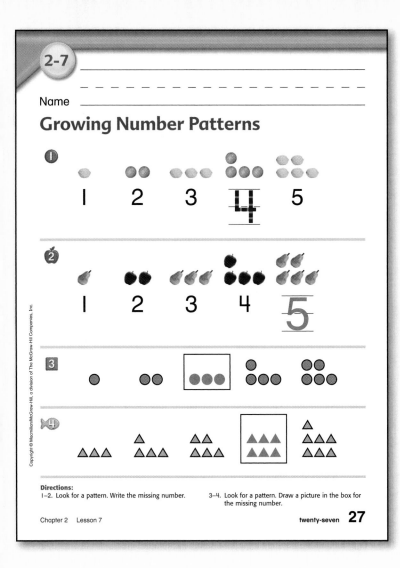

Directions:
1–2. Look for a pattern. Write the missing number.
3–4. Look for a pattern. Draw a picture in the box for the missing number.

Chapter 2 Lesson 7

twenty-seven **27**

③ Practice

Direct students to page 27 in their student workbooks. Read the directions at the bottom of the student page as they complete the exercises.

Help students see patterns by counting the number of objects in each group aloud with students. When students come to the missing picture, review the numbers they have already counted and ask what number comes next.

④ Assess

See It Show students one circle, then two circles and three circles. Ask students how many circles would be next if the pattern continues.

Say It Have students count in ascending order from 1 to 10 as they use counters to model each number.

Do It Give students a set of cards, modeling 1 to 5 with pictures in rows. Have students arrange the cards in ascending order.

Write It Have students draw pictures to show numbers ascending from 1 to 3.

⚠ Common Error Alert

Students may have difficulty recognizing number patterns. Arrange number cards in ascending order and have students model each number with counters. Show students how to arrange the counters in rows, one under the other, so that the pattern can be more easily seen.

Intervention Strategy   Auditory Learners

Rhythmic Patterns One way to help students identify patterns is to have them clap, snap, or tap their fingers while reciting number patterns aloud. Students can then repeat, identify, and extend the pattern. Clap, snap, or tap along with students as they repeat and extend the patterns.

Lesson 2-7 Growing Number Patterns **27**

More Number Patterns

Lesson Planner

Objective
Identify, duplicate, and extend descending number patterns.

Vocabulary

fewer   **less**

least   **most**

Other Resources

Materials
picture cards (numbers
  1 through 9 with pictures
  for each number)
pencils
paper

Manipulatives
connecting cubes
color tiles

 **On-Hand
Manipulatives**
objects for counting and
  making patterns (paper
  clips, crayons, pencils)

CRM Chapter Resource Masters
Vocabulary and English Language
  Development (p. A54)
Skills Practice (p. A55)
Practice at Home (p. A56)

Teacher Tech Tools
○ TeacherWorks™ Plus
Math Online ▷ macmillanmh.com
Advance Tracker

Student Tech Tools
○ StudentWorks™ Plus
Math Online ▷ macmillanmh.com
eGlossary

1 Introduce

- Give students nine linked connecting cubes.
- **How many cubes do you have?** 9
- Have student remove one cube.
- **Now how many cubes do you have?** 8
- Continue until all the connecting cubes are removed.
  Explain that they are using fewer cubes each time.

2 Teach

Key Concept

Foundational Skills and Concepts   Show
students picture cards from 1 to 9.
- **Which card has the most pictures?** 9
- Set the 9 card aside.
- **Now which card has the most pictures?** 8
- Repeat in descending order through number 1.
  Discuss the pattern.
- Point to each card and count backward aloud with
  students. Then, remove a card and have students
  name the missing number.

Using Manipulatives

Connecting Cubes   Make sure pairs have
15 connecting cubes.

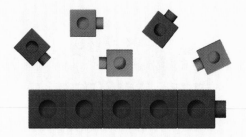

- Have students make cube trains of five, four, three,
  two, and one cubes.
- Have students arrange his or her trains from greatest
  to least.
- One student closes his or her eyes while the other
  removes one of the trains.
- Have the student open his or her eyes and count
  backward to find the missing train.
- Have students take turns.

Intervention Strategy   Visual Learners

Picture Number LInes   Have students practice making
descending number patterns using picture cards with different
numbers of objects. Have students put the card with the greatest
number of pictures first, working down to the card with the
fewest pictures.

Name _____

More Number Patterns

1.

8　　7　　*6*　　5

2.

9　　8　　*7*　　6　　5

3.

8　7　*6*　5　4　*3*　2

Directions:
1–2. Look for a pattern. Write the missing number.　　3. Look for a pattern. Write the missing numbers.

28　twenty-eight

Chapter 2　Lesson 8

Copyright © Macmillan/McGraw-Hill, a division of The McGraw-Hill Companies, Inc.

③ Practice

Direct students to page 28 in their student workbooks. Read the directions at the bottom of the student page as they complete the exercise.

Encourage students to count aloud as they complete Exercises 1–3.

④ Assess

See It　Have students use color tiles to make their own descending number patterns.

Say It　Begin to count backward from 10, and have students help you by supplying the next number in the pattern.

Do It　Have students create descending number patterns by clapping. First clap seven times, then clap six times, and so on. Help students keep track of the descending pattern by using number cards.

Write It　Have students write numbers 0 to 5 in order. Ask students to count backward and draw sets of pictures starting under the 5 and continuing to 0.

Math Coach Notes

Strategies　Have students compare two objects or pictures and add another picture until students are comparing up to five objects. Encourage students to describe the patterns they see in the concrete and pictorial representations, using math terms such as *more, fewer, greater than,* and *less than.* Prompt them with questions such as: "Which picture has fewer?"

Progress Check 2

Formative Assessment

Use the Progress Check to assess students' mastery of the previous lessons. Have students review the lesson indicated for the problems they answered incorrectly.

 Common Error Alert

Comparing Sets If students have difficulty comparing sets, have them draw lines to match items in each set. Another way is to have them model sets with counters or other objects, then match counters one-to-one to compare quantities in the two sets.

Exercise 2 Have students model five and four with connecting cubes, then arrange trains in order from shortest to longest to identify the lesser group.

Exercise 4 Be sure students are able to identify the number pattern as descending. Allow students to clap or hop as they read each number.

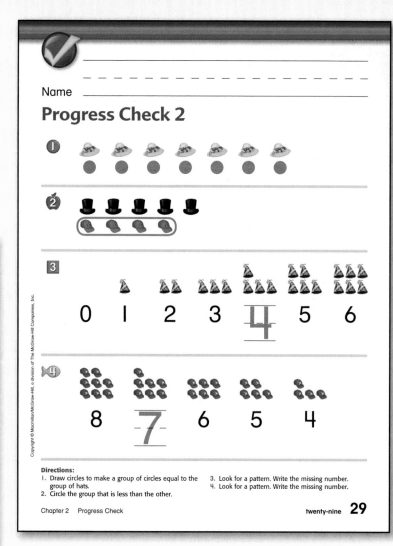

Data-Driven Decision Making

Students missing Exercises . . .	Have trouble with . . .	Should review and practice . . .
1	identifying equal sets.	TE Lesson 2-5, p. 25 CRM Skills Practice, p. A46
2	identifying sets that are greater than or less than.	TE Lesson 2-6, p. 26 CRM Skills Practice, p. A49
3–4	identifying ascending and descending number patterns.	TE Lessons 2-7 and 2-8, pp. 27–28 CRM Skills Practice, pp. A52 and A55

Name _____

Replay

Number line: 0 1 2 3 4 5 6 7 8 9 10

5 purple	1 orange	2 orange
6 purple	4	8 purple
9 purple	7 purple	10 purple

2 (4) 9

4

Directions:
How many apples did the pig eat?
Step 1 In the table, find the numbers greater than 4. Color them purple.
Step 2 In the table, find the numbers less than 3. Color them orange.

Step 3 Look at the apples. Circle the apple with the number that is not colored.
Step 4 Write the number.

30 thirty

Chapter 2 Replay

Replay

Use the Replay activity to review and reinforce concepts and skills presented in Lessons 2-5, 2-6, 2-7, and 2-8.

Instructions

Explain to students that they need to complete Steps 1, 2, and 3 before they complete Steps 4 and 5. Remind students that *greater than* means more and *less than* means fewer.

Student Technology

Students can use the following technology resources to reinforce chapter content.

StudentWorks™ Plus

Math Online macmillanmh.com
- eGames
- eGlossary

Review

Vocabulary

Before beginning the exercises, review vocabulary introduced in the chapter. Refer to the page numbers to revisit vocabulary activities in the lessons.

after (p. 19A)	**greater than** (p. 26A)	**less than** (p. 26A)
before (p. 19A)	**greatest** (p. 27A)	**more** (p. 27A)
equal (p. 25A)	**growing** (p. 27A)	**most** (p. 28A)
fewer (p. 28A)	**last** (p. 20A)	**next** (p. 20A)
fifth (p. 22A)	**least** (p. 27A)	**second** (p. 21A)
first (p. 20A)	**less** (p. 28A)	**third** (p. 21A)
fourth (p. 22A)		
greater (p. 27A)		

Vocabulary Review Strategies

Have students make a class chapter dictionary, incorporating or listing words on a picture. For example: a student who is *last* in line (simple stick figures) is wearing a shirt on which appears the vocabulary word *last*.

Write out each vocabulary word. Have students draw a picture of what each word means to them. Then, to reinforce the meaning, have students explain their pictures orally to the group.

Concepts

The exercises in this section are grouped to cover content from each lesson in the chapter.

Exercise 1: Lesson 2-1 (p. 19)
Exercise 2: Lessons 2-2, 2-3, 2-4 (pp. 20-22)
Exercise 3: Lesson 2-5 (p. 25)
Exercises 4–5: Lesson 2-6 (p. 26)
Exercise 6: Lessons 2-7, 2-8 (pp. 27-28)

CRM Find Extra Practice for these concepts in the Practice Worksheets, pp. A33–A56.

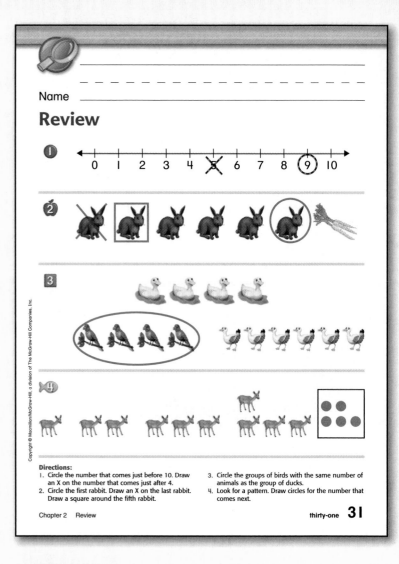

Name

Review

Directions:
1. Circle the number that comes just before 10. Draw an X on the number that comes just after 4.
2. Circle the first rabbit. Draw an X on the last rabbit. Draw a square around the fifth rabbit.
3. Circle the groups of birds with the same number of animals as the group of ducks.
4. Look for a pattern. Draw circles for the number that comes next.

Chapter 2　Review

thirty-one **31**

 **Dinah Zike's Foldables**

Have students use the Foldable they created at the beginning of the chapter to review and reinforce the concepts and skills they learned during the chapter. (See Chapter Resource Masters p. A29 for instructions.)

Intervention Strategy　Kinesthetic Learners

Counters or Cubes One alternative way to help students is to have them use two-colored counters or connecting cubes to model the numbers and sets in each exercise. Have students write the number that each model represents underneath the model, then use the models to help complete the exercise.

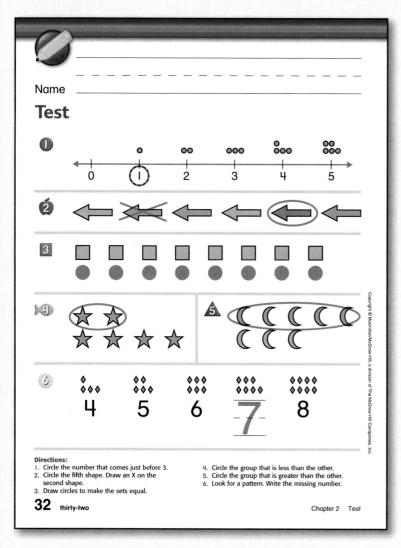

Name _____

Test

①
```
    o      oo     ooo    ooo    ooo
                         ooo    ooo
  |---|---|---|---|---|---|
  0  (1)  2   3   4   5
```

②

③

④

⑤

⑥
```
  ◊◊   ◊◊   ◊◊◊   ◊◊◊   ◊◊◊◊
  ◊◊◊  ◊◊◊  ◊◊◊   ◊◊◊   ◊◊◊◊
   4    5    6    7    8
```

Directions:
1. Circle the number that comes just before 3.
2. Circle the fifth shape. Draw an X on the second shape.
3. Draw circles to make the sets equal.
4. Circle the group that is less than the other.
5. Circle the group that is greater than the other.
6. Look for a pattern. Write the missing number.

32 thirty-two   Chapter 2   Test

Test

Chapter Resource Masters

Additional forms of the Chapter 2 Tests are available.

Test Format	Where to Find it
Chapter 2 Test	Math Online ▷ macmillanmh.com
Blackline Masters	Assessment Masters, pp. 22–23

Alternative Assessment

Use Manipulatives   Have students use manipulatives to model equal sets, sets that are greater than another set, and sets that are less than other sets. Use color tiles and have students arrange tiles according to directions involving the terms *before*, *after*, *first*, *next*, *last*, *second*, *third*, *fourth*, and *fifth*. Have students use connecting cubes or draw pictures to create ascending and descending number patterns.

ExamView®
Assessment Suite

Customize and create multiple versions of your chapter tests and their answer keys. All of these questions from the chapter tests are available on ExamView® Assessment Suite.

Advance TRACKER

This online assessment tool allows teachers to track student progress with easily accessible, comprehensive reports available for every student. Assess students using any internet-ready computer.

Exercises 4 and 5   Students might be confused because all of the shapes are the same. Explain that it is the color that makes the groups different. Make two columns on the board, one labeled "Same" and the other labeled "Different." Have students identify characteristics for each column. Explain that for two shapes to be the same, there must be nothing in the "Different" column.

Data-Driven Decision Making

Students missing Exercises . . .	Have trouble with . . .	Should review and practice . . .
1	concepts of *before* and *after*.	TE Lesson 2-1, p. 19 CRM Skills Practice, p. A34
2	ordinal numbers *second* through *fifth*.	TE Lessons 2-2, 2-3, 2-4, pp. 20–22 CRM Skills Practice, pp. A37, A40, A43
3	identifying equal sets.	TE Lesson 2-5, p. 25 CRM Skills Practice, p. A46
4–5	identifying *greater than* and *less than*.	TE Lesson 2-6, p. 26 CRM Skills Practice, p. A49
6	identifying ascending and descending number patterns.	TE Lessons 2-7, 2-8, pp. 27–28 CRM Skills Practice, pp. A52 and A55

Chapter Overview

Chapter-at-a-Glance

Lesson	Math Objective	State/Local Standards
3-1 Sums of 1 and 2 (pp. 35A–35)	Join sets to make groups of one and two.	
3-2 Sums of 3 and 4 (pp. 36A–36)	Join sets to make groups of three and four.	
3-3 Sums of 5 (pp. 37A–37)	Join sets to make groups of five.	
3-4 Sums of 6 (pp. 38A–38)	Join sets to make groups of six.	
Progress Check 1 (p. 39)		
3-5 Sums of 7 (pp. 41A–41)	Join sets to make groups of seven.	
3-6 Sums of 8 (pp. 42A–42)	Join sets to make groups of eight.	
3-7 Sums of 9 (pp. 43A–43)	Join sets to make groups of nine.	
Progress Check 2 (p. 44)		

Content-at-a-Glance

The diagram below summarizes and unpacks Chapter 3 content.

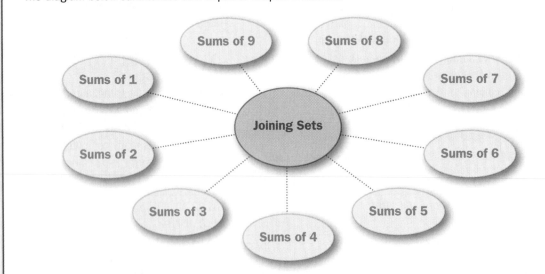

Chapter Assessment Manager

Diagnostic Diagnose students' readiness.

	Student Study Guide/ Teacher Edition	Assessment Masters	Technology
Intensive Intervention Placement Test		1–4	● ExamView® Assessment Suite
Section Pretest (Chapters 1–4)		6–7	● ExamView® Assessment Suite
Chapter 3 Pretest		29–30	● ExamView® Assessment Suite
Get Ready	SSG 34		Math Online ▷ macmillanmh.com StudentWorks™ Plus

Formative Identify students' misconceptions of content knowledge.

	Student Study Guide/ Teacher Edition	Assessment Masters	Technology
Progress Checks	SSG 39, 44		Math Online ▷ macmillanmh.com StudentWorks™ Plus
Vocabulary Review	TE 45		Math Online ▷ macmillanmh.com
Lesson Assessments			● ExamView® Assessment Suite

Summative Determine student success in learning the concepts in the lesson, chapter, or section.

	Student Study Guide/ Teacher Edition	Assessment Masters	Technology
Chapter 3 Test	SSG 46	32–33	● ExamView® Assessment Suite
Alternative Assessment	TE 46	37–38	● ExamView® Assessment Suite
See It, Say It, Do It, Write It	TE 35, 36, 37, 38, 41, 42, 43		
Section Test (Chapters 1–4)		39–40	● ExamView® Assessment Suite

Backmapping and Vertical Alignment McGraw-Hill's *Math Triumphs* intervention program was conceived and developed with the final result in mind: student success in grade-level mathematics, including Algebra 1 and beyond. The authors, using the **NCTM Focal Points and Focal Connections** as their guide, developed this brand-new series by backmapping from grade-level and Algebra 1 concepts, and vertically aligning the topics so that they build upon prior skills and concepts and serve as a foundation for future topics.

Chapter Resource Manager

TeacherWorks *Plus* ™
All-In-One Planner and Resource Center

	Lesson 3-1	**Lesson 3-2**	**Lesson 3-3**	**Lesson 3-4**
Concept	Sums of 1 and 2	Sums of 3 and 4	Sums of 5	Sums of 6
Objective	Join sets to make groups of one and two.	Join sets to make groups of three and four.	Join sets to make groups of five.	Join sets to make groups of six.
Math Vocabulary	add one two zero	four three	five	six
Lesson Resources	**Materials** • crayons **Manipulatives** • two-color counters **Other Resources** CRM Vocabulary and English Language Development CRM Skills Practice CRM Practice at Home	**Materials** • markers **Manipulatives** • two-color counters **Other Resources** CRM Vocabulary and English Language Development CRM Skills Practice CRM Practice at Home	**Materials** • paper **Manipulatives** • two-color counters **Other Resources** CRM Vocabulary and English Language Development CRM Skills Practice CRM Practice at Home	**Materials** • number cards • boxes **Manipulatives** • connecting cubes **Other Resources** CRM Vocabulary and English Language Development CRM Skills Practice CRM Practice at Home
Technology	**Math Online** ⟩ macmillanmh.com StudentWorks™ Plus ⊙ ExamView® Assessment Suite	**Math Online** ⟩ macmillanmh.com StudentWorks™ Plus ⊙ ExamView® Assessment Suite	**Math Online** ⟩ macmillanmh.com StudentWorks™ Plus ⊙ ExamView® Assessment Suite	**Math Online** ⟩ macmillanmh.com StudentWorks™ Plus ⊙ ExamView® Assessment Suite

Lesson 3-5	Lesson 3-6	Lesson 3-7	
Sums of 7	Sums of 8	Sums of 9	**Concept**
Join sets to make groups of seven.	Join sets to make groups of eight.	Join sets to make grorups of nine.	**Objective**
seven	eight	nine	**Math Vocabulary**
Materials • number cards	**Materials** • cardboard paper • crayons • number cards or index cards • paper • tape	**Materials** • box • colored paper • crayons • number line • pencils • self-stick notes	**Lesson Resources**
Manipulatives • counters	**Manipulatives** • connecting cubes • counters	**Manipulatives** • connecting cubes	
Other Resources **CRM** Vocabulary and English Language Development **CRM** Skills Practice **CRM** Practice at Home	**Other Resources** **CRM** Vocabulary and English Language Development **CRM** Skills Practice **CRM** Practice at Home	**Other Resources** **CRM** Vocabulary and English Language Development **CRM** Skills Practice **CRM** Practice at Home	
Math Online macmillanmh.com StudentWorks™ Plus 💿 ExamView® Assessment Suite	**Math Online** macmillanmh.com StudentWorks™ Plus 💿 ExamView® Assessment Suite	**Math Online** macmillanmh.com StudentWorks™ Plus 💿 ExamView® Assessment Suite	**Technology**

Chapter Notes

Home Connection

- Read the Home Connection letter with students and have them write their name in the space below.
- Read and explain the activity under Help at Home. If time allows, complete a portion of the activity so students can introduce the activity to a parent or other caregiver.

Real-World Applications

- Explain to students that we use addition and join sets for many things. Sometimes we need to use addition to count money.
- Show them a clear piggy bank, or other container, and drop in a penny. Ask how many pennies are in the bank. Continue, one penny at a time, up to nine.
- Empty the container and have students come up and drop in one penny at a time, counting the pennies in the container.

Math Online

Visit macmillanmh.com for ongoing support of chapter content and instruction, including:
- Online Games
- Concepts in Motion

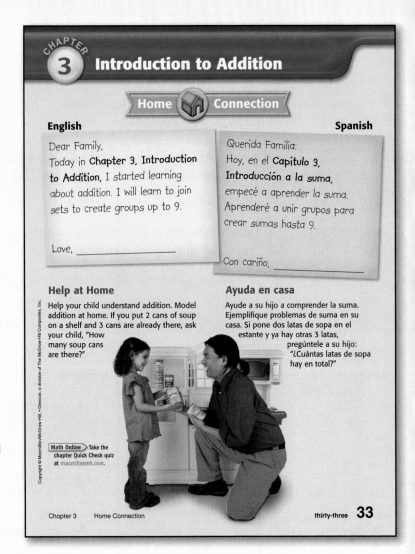

CHAPTER 3 **Introduction to Addition**

Home Connection

English

Dear Family,
Today in **Chapter 3, Introduction to Addition**, I started learning about addition. I will learn to join sets to create groups up to 9.

Love, _____

Spanish

Querida Familia:
Hoy, en el **Capítulo 3, Introducción a la suma,** empecé a aprender la suma. Aprenderé a unir grupos para crear sumas hasta 9.

Con cariño, _____

Help at Home

Help your child understand addition. Model addition at home. If you put 2 cans of soup on a shelf and 3 cans are already there, ask your child, "How many soup cans are there?"

Ayuda en casa

Ayude a su hijo a comprender la suma. Ejemplifique problemas de suma en su casa. Si pone dos latas de sopa en el estante y ya hay otras 3 latas, pregúntele a su hijo: "¿Cuántas latas de sopa hay en total?"

Math Online > Take the chapter Quick Check quiz at macmillanmh.com.

Chapter 3   Home Connection   thirty-three **33**

Key Vocabulary

Find interactive definitions in 13 languages in the **eGlossary** at macmillanmh.com.

English   Español *Introduce the most important vocabulary terms from Chapter 3.*

add   sumar
to join together sets to find the total or sum (p. 35A)

○   ○○   ○○○
1   2   3 in all

zero   cero
the number zero equals none or nothing (p. 35A)

one   uno
one more than zero (p. 35A)

○

two   dos
one more than one (p. 35A)

○○

three   tres
one more than two (p. 36A)

○○○

four   cuatro
one more than three (p. 36A)

○○○○

five   cinco
one more than four (p. 37A)

○○○○○

six   seis
one more than five (p. 38A)

○○○○○○

seven   siete
one more than six (p. 41A)

○○○○○○○

eight   ocho
one more than seven (p. 42A)

○○○○○○○○

Name _____

Get Ready

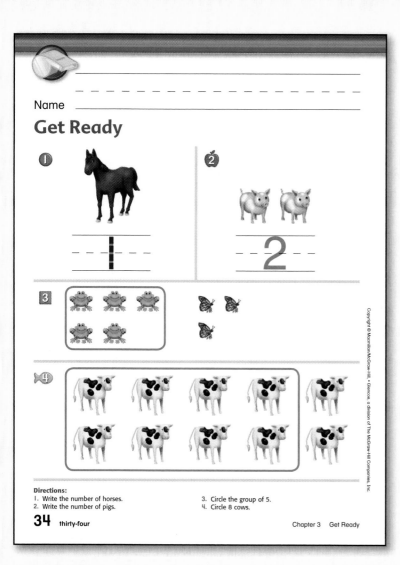

①

_____

②

_____

③

④

Directions:
1. Write the number of horses.
2. Write the number of pigs.
3. Circle the group of 5.
4. Circle 8 cows.

34 thirty-four

Chapter 3 Get Ready

Get Ready

Diagnostic Assessment

Have students complete the Get Ready exercises to assess readiness. Refer to the lessons below for additional support for prerequisite skills.

Exercises 1–4: Grade K, Chapter 1, Lessons 5–8 (pp. 9-12)

You may also assess student readiness with:
Assessment Masters: Chapter Pretest (pp. 29-30)

Math Online > macmillanmh.com
Online Readiness Quiz

Intervention Strategy

Use the following multi-step project to help students discover and explore all chapter concepts.

Step 1 Have students count classroom objects that number between one and nine, for example, clocks, doors, windows, lights.

Step 2 Have students draw a representation of each object and write its number.

Dinah Zike's Foldables

Guide students through the directions on p. A57 in the Chapter Resource Masters to create their own Foldable graphic organizer for use with this chapter.

 **Professional Development**

Targeted professional development has been articulated throughout the **McGraw-Hill's** *Math Triumphs* intervention program. The **McGraw-Hill Professional Development Video Library** provides short videos that support the **NCTM Focal Points and Focal Connections.** For more information, visit macmillanmh.com.

Model Lessons | Instructional Strategies

Vocabulary Preview

- Before students begin the chapter, write the vocabulary words on the board and read them to the class.
- Introduce the vocabulary words to the class, using picture definitions.
- Make index cards of the vocabulary words. Use the cards to remind students what they stand for or mean before every lesson.

Lesson 3-1

Sums of 1 and 2

Lesson Planner

Objective

Develop an understanding of joining sets to make groups of one and two.

Vocabulary

add   **two**

one   **zero**

Other Resources

Materials
crayons

Manipulatives
two-color counters

**On-Hand Manipulatives**
pennies

[CRM] Chapter Resource Masters
Vocabulary and English Language
  Development (p. A61)
Skills Practice (p. A62)
Practice at Home (p. A63)

Teacher Tech Tools
TeacherWorks™ Plus
Math Online > macmillanmh.com
Advance Tracker

Student Tech Tools
StudentWorks™ Plus
Math Online > macmillanmh.com
eGlossary

1 Introduce

- Tell students to hold out their hands, palms up. Ask how many pennies they are holding.
- Walk around the room and put a penny in each student's hand.
- Explain that you have *added* one penny to zero and repeat.
- Ask how many pennies they now have.
- Add another penny to each student's hand.
- Ask how many pennies they have now.

2 Teach

Key Concept

Foundational Skills and Concepts

- Tell students you will model addition of crayons.
- Show students one crayon in your hand and tell them that you will model *addition* of crayons by joining two groups.
- Put another crayon in your other hand and tell them that you have added one crayon to another crayon.
- **How many crayons are there in all?** 2
- Put down those crayons and pick up a new group of two crayons in one hand.
- Show the students your other, empty hand and ask how many crayons are in it. Tell them that they can add zero and ask how many crayons you have after adding zero. 2

Using Manipulatives

Two-Color Counters   Provide each student with 2 two-color counters and a sheet of paper.

- Have students draw a line down the center of the paper.
- Have students place one counter on one side of the paper.
- **How many counters are on the paper?** 1
- Have students place a counter to the other side of the paper.
- **How many counters are on the paper in all?** 2

Intervention Strategy

Kinesthetic Learners

Model Addition   One way to help students understand the concept of addition is modeling. To model making groups of one, create a large yarn circle. Tell students that when the circle is empty, it has zero people in it. Invite a student to enter the circle. Have students tell how many in all. To model a group of two, have another student join the first. Then have students tell how many in all.

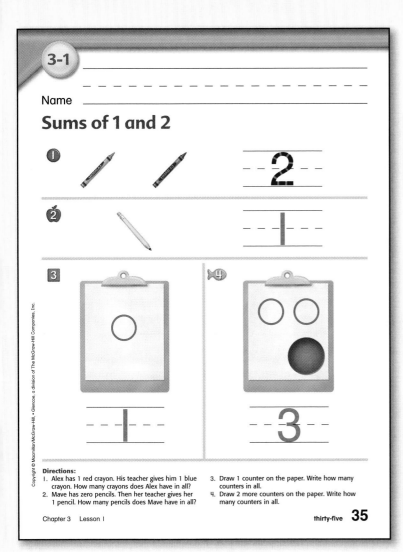

3-1

Name _____

Sums of 1 and 2

1. ✏️ ✏️   **2**

2. 🍎 ✏️   **1**

3. 📋 ○   **1**

4. 🐟 📋 ○ ○ ●   **3**

Directions:
1. Alex has 1 red crayon. His teacher gives him 1 blue crayon. How many crayons does Alex have in all?
2. Mave has zero pencils. Then her teacher gives her 1 pencil. How many pencils does Mave have in all?
3. Draw 1 counter on the paper. Write how many counters in all.
4. Draw 2 more counters on the paper. Write how many counters in all.

Chapter 3   Lesson 1

thirty-five **35**

③ Practice

Direct students to page 35 in their workbooks. Read the directions at the bottom of the student page as they complete the exercises.

For Exercises 1–4, give students counters so they can model the sets.

④ Assess

See It   Draw figures to show groups of 1 and 2, and have students identify how many in all.

Say It   Show students an addition scene or model a problem, and have them recite how one set joins another.

Do It   Pass out counters and have students model joining sets to get groups of 1 and 2.

Write It   Create addition story problems with groups of 1 and 2. Have students draw representations of the two groups and write how many in all.

English Learner Strategy

Rhyme Numbers   For students speaking English as a second language, invite them to make up rhymes to remember numbers *zero, one* and *two.* Suggested rhymes might include: "zero is a hero," "one is fun," and "two is blue."

Lesson 3-2

Sums of 3 and 4

Lesson Planner

Objective
Develop an understanding of joining sets to make groups of three and four.

Vocabulary

four

three

Other Resources

Materials
markers

Manipulatives
two-color counters

On-Hand Manipulatives
pencils

CRM Chapter Resource Masters
Vocabulary and English Language
  Development (p. A64)
Skills Practice (p. A65)
Practice at Home (p. A66)

Teacher Tech Tools
TeacherWorks™ Plus
Math Online > macmillanmh.com
Advance Tracker

Student Tech Tools
StudentWorks™ Plus
Math Online > macmillanmh.com
eGlossary

1 Introduce

- Create simple stories that involve joining sets.
- Have two students stand in front of the class.
- Tell a basic story that requires one more student and have a third student join.
- Then tell a story that requires two more students. Invite students to help create "joining" stories.

2 Teach

Key Concept

Foundational Skills and Concepts

- Tell students you will model addition of markers. Show them two markers. Tell them to count the markers.
- Then add one more marker.
- Discuss ways to say there were two markers joined by one.
- Ask them to tell how many markers there are in all. Repeat, modeling a group of four.

Using Manipulatives

Connecting Cubes   Provide each student with two connecting cubes already connected. Provide each student with a third connecting cube. Tell students to join two and one.

- **How many cubes do you have in all?** 3
- Distribute a fourth connecting cube and ask students to join three and one.
- **How many are there in all?** 4
- Ask students what other combination of cubes makes four. 0 and 4, 2 and 2, 1 and 3

Intervention Strategy   Visual Learners

Tree Models   Use visual models to help students comprehend addition. Distribute to each student a picture of a tree and four counters. Tell students the counters will be called "birds." Using the counters, have students copy as you model joining sets of "birds" to make groups of 3 and 4. Then have students draw their own birds on either side of the tree to model groups of 3 and 4.

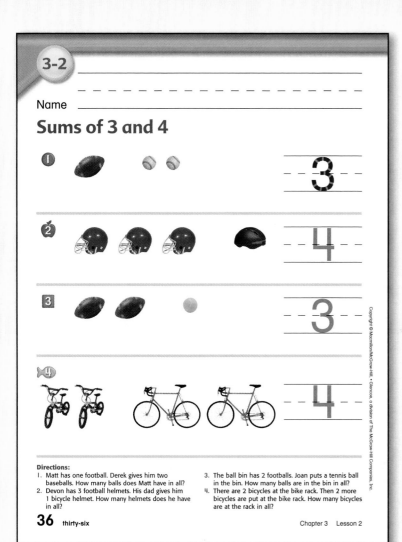

3-2

Name _____

Sums of 3 and 4

① 🏈 ⚾⚾ 3

② 🪖🪖🪖   🪖 4

③ 🏈🏈   ⚪ 3

④ 🚲🚲   🚴🚴 4

Directions:
1. Matt has one football. Derek gives him two baseballs. How many balls does Matt have in all?
2. Devon has 3 football helmets. His dad gives him 1 bicycle helmet. How many helmets does he have in all?
3. The ball bin has 2 footballs. Joan puts a tennis ball in the bin. How many balls are in the bin in all?
4. There are 2 bicycles at the bike rack. Then 2 more bicycles are put at the bike rack. How many bicycles are at the rack in all?

36 thirty-six

Chapter 3   Lesson 2

Direct students to page 36 in their workbooks. Read the directions at the bottom of the student page as they complete the exercises.

You might have students model the exercises with two-color counters.

4 Assess

See It Draw figures to show joining sets to get three and four, and have students identify how many there are in all.

Say It Show students an addition scene or model a problem, and have them say how one set joins another.

Do It Pass out connecting cubes and have students model joining sets to create groups of three and four.

Write It Have students draw scenarios showing people joining hands to create groups of three and four.

English Learner Strategy

Word Meanings Students may be confused by the fact that there are several words and expressions that mean the same things as the word *add*. Review all of these expressions (add, join, put together) with the students.

Sums of 5

Lesson Planner

Objective
Develop an understanding of joining sets to make groups of five.

Vocabulary
five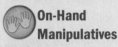

Other Resources

Materials
paper

Manipulatives
two-color counters

On-Hand Manipulatives
pennies

CRM Chapter Resource Masters
Vocabulary and English Language Development (p. A67)
Skills Practice (p. A68)
Practice at Home (p. A69)

Teacher Tech Tools
TeacherWorks™ Plus
Math Online > macmillanmh.com
Advance Tracker

Student Tech Tools
StudentWorks™ Plus
Math Online > macmillanmh.com
eGlossary

Intervention Strategy
Interpersonal Learners

Draw and Paste Animals Break students into pairs and assign each pair a type of animal (dogs, birds, fish). Tell one student in each pair to draw one animal and the other student to draw two animals. Have students cut and paste their animals onto one sheet of paper. Tell students that they have added, or joined, their animals. Ask how many animals they have in all.

1 Introduce

Invite four students to the front of the room. Show how different numbers of students combine to make groups of one, two, three, and four. Explain that when we make a group of two, we say, "One and one is two." Demonstrate making groups of three and four with student volunteers.

2 Teach

Key Concept
Foundational Skills and Concepts

- Draw five stars on the board. Ask how many stars there are. 5
- Circle the first star and put a box around the remaining four stars.
- **How many stars are in the circle?** 1 **How many stars are in the box?** 4 Tell students that this shows that a group of one and four is five.
- Draw five more stars on the board.
- Draw a circle around two stars and a box around the remaining three stars.
- **How many stars are in the circle?** 2 **How many stars are in the box?** 3 Tell students that this shows that the group of two and three is five.

Using Manipulatives

Two-Color Counters   Have students work with a partner. Provide one partner with two counters and the other partner with three counters.

- Ask students how many counters they have. Some will say two; some will say three.
- Ask students with three counters to give the counters to their partner.
- Ask students to count how many counters in all. 5

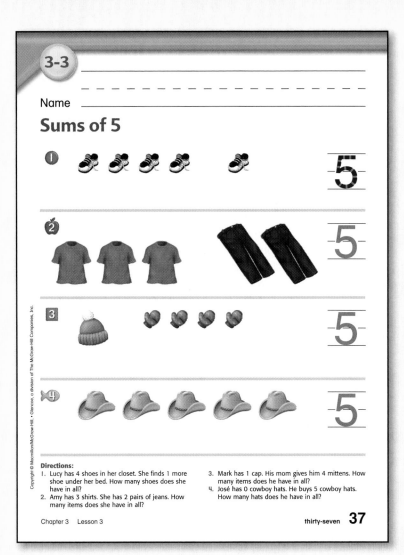

3-3

Name _____

Sums of 5

① 5

② 5

③ 5

④ 5

Directions:
1. Lucy has 4 shoes in her closet. She finds 1 more shoe under her bed. How many shoes does she have in all?
2. Amy has 3 shirts. She has 2 pairs of jeans. How many items does she have in all?
3. Mark has 1 cap. His mom gives him 4 mittens. How many items does he have in all?
4. José has 0 cowboy hats. He buys 5 cowboy hats. How many hats does he have in all?

Chapter 3 Lesson 3

thirty-seven **37**

③ Practice

Direct students to page 37 in their workbooks. Read the directions at the bottom of the student page as they complete the exercises.

Students can model the exercises with two-color counters.

④ Assess

See It   Show students two fingers on one hand and three fingers on the other hand. Ask how many fingers are showing in all. 5

Say It   Show students two sets of stars adding to five and have them give a sentence aloud, using "and" and "is." Sample answer: Two stars and three stars is five stars.

Do It   Pass out base-ten blocks and have students model joining sets to make groups of five.

Write It   Have students draw two sets of circles that equal five.

 Common Error Alert

Separating Counters   Some students may have difficulty keeping their counters separate. Tell students that they should use both hands as they count the counters. Have students move one counter at a time as they count to find how many there are in all.

Sums of 6

Lesson Planner

Objective
Develop an understanding of joining sets to make groups of six.

Vocabulary
six

Other Resources

Materials
boxes
number cards

Manipulatives
connecting cubes

 **On-Hand Manipulatives**
paper clips

CRM Chapter Resource Masters
Vocabulary and English Language Development (p. A70)
Skills Practice (p. A71)
Practice at Home (p. A72)

Teacher Tech Tools
TeacherWorks™ Plus
Math Online > macmillanmh.com
Advance Tracker

Student Tech Tools
StudentWorks™ Plus
Math Online > macmillanmh.com
eGlossary

① Introduce

- Ask three students to stand in front of the board.
- Write the number "3" on the board above the students.
- Say that you need three more students. Ask them to stand in front of the board, but away from the other group of students. Write the number "3" on the board above this group of students.
- Have students count how many students there are in all. Write this number to the right of the two groups.

② Teach

Key Concept

Foundational Skills and Concepts
- Show students a set of four boxes. Have students count the boxes as you point to each box in the set.
- Show students a set of two boxes. Have students count the boxes as you point to each box in the set.
- Invite a volunteer to join the sets. Ask students to count the boxes as you point to each box in the joined sets.
- Explain to students that joining the sets makes a group of six.

Using Manipulatives

Connecting Cubes Provide each student with six connected cubes.
- Have students break the cubes into two groups, or sets.
- **How many connecting cubes are in each group?**
  Sample answers: 5 and 1; 4 and 2; 3 and 3
- Tell students to reconnect the cubes. Ask students to break the cubes again, making sets with different numbers each time.

Intervention Strategy
Interpersonal Learners

Join Sets Organize students into pairs. Have each pair create an addition story. Have students draw pictures representing the joining of two sets of people, animals, or objects. Student pairs then use number cards to represent the sets and the sum. Invite pairs to present their work to the class.

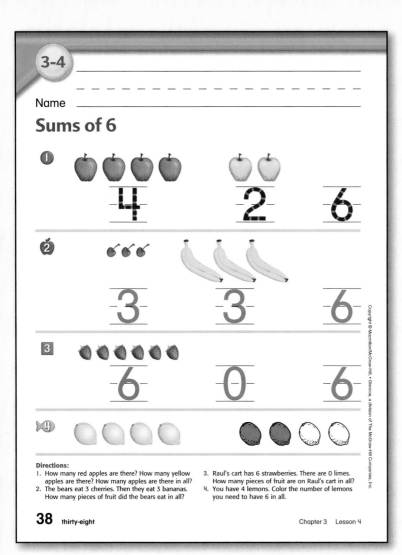

3-4

Name _____

Sums of 6

1. 🍎🍎🍎🍎   🍏🍏
   4   2   6

2. 🍒🍒🍒   🍌🍌🍌
   3   3   6

3. 🍓🍓🍓🍓🍓🍓
   6   0   6

4. 🍋🍋🍋🍋   🥔🥔🍋🍋

Directions:
1. How many red apples are there? How many yellow apples are there? How many apples are there in all?
2. The bears eat 3 cherries. Then they eat 3 bananas. How many pieces of fruit did the bears eat in all?
3. Raul's cart has 6 strawberries. There are 0 limes. How many pieces of fruit are on Raul's cart in all?
4. You have 4 lemons. Color the number of lemons you need to have 6 in all.

38 thirty-eight

Chapter 3   Lesson 4

③ Practice

Direct students to page 38 in their workbooks. Read the directions at the bottom of the student page as they complete the exercises.

For Exercise 4, suggest that students count on from four.

④ Assess

See It   Use manipulatives or draw figures to show sets of one through five. Have students select the appropriate sets to make six.

Say It   Show students a set of two and then a set of four. Have students give an explanation of joining the sets. Sample answer: "If I have two and a friend gives me four more, then I have six in all."

Do It   Pass out counters and have students model joining sets to make groups of six.

Write It   Draw figures to show joining sets that make a group of six. Have students write the number in each set and how many in all.

Math Coach Notes

Finding Sums   Focus on one sum at a time, rather than stressing the addition of particular addends. Students may become confused if they are asked to add groups of numbers with different sums.

Progress Check 1

Formative Assessment

Use the Progress Check to assess students' mastery of the previous lessons. Have students review the lesson indicated for the problems they answered incorrectly.

 Common Error Alert

Adding with Zero Make sure students understand that adding zero to a number does not change the number at all. They should not put a zero in the ones place (for example, one and zero is ten) or alter the number in any other way. Remind them that joining a number with zero means there will be the same number in all.

Vocabulary Make sure students understand that adding two numbers is the same as counting how many objects they have in all.

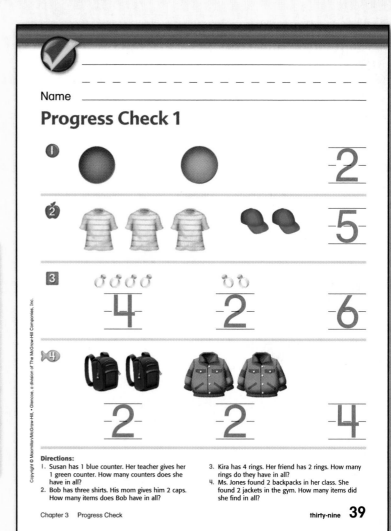

Directions:
1. Susan has 1 blue counter. Her teacher gives her 1 green counter. How many counters does she have in all?
2. Bob has three shirts. His mom gives him 2 caps. How many items does Bob have in all?
3. Kira has 4 rings. Her friend has 2 rings. How many rings do they have in all?
4. Ms. Jones found 2 backpacks in her class. She found 2 jackets in the gym. How many items did she find in all?

Chapter 3   Progress Check   thirty-nine **39**

Data-Driven Decision Making

Students missing Exercises . . .	Have trouble with . . .	Should review and practice . . .
1	groups of one and two.	TE Lesson 3-1, p. 35 CRM Skills Practice, p. A62
2	groups of five.	TE Lesson 3-3, p. 37 CRM Skills Practice, p. A68
3	groups of six.	TE Lesson 3-4, p. 38 CRM Skills Practice, p. A71
4	groups of three and four.	TE Lesson 3-2, p. 36 CRM Skills Practice, p. A65

Name

Replay

Directions:

Step 1: Color the engine blue. How many cars have you colored in all?

Step 2: Color 2 train cars red. How many cars have you colored in all?

Step 3: Color 1 train car green. How many cars have you colored in all?

Step 4: Color 2 train cars yellow. How many cars have you colored in all?

40 forty

Chapter 3 Replay

Replay

Use the Replay activity to review and reinforce concepts and skills presented in Lessons 3-1, 3-2, 3-3, and 3-4.

Instructions

Explain that the engine is the first car of the train. Tell students to color the number of train cars as you direct them. Then, after each step, have them count how many train cars are colored.

Student Technology

Students can use the following technology resources to reinforce chapter content.

🔵 StudentWorks™ Plus

Math Online ▷ macmillanmh.com

- eGames
- eGlossary

Sums of 7

Lesson Planner

Objective
Develop an understanding of joining sets to make groups of 7.

Vocabulary
seven

Other Resources

Materials
number cards

Manipulatives
counters

 **On-Hand
Manipulatives**
paper clips

CRM Chapter Resource Masters
Vocabulary and English Language
  Development (p. A73)
Skills Practice (p. A74)
Practice at Home (p. A75)

Teacher Tech Tools
TeacherWorks™ Plus
Math Online > macmillanmh.com
Advance Tracker

Student Tech Tools
StudentWorks™ Plus
Math Online > macmillanmh.com
eGlossary

1 Introduce

- Show students a clear glass.
- Add one ounce of water three separate times. Use a marker to mark the level of the water after each ounce is added.
- Have a student add four ounces of water separately to the glass. Use a marker to mark the new level of the water.
- Students should be able to see that when they join the waters, the level of water in the glass increases.

2 Teach

Key Concept

Foundational Skills and Concepts   Show students seven connecting cubes. Tell students that there are many ways to join sets to make a group of seven.

- Have volunteers suggest possible combinations.
- Model each combination to see if it makes a group of seven. If a suggested combination does not make a group of seven, have students count the blocks to find out why.

Using Manipulatives

Connecting Cubes   Distribute seven connecting cubes to each student.

As you demonstrate the combinations that make seven, have students copy the combinations at their desks using their cubes.

Intervention Strategy   Logical Learners

Connecting Cubes   Use connecting cubes to show joining of the following sets: seven and zero, zero and seven; six and one, one and six; five and two, two and five; three and four, four and three. Discuss whether each pair is the same or not. Show students that joining sets is not affected by the order of the sets.

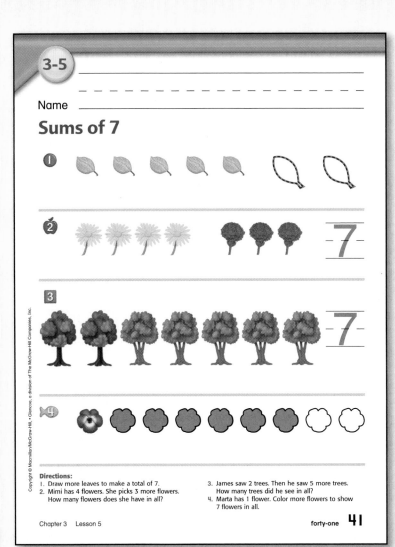

3-5

Name _____

Sums of 7

① 🍃 🍃 🍃 🍃 🍃 🍃 🍃

② 🌼 🌼 🌼 🌼   🌸 🌸 🌸   7

③ 🌳 🌳 🌳 🌳 🌳 🌳 🌳   7

④ 🌸 🌸 🌸 🌸 🌸 🌸 🌸 🌸 🌸

Directions:
1. Draw more leaves to make a total of 7.
2. Mimi has 4 flowers. She picks 3 more flowers. How many flowers does she have in all?
3. James saw 2 trees. Then he saw 5 more trees. How many trees did he see in all?
4. Marta has 1 flower. Color more flowers to show 7 flowers in all.

Chapter 3   Lesson 5

forty-one **41**

③ Practice

Direct students to page 41 in their workbooks. Read the directions at the bottom of the student page as they complete the exercises.

For Exercises 1 and 4, suggest that students count on to color the total number of items.

④ Assess

See It   Use manipulatives or draw figures to show joining sets to make seven. Then use number cards to show the addition sentence.

Say It   Draw a set of figures and ask students how many they need to make seven. Write the number in each set and the number for how many there are in all.

Do It   Distribute counters and have students model joining sets to make groups of seven.

Write It   Draw a set of three figures and a set of four figures. Have students write the numbers in each group and draw how many there are in all.

Intervention Strategy   Auditory Learners

Joining Sets   Reinforce the concept of addition as putting two groups together. Provide sentences to help students verbalize: seven and zero is seven, one and six is seven, five and two is seven, three and four is seven.

Sums of 8

Lesson Planner

Objective
Develop an understanding of joining sets to make groups of eight.

Vocabulary
eight

Other Resources

Materials
cardboard paper
crayons
number cards or index cards
paper
tape

Manipulatives
connecting cubes
counters

 **On-Hand Manipulatives**
paper clips
pennies

CRM Chapter Resource Masters
Vocabulary and English Language
    Development (p. A76)
Skills Practice (p. A77)
Practice at Home (p. A78)

Teacher Tech Tools
TeacherWorks™ Plus

Math Online > macmillanmh.com
Advance Tracker

Student Tech Tools
StudentWorks™ Plus

Math Online > macmillanmh.com
eGlossary

Intervention Strategy
Interpersonal Learners

Drawing Addition   Give each student a sheet of paper and crayons. Each student will draw one to four people on a sheet. Organize students into pairs. Have pairs display their drawings and tell how many people there are in all. Encourage students to create addition sentences using number cards. If there is time, have students rotate partners and create new sentences.

① Introduce

- Make index cards with one of the following numbers: 0, 1, 2, 3, 4, 5, 6, 7, 8.
- Have nine students each hold one card.
- Have these students and the rest of the class work together to find pairs that make a group of eight.
- When all students are paired, explain that there are several ways to join sets to have eight in all.

② Teach

Key Concept
Foundational Skills and Concepts
- On the board, tape eight sheets of paper in two rows of four. Ask students to count the sheets of paper as you point to them. Write "8" below the papers.
- Move one sheet of paper to the other side of the board.
- Ask students to count the sheets of paper in each set as you point to them. Erase "8" and write "7" under the set of seven and a "1" under the set of one. Explain to students that the set of seven and one is eight.
- Continue moving and counting sheets of paper until all eight sheets have been moved.

Using Manipulatives

Connecting Cubes   Give each student cubes connected in the following sets: one red, two orange, three purple, four yellow, five green, six red, seven orange. Have students arrange their cubes from longest to smallest.
- **How many cubes are connected in your longest set?** 7
- **Which set could you join with these seven cubes to have eight in all?** the set of one cube
- Repeat with the remaining sets of cubes until all the sets have been joined to make eight.

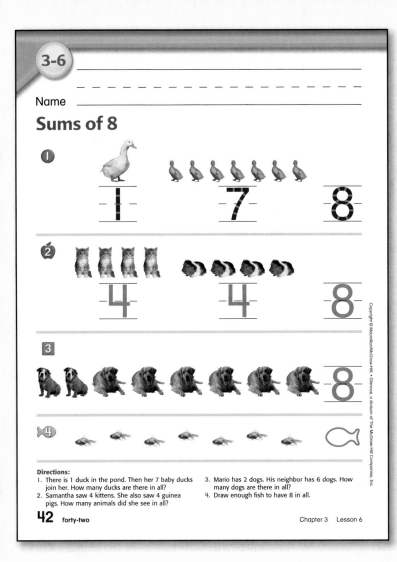

3-6

Name _____

Sums of 8

① = 1 ... 7 = 8

② = 4 ... 4 = 8

③ = 8

④ = ◇

Directions:
1. There is 1 duck in the pond. Then her 7 baby ducks join her. How many ducks are there in all?
2. Samantha saw 4 kittens. She also saw 4 guinea pigs. How many animals did she see in all?
3. Mario has 2 dogs. His neighbor has 6 dogs. How many dogs are there in all?
4. Draw enough fish to have 8 in all.

42 forty-two

Chapter 3 Lesson 6

Copyright © Macmillan/McGraw-Hill • Glencoe, a division of The McGraw-Hill Companies, Inc.

---

③ Practice

Direct students to page 42 in their workbooks. Read the directions at the bottom of the student page as they complete the exercises.

For Exercise 4, be sure that students count the seven fish correctly.

④ Assess

See It Use manipulatives or draw figures to show joining sets to make eight. Then use number cards to show how many are in each set and how many there are in all.

Say It Have students recite the following rhyme: "Four plus four, it equals eight. Adding numbers is so great."

Do It Distribute counters and have students model joining sets to make groups of eight.

Write It Give students papers with numbers "1" through "7" on them. Have students draw additional figures or Xs to make eight in all.

⚠ Common Error Alert

Students make occasional errors in counting. Emphasize that when counting sets of objects students should start at the top or the left. They should place a finger on the first object and carefully count down or to the right. Encourage students to count aloud while pointing to each object in a set, or mark each object to make sure each is counted and that none are left out.

Lesson 3-6 Sums of 8   **42**

Sums of 9

Lesson Planner

Objective
Develop an understanding of addition and successfully make groups of nine.

Vocabulary
nine

Materials
box
colored paper
crayons
number line
pencils
self-stick notes

Manipulatives
connecting cubes

 **On-Hand Manipulatives**
paper clips

Other Resources

 **Chapter Resource Masters**
Vocabulary and English Language Development (p. A79)
Skills Practice (p. A80)
Practice at Home (p. A81)

Teacher Tech Tools
TeacherWorks™ Plus
Math Online ＞ macmillanmh.com
Advance Tracker

Student Tech Tools
StudentWorks™ Plus
Math Online ＞ macmillanmh.com
eGlossary

① Introduce

- Draw eight stars on the board in two rows of four.
- Ask the students to count the stars as you point to them.
- Ask a student to draw another star below the eight stars.
- Ask the students to count the stars again as you point to them.
- Explain to students that you had eight stars, the volunteer gave you one more and now there are nine in all.

② Teach

Key Concept

Foundational Skills and Concepts
- Place nine markers in a box.
- Ask a student to take some markers out of the box. As a class, count the markers. Write this number on the board.
- Ask another student to grab the rest of the markers out of the box. As a class, count the markers. Write this number on the board.
- Then count all the markers from both students. Write this number on the board.
- Place all nine markers back in the box and repeat the exercise again with different students.

Using Manipulatives

Connecting Cubes Arrange the class in pairs. Give ten connecting cubes and a sheet of colored paper to each pair.
- Tell one partner to make a pile of five cubes on the paper.
- Tell the other partner to add four more cubes to the pile on the paper.
- **How many cubes are now on the paper?** 9
- Write the number "9" on the board.
- Discuss different addition sentences that make nine and have students model them with their cubes.

Intervention Strategy   Visual Learners

Number Line Supply students with a number line and some self-stick notes. Instruct the class that the self-stick notes can serve as markers for counting on. Give students sets of numbers such as two and four. Instruct them to place the marker at the number two, and then to count up four more to find the answer. Assist any student having difficulty.

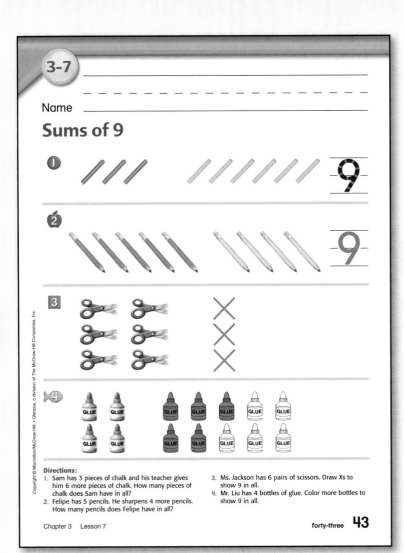

Name

Sums of 9

Directions:

1. Sam has 3 pieces of chalk and his teacher gives him 6 more pieces of chalk. How many pieces of chalk does Sam have in all?
2. Felipe has 5 pencils. He sharpens 4 more pencils. How many pencils does Felipe have in all?
3. Ms. Jackson has 6 pairs of scissors. Draw Xs to show 9 in all.
4. Mr. Liu has 4 bottles of glue. Color more bottles to show 9 in all.

Chapter 3   Lesson 7

forty-three **43**

③ Practice

Direct students to page 43 in their workbooks. Read the directions at the bottom of the student page as they complete the exercises.

For Exercises 1 and 4, have students count on to nine.

④ Assess

See It   Show students four crayons and five pencils. Have them say how many there are in all.

Say It   Have students recite the following rhyme: "Five plus four, it equals nine. Adding numbers is so fine."

Do It   Ask students to use manipulatives to create a group of two objects and a group of seven objects. Have them say how many there are in all.

Write It   Have students divide a piece of paper in half. Ask students to draw a circle on each side of the paper. Have them continue drawing circles until they have drawn nine circles in all.

Progress Check 2

Formative Assessment

Use the Progress Check to assess students' mastery of the previous lessons. Have students review the lesson indicated for the problems they answered incorrectly.

 Common Error Alert

Counting to Add Make sure that students understand it is easiest to count from left to right when finding the number of objects in a group or when adding groups of objects.

Exercises 2 and 4 Be sure students understand that they are counting all the pieces of fruit, not the types of fruit.

Exercise 5 Be sure students understand that they are not being asked to draw seven more oranges. They are being asked to draw enough oranges so that there are seven oranges altogether.

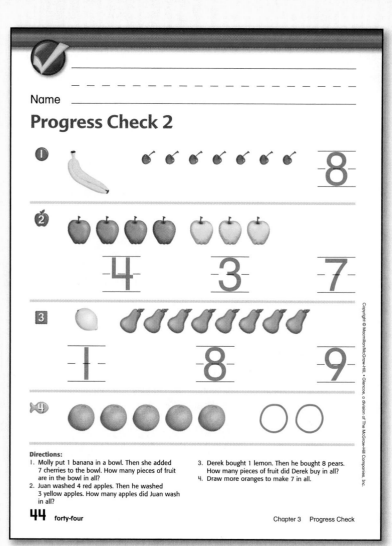

Name _____

Progress Check 2

① 8

② 4   3   7

③ 1   8   9

④

Directions:
1. Molly put 1 banana in a bowl. Then she added 7 cherries to the bowl. How many pieces of fruit are in the bowl in all?
2. Juan washed 4 red apples. Then he washed 3 yellow apples. How many apples did Juan wash in all?
3. Derek bought 1 lemon. Then he bought 8 pears. How many pieces of fruit did Derek buy in all?
4. Draw more oranges to make 7 in all.

44 forty-four

Chapter 3 Progress Check

Data-Driven Decision Making

Students missing Exercises . . .	Have trouble with . . .	Should review and practice . . .
1	groups of 8.	**TE** Lesson 3-6, p. 42 **CRM** Skills Practice, p. A77
2	groups of 7.	**TE** Lesson 3-5, p. 41 **CRM** Skills Practice, p. A74
3	groups of 9.	**TE** Lesson 3-7, p. 43 **CRM** Skills Practice, p. A80
4	groups of 7.	**TE** Lesson 3-5, p. 41 **CRM** Skills Practice, p. A74

Intervention Strategies

Sums with Strings Activity

Materials:

- 9 large beads, buttons, or tube-shaped pasta
- cardboard paper
- length of yarn or string

Step 1   Organize students into pairs.

Step 2   Distribute to each pair of students a length of yarn or string and 9 large beads, buttons, or pasta.

Step 3   Have pairs say how many pieces are on the string. zero
Have pairs add one piece to the string. Ask how many pieces are now on the string. one
Have pairs add another piece to the string. Ask how many pieces there are on the string. two
Have pairs continue the activity until they have put all nine pieces on the string.

Step 4   Repeat, starting with one or two pieces, adding more than one at a time. Continue using pieces to get sums with different addends. Use all one color or kind of object to represent each addend.

Step 5   Give pairs a sheet of cardboard paper. On it, have them paste the string and some of the objects to create a visual representation. Have them write the number of objects represented.

Sums to 9

Materials: none

Step 1   Tell students they are going to role-play making groups of 9.

Step 2   Have students act out the following scenario: two students are in the reading room; two students join them.

Step 3   Ask how many students are now in the reading room. four

Step 4   Have students act out other scenarios. Instruct them to tell how many students there are in all. Suggested scenarios:

- Three students are having lunch. Five students join them.
- Five students are in line. Three students join them.
- Three birds are on a wire. Four birds join them.
- One cow is eating hay. Six more cows join the cow.

Verbal Instructions

In verbal instructions, give an example of what is expected. Help students understand and accomplish oral instructions by copying the example.

Time Management

Use this activity at any point during the course of the chapter instruction. Modify it by having students use stamps and stamp pads in place of string and objects with holes.

Time Management

Use this activity as a post-chapter activity. Modify it by assigning numbers to individual students and having one student join another. Classmates would then state the addition sentence and tell how many students there are. Encourage students to use their own scenarios.

Review

Vocabulary

If students have difficulty answering exercises 1–4, use the page references below to review the vocabulary words, or refer to them in the glossary.

add (p. 35A)	**seven** (p. 41A)
eight (p. 42A)	**six** (p. 38A)
five (p. 37A)	**three** (p. 36A)
four (p. 36A)	**two** (p. 35A)
nine (p. 43A)	**zero** (p. 35A)
one (p. 35A)	

Vocabulary Review Strategies

Write numbers "1" through "9" on index cards. Place two number cubes on each index card. Ask the students to arrange the number cubes so that when they join the numbers on the number cubes the sum is the same as the number on the index card.

Concepts

The exercises in this section are grouped to cover content from each lesson in the chapter.

Exercise 1: Lesson 3-4
Exercise 2: Lesson 3-6
Exercise 3: Lesson 3-3
Exercise 4: Lesson 3-5

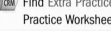 Find Extra Practice for these concepts in the Practice Worksheets, pp. A61–A81.

 **Dinah Zike's Foldables**

Have students use the Foldable they created at the beginning of the chapter to review and reinforce the concepts and skills they learned during the chapter. (See Chapter Resource Masters p. A57 for instructions.)

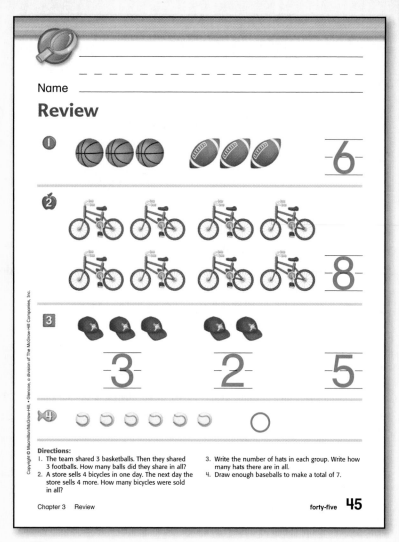

Name _____

Review

① ⚫⚫⚫ 🏈🏈🏈   6

② 🚲🚲🚲🚲 🚲🚲🚲🚲   8

③ 🧢🧢🧢   🧢🧢   3   2   5

④ ◡◡◡◡◡◡   ○

Directions:
1. The team shared 3 basketballs. Then they shared 3 footballs. How many balls did they share in all?
2. A store sells 4 bicycles in one day. The next day the store sells 4 more. How many bicycles were sold in all?
3. Write the number of hats in each group. Write how many hats there are in all.
4. Draw enough baseballs to make a total of 7.

Chapter 3 Review

⚠️ **Common Error Alert**

Addition as Combining   Make sure that students understand addition is a process of combining two groups, not counting each group separately. Emphasize that even in problems that single out separate sets, this is a leaping off point to explain how numbers change with addition (they combine and grow).

Intervention Strategy   **Visual Learners**

Zero Concepts   Show an empty bag to the class. Make sure students understand there is nothing in the bag. Write the number "0" on the board. Have a volunteer place three balls in the bag. Write "3" on the board. Ask the class how many balls are in the bag now. Write "3" on the board again.

Review the meaning of the numbers with the students. Say, "I had zero balls in the bag. You put three balls in the bag. Now there are three balls in all in the bag," pointing to each symbol as you say it. Then repeat the process, starting with one ball and adding more.

Test

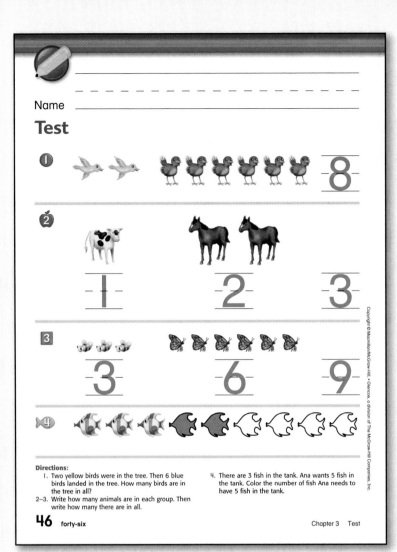

1.  8

2. 1   2   3

3. 3   6   9

4.

Directions:
1. Two yellow birds were in the tree. Then 6 blue birds landed in the tree. How many birds are in the tree in all?
2–3. Write how many animals are in each group. Then write how many there are in all.

4. There are 3 fish in the tank. Ana wants 5 fish in the tank. Color the number of fish Ana needs to have 5 fish in the tank.

46 forty-six

Chapter 3   Test

Test

Chapter Resource Masters

Additional forms of the Chapter 3 Tests are available.

Test Format	Where to Find it
Chapter 3 Test	**Math Online** ⟩ macmillanmh.com
Blackline Masters	Assessment Masters, pp. 32–33

Alternative Assessment

Assess students' proficiency with addition by monitoring portfolios of their work, by watching them solve problems on the board, and by using models, number lines, or drawings. Students who have trouble with paper-testing can demonstrate mastery by modeling addition with connecting cubes and describing the groups.

ExamView®
Assessment Suite

Customize and create multiple versions of your chapter tests and their answer keys. All of these questions from the chapter tests are available on ExamView® Assessment Suite.

Advance TRACKER

This online assessment tool allows teachers to track student progress with easily accessible, comprehensive reports available for every student. Assess students using any internet-ready computer.

Data-Driven Decision Making

Students missing Exercises . . .	Have trouble with . . .	Should review and practice . . .
1	groups of eight.	TE Lesson 3-6, p. 42 CRM Skills Practice, p. A77
2	groups of three and four.	TE Lesson 3-2, p. 36 CRM Skills Practice, p. A65
3	groups of nine.	TE Lesson 3-7, p. 43 CRM Skills Practice, p. A80
4	groups of five.	TE Lesson 3-3, p. 37 CRM Skills Practice, p. A68

Chapter Overview

Chapter-at-a-Glance

Lesson	Math Objective	State/Local Standards
4-1 Take Away from 1 and 2 (pp. 49A–49)	Learn to subtract from 1 and 2.	
4-2 Take Away from 3 and 4 (pp. 50A–50)	Learn to subtract from 3 and 4.	
4-3 Take Away from 5 (pp. 51A–51)	Learn to subtract from 5.	
4-4 Take Away from 6 (pp. 52A–52)	Learn to subtract from 6.	
Progress Check 1 (p. 53)		
4-5 Take Away from 7 (pp. 55A–55)	Learn to subtract from 7.	
4-6 Take Away from 8 (pp. 56A–56)	Learn to subtract from 8.	
4-7 Take Away from 9 (pp. 57A–57)	Learn to subtract from 9.	
Progress Check 2 (p. 58)		

Content-at-a-Glance

The diagram below summarizes and unpacks Chapter 4 content.

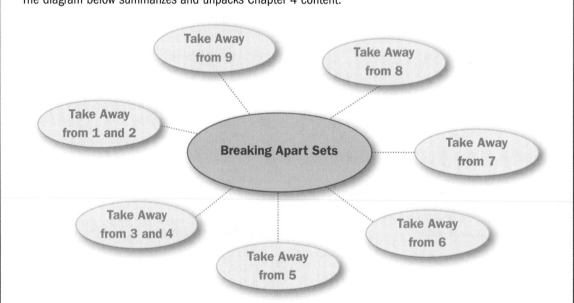

Chapter Assessment Manager

Diagnostic Diagnose students' readiness.

	Student Study Guide/ Teacher Edition	Assessment Masters	Technology
Intensive Intervention Placement Test		1–4	● ExamView® Assessment Suite
Section Pretest (Chapters 1–4)		42–43	● ExamView® Assessment Suite
Chapter 4 Pretest		45–46	● ExamView® Assessment Suite
Get Ready	SSG 48		Math Online ▷ macmillanmh.com StudentWorks™ Plus

Formative Identify students' misconceptions of content knowledge.

	Student Study Guide/ Teacher Edition	Assessment Masters	Technology
Progress Checks	SSG 53, 58		Math Online ▷ macmillanmh.com StudentWorks™ Plus
Vocabulary Review	TE 59		Math Online ▷ macmillanmh.com
Lesson Assessments			● ExamView® Assessment Suite

Summative Determine student success in learning the concepts in the lesson, chapter, or section.

	Student Study Guide/ Teacher Edition	Assessment Masters	Technology
Chapter 4 Test	SSG 60	48–49	● ExamView® Assessment Suite
Alternative Assessment	TE 60	53–54	● ExamView® Assessment Suite
See It, Say It, Do It, Write It	TE 49, 50, 51, 52, 55, 56, 57		
Section Test (Chapters 1–4)		75–76	● ExamView® Assessment Suite

Backmapping and Vertical Alignment McGraw-Hill's *Math Triumphs* intervention program was conceived and developed with the final result in mind: student success in grade-level mathematics, including Algebra 1 and beyond. The authors, using the **NCTM Focal Points and Focal Connections** as their guide, developed this brand-new series by backmapping from grade-level and Algebra 1 concepts, and vertically aligning the topics so that they build upon prior skills and concepts and serve as a foundation for future topics.

TeacherWorks™ Plus
All-In-One Planner and Resource Center

	Lesson 4-1	Lesson 4-2	Lesson 4-3	Lesson 4-4
Concept	Take Away from 1 and 2	Take Away from 3 and 4	Take Away from 5	Take Away from 6
Objective	Learn to subtract from 1 and 2.	Learn to subtract from 3 and 4.	Learn to subtract from 5.	Learn to subtract from 6.
Math Vocabulary	one subtract take away two	four three	five	six
Lesson Resources	**Materials** • boxes • crayons • paper • pencils **Manipulatives** • two-color counters **Other Resources** CRM Vocabulary and English Language Development CRM Skills Practice CRM Practice at Home	**Materials** • books • paper clips • pennies **Manipulatives** • connecting cubes • two-color counters **Other Resources** CRM Vocabulary and English Language Development CRM Skills Practice CRM Practice at Home	**Materials** • buttons • erasers • markers • small objects **Manipulatives** • attribute buttons • two-color counters **Other Resources** CRM Vocabulary and English Language Development CRM Skills Practice CRM Practice at Home	**Materials** • balls or eggs • colored paper • egg carton • paper clips • small objects **Manipulatives** • connecting cubes **Other Resources** CRM Vocabulary and English Language Development CRM Skills Practice CRM Practice at Home
Technology	**Math Online**⟩ macmillanmh.com StudentWorks™ Plus 🔘 ExamView® Assessment Suite	**Math Online**⟩ macmillanmh.com StudentWorks™ Plus 🔘 ExamView® Assessment Suite	**Math Online**⟩ macmillanmh.com StudentWorks™ Plus 🔘 ExamView® Assessment Suite	**Math Online**⟩ macmillanmh.com StudentWorks™ Plus 🔘 ExamView® Assessment Suite

Lesson 4-5	Lesson 4-6	Lesson 4-7	
Take Away from 7	Take Away from 8	Take Away from 9	**Concept**
Learn to subtract from 7.	Learn to subtract from 8.	Learn to subtract from 9.	**Objective**
seven	eight	nine	**Math Vocabulary**
Materials • buttons • paper • pencils • teacher-prepared picture cards **Manipulatives** • color tiles • pennies • spinner • two-color counters **Other Resources** CRM Vocabulary and English Language Development CRM Skills Practice CRM Practice at Home	**Materials** • buttons • crayons • paper • pencils • small bags • teacher-prepared subtraction page **Manipulatives** • connecting cubes • two-color counters **Other Resources** CRM Vocabulary and English Language Development CRM Skills Practice CRM Practice at Home	**Materials** • index cards • pictures • teacher-prepared number cards **Manipulatives** • connecting cubes **Other Resources** CRM Vocabulary and English Language Development CRM Skills Practice CRM Practice at Home	**Lesson Resources**
Math Online macmillanmh.com StudentWorks™ Plus ● ExamView® Assessment Suite	**Math Online** macmillanmh.com StudentWorks™ Plus ● ExamView® Assessment Suite	**Math Online** macmillanmh.com StudentWorks™ Plus ● ExamView® Assessment Suite	**Technology**

Chapter Notes

Home Connection

- Read the Home Connection letter with students and have them write their names in the space below.
- Read and explain the activity under Help at Home. If time allows, complete a portion of the activity so students can introduce the activity to a parent or other caregiver.

Real-World Applications

- Arrange students in groups of 4. Give one student in each group 6 to 8 crayons.
- Have students tell how many crayons they have.
- Tell students to give 1 crayon to another group member.
- **Now how many crayons do you have?** See students' work.
- Instruct students to give away 2 more crayons. Repeat the question. Discuss how sets become smaller when objects are taken away.
- Give the set of crayons to another student and repeat the activity.

| Math Online >

Visit macmillanmh.com for ongoing support of chapter content and instruction, including:
- Online Games
- Concepts in Motion

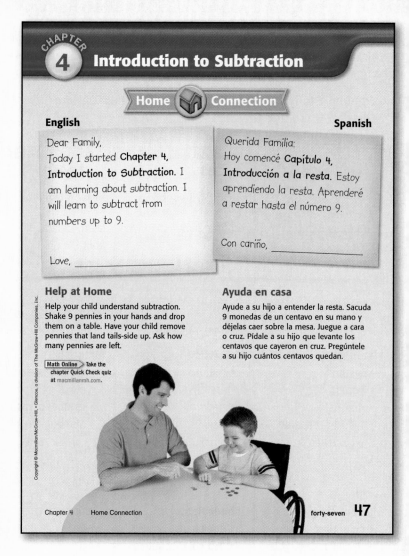

Introduction to Subtraction

Home Connection

English

Dear Family,
Today I started **Chapter 4, Introduction to Subtraction.** I am learning about subtraction. I will learn to subtract from numbers up to 9.

Love, _____

Spanish

Querida Familia:
Hoy comencé **Capítulo 4, Introducción a la resta.** Estoy aprendiendo la resta. Aprenderé a restar hasta el número 9.

Con cariño, _____

Help at Home

Help your child understand subtraction. Shake 9 pennies in your hands and drop them on a table. Have your child remove pennies that land tails-side up. Ask how many pennies are left.

Math Online > Take the chapter Quick Check quiz at macmillanmh.com.

Ayuda en casa

Ayude a su hijo a entender la resta. Sacuda 9 monedas de un centavo en su mano y déjelas caer sobre la mesa. Juegue a cara o cruz. Pídale a su hijo que levante los centavos que cayeron en cruz. Pregúntele a su hijo cuántos centavos quedan.

Copyright © Macmillan/McGraw-Hill, a division of The McGraw-Hill Companies, Inc.

Key Vocabulary

Find interactive definitions in 13 languages in the **eGlossary** at macmillanmh.com.

English   Español *Introduce the most important vocabulary terms from Chapter 4.*

one uno (p. 49A)	1	○
two dos (p. 49A)	2	○○
three tres (p. 50A)	3	○○○
four cuatro (p. 50A)	4	○○○○
five cinco (p. 51A)	5	○○○○○

six seis (p. 52A)	6	○○○○○○
seven siete (p. 55A)	7	○○○○○○○
eight ocho (p. 56A)	8	○○○○○○○○
nine nueve (p. 57A)	9	○○○○○○○○○

subtract   restar To take away, take apart, separate, or find the difference between two sets. The opposite of addition. (p. 49A)

Name _____

Get Ready

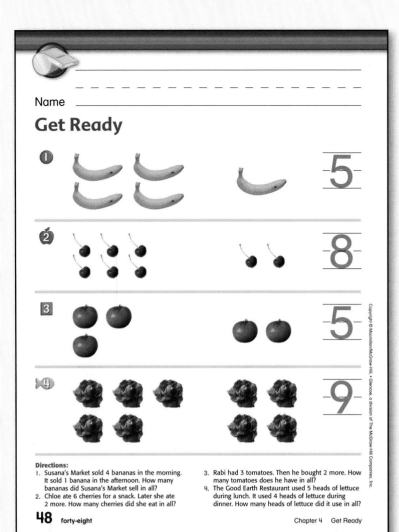

1. 5

2. 8

3. 5

4. 9

Directions:
1. Susana's Market sold 4 bananas in the morning. It sold 1 banana in the afternoon. How many bananas did Susana's Market sell in all?
2. Chloe ate 6 cherries for a snack. Later she ate 2 more. How many cherries did she eat in all?
3. Rabi had 3 tomatoes. Then he bought 2 more. How many tomatoes does he have in all?
4. The Good Earth Restaurant used 5 heads of lettuce during lunch. It used 4 heads of lettuce during dinner. How many heads of lettuce did it use in all?

48 forty-eight

Chapter 4 Get Ready

Get Ready

Diagnostic Assessment

Have students complete the Get Ready exercises to assess readiness. Refer to the lessons below for additional support for prerequisite skills.

Exercises 1–4: Grade K, Chapter 3, Lessons 3–7 (pp. 37–43)

You may also assess student readiness with the following resources:

Assessment Masters: Chapter Pretest (pp. 45–46)

Math Online macmillanmh.com
Online Readiness Quiz

Intervention Strategy

Step 1 Provide students with drawing paper.

Step 2 Have students draw pictures that model the process of subtraction. Provide suggestions, such as: "If you had 3 grapes on a plate and ate 1, how many grapes are left?"

Step 3 Have students put their pictures together in a book titled "My Subtraction Book." Invite them to tell the class about each of their pictures.

Dinah Zike's Foldables

Guide students through the directions on p. A82 in the Chapter Resource Masters to create their own Foldable graphic organizer for use with this chapter.

Vocabulary Preview

- Make a word wall with vocabulary words from the chapter. Refer to review page 59.
- Read each word aloud, and have students offer to explain what the word means. If students are unfamiliar with the word, provide a definition.
- Have students create drawings for each word on the word wall and attach their drawings to the wall.

Professional Development

Targeted professional development has been articulated throughout **McGraw-Hill's Math Triumphs** intervention program. The **McGraw-Hill Professional Development Video Library** provides short videos that support the **NCTM Focal Points and Focal Connections.** For more information, visit macmillanmh.com.

Model Lessons   Instructional Strategies

Take Away from 1 and 2

Lesson Planner

Objective
Learn how to subtract from 1 and 2.

Vocabulary

one

subtract

take away

two

Other Resources

Materials
boxes
crayons
paper

Manipulatives
two-color counters

 **On-Hand Manipulatives**
pennies

CRM Chapter Resource Masters
Vocabulary and English Language
  Development (p. A86)
Skills Practice (p. A87)
Practice at Home (p. A88)

Teacher Tech Tools
 TeacherWorks™ Plus
Math Online macmillanmh.com
Advance Tracker

Student Tech Tools
 StudentWorks™ Plus
Math Online macmillanmh.com
eGlossary

Intervention Strategy
Kinesthetic Learners

Using Hands   Have students raise both hands above their heads. Ask students how many hands they each have in the air. Then ask them to put down, or take away, one hand and tell how many are still in the air. Repeat with other body parts such as holding up two fingers and then putting one down, or standing on two feet, and then lifting up one.

---

1 Introduce

- Arrange 6 chairs to model seats on a bus.
- **Who wants to go for a ride on the bus?** Select 7 students, and then point out that the group is too big for the bus.
- **How can we make the group smaller?** Listen to students' suggestions.
- **If we take away 1 person, we will have enough chairs.**
- Model taking away 1 student to make the group smaller.

2 Teach

Key Concept

Foundational Skills and Concepts
- Display two objects to represent fish in a pond, and tell this subtraction story.
- **Two fish are swimming in a pond. A boat comes by and takes away 1 fish.** Draw an X over one of the "fish." Explain that the X represents the fish you are taking away. Remove one of the objects.
- **How many fish are left in the pond?** 1
- Continue the story. **Then another boat takes 1 fish.**
- Remove the other object.
- **How many fish are left in the pond now?** 0
- Have students draw pictures to illustrate their own subtraction story, and then share them with the class.

Using Manipulatives

Two-Color Counters   Organize students into pairs, and provide them with a small box and 2 two-color counters.
- Tell students to place both counters in the box.
- Have one student hold the box while the other student removes 1 counter at a time from the box. Ask students to count how many counters are left in the box after each counter is taken away.
- Repeat the activity, but have the student take away 2 counters at one time.

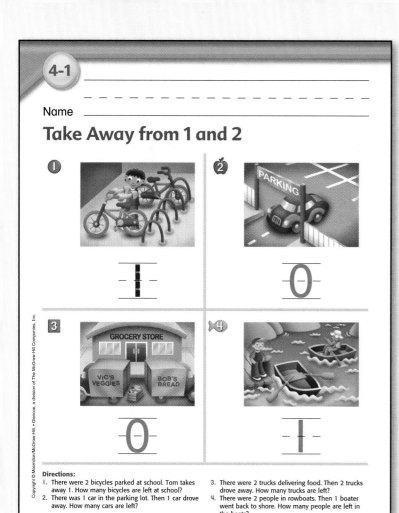

4-1

Name _____

Take Away from 1 and 2

① ____ — **I**

② ____ — **0**

③ ____ — **0**

④ ____ — **I**

Directions:
1. There were 2 bicycles parked at school. Tom takes away 1. How many bicycles are left at school?
2. There was 1 car in the parking lot. Then 1 car drove away. How many cars are left?
3. There were 2 trucks delivering food. Then 2 trucks drove away. How many trucks are left?
4. There were 2 people in rowboats. Then 1 boater went back to shore. How many people are left in the boats?

Chapter 4   Lesson 1   forty-nine   **49**

③ Practice

Direct students to page 49 in their student workbook. Read the directions at the bottom of the student page as they complete the exercise.

Ask students to count back from the starting number.

④ Assess

See It   Draw 2 flowers on the chalkboard. Draw an X on one. **How many flowers did I take away?** 1 **How many flowers are there now?** 1

Say It   Have students tell a subtraction story for 2 take away 1 or 2 take away 2 using concrete objects, such as toy animals.

Do It   Have students model 2 take away 1 using their hands or fingers.

Write It   Have students draw a picture showing 2 take away 1 or 2.

Math Coach Notes

Math Talk   Encourage students to communicate mathematically during all activities involving subtraction. Model the use and interchangeability of the terms *subtract* and *take away*. Ask questions that will elicit responses that contain the target words. **How can we make this group of birds smaller? What happens when we take one away (or, subtract one) from this group?** Help students form complete thoughts and sentences when responding to your question. **We had 2 counters. When we take one away, we have one left.**

Reinforce the concept of subtraction by modeling throughout the day. Whenever a situation involves taking away from 1 or 2, narrate the "take away" as it is happening, such as "You have one paper. I take it away. Now you have zero papers left."

Take Away from 3 and 4

Lesson Planner

Objective
Learn how to subtract from 3 and 4.

Vocabulary
four

three

Other Resources

Materials
books

Manipulatives
connecting cubes
two-color counters

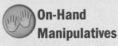 **On-Hand Manipulatives**
paper clips
pennies

CRM Chapter Resource Masters
Vocabulary and English Language
   Development (p. A89)
Skills Practice (p. A90)
Practice at Home (p. A91)

Teacher Tech Tools
TeacherWorks™ Plus
Math Online > macmillanmh.com
Advance Tracker

Student Tech Tools
StudentWorks™ Plus
Math Online > macmillanmh.com
eGlossary

Intervention Strategy
Linguistic Learners

Using Counters Have students explain to you how to use counters to model the subtraction. You may want to prompt students with questions, such as: **Why do I take away 3 counters?** or **Why is there only 1 cube left?** Encourage students to respond in complete sentences and to use mathematical terms.

1 Introduce

- Arrange a group of 3 students at the front of the class, sitting on the floor.
- Tell a subtraction story and have students model it.
- **Three turtles are sitting on a log. One turtle goes home. Take 1 turtle away from the log.**
- Have 1 student return to his or her chair.
- Draw a picture of 3 turtles on the board. When each student leaves the "log," draw an X through 1 of the turtles on the board.
- **How many turtles are left?** 2 **Three turtles take away 1 turtle is 2 turtles.**
- Repeat with other subtraction stories. Ask students to contribute by naming the objects used in the subtraction story.

2 Teach

Key Concept

Foundational Skills and Concepts Draw 4 circles on the chalkboard.
- **How many circles do I have on the chalkboard?** 4
- Draw an X through 1 circle and tell students you are taking away 1 circle. Explain to students that drawing an X through an object represents taking away that object.
- **How many circles have an X on them?** 1 **How many circles did I take away?** 1
- **How many circles are left?** 3
- Repeat the activity with different numbers.

Using Manipulatives

Connecting Cubes
- Write a large 4 on the chalkboard. Have students model 4 with connecting cubes. Relate the symbol on the chalkboard to their 4-cube chains.
- Show how to model 4 take away 1 by removing one cube, and then have students do the same.
- **How many cubes are left?** 3
- Repeat with other examples of take away from 3 and 4.

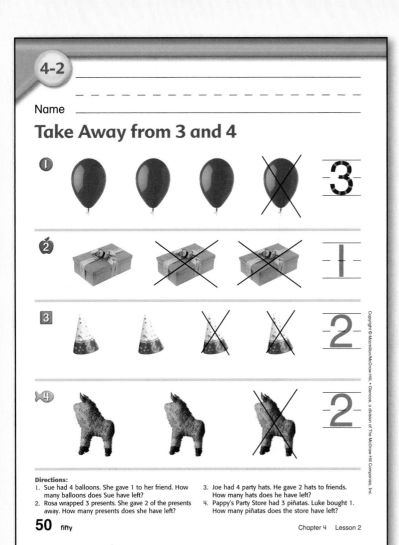

Name

Take Away from 3 and 4

① ✕ 3

② ✕ ✕ 1

③ ✕ ✕ 2

④ ✕ 2

Copyright © Macmillan/McGraw-Hill • Glencoe, a division of The McGraw-Hill Companies, Inc.

Directions:

1. Sue had 4 balloons. She gave 1 to her friend. How many balloons does Sue have left?
2. Rosa wrapped 3 presents. She gave 2 of the presents away. How many presents does she have left?
3. Joe had 4 party hats. He gave 2 hats to friends. How many hats does he have left?
4. Pappy's Party Store had 3 piñatas. Luke bought 1. How many piñatas does the store have left?

50 fifty

Chapter 4   Lesson 2

③ Practice

Direct students to page 50 in their student workbook. Read the directions at the bottom of the student page as they complete the exercise.

Encourage students to draw an X on the pictures to show that they have been "taken away."

④ Assess

See It   Draw 4 circles on the chalkboard and place an X through 1 of the circles. Have students explain the drawing using a subtraction story.

Say It   Have students explain to a partner how to find what is left when you take away 2 from 3. Allow students to use manipulatives.

Do It   Start with a group of 4 students. Ask the students to model 4 take away 3.

Write It   Place 4 books on a desk, and then remove 1. Have students draw a picture to model the subtraction story.

English Learner Strategy

Vocabulary   To assess student understanding of the term "take away," show students you have 4 pennies. Ask one student to "take away" 1 penny. How many pennies are left? Explain that the word "left" has multiple meanings. In this case it does not mean the opposite of right. It means how many remain. Clarify the term "left" with students.

Take Away from 5

Lesson Planner

Objective
Learn how to subtract from 5.

Vocabulary
five

Other Resources

Materials
erasers
markers

Manipulatives
attribute buttons
two-color counters

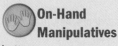 **On-Hand Manipulatives**
buttons
small objects for counting

CRM Chapter Resource Masters
Vocabulary and English Language
  Development (p. A92)
Skills Practice (p. A93)
Practice at Home (p. A94)

Teacher Tech Tools
TeacherWorks™ Plus
Math Online > macmillanmh.com
Advance Tracker

Student Tech Tools
StudentWorks™ Plus
Math Online > macmillanmh.com
eGlossary

---

1 Introduce
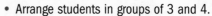

- Arrange students in groups of 3 and 4.
- Write a subtraction sentence for 3 or 4 on the chalkboard.
- Choose a group to make up a subtraction story for the sentence, and then act out the story in front of the class.
- Repeat until all groups have participated.

2 Teach

Key Concept

Foundational Skills and Concepts   Stand in front of the students, holding 5 erasers. Count the erasers aloud with the class. Ask a student to take away 2 from you.
- **How many erasers do I have left?** 3
- Pick up 5 markers. Count the markers aloud with the class. Ask a student to take away 3 from you.
- **How many markers do I have left?** 2
- Repeat until all possibilities of taking away from 5 have been modeled.

Using Manipulatives

Attribute Buttons   Provide each student with 5 attribute buttons. Draw pictures and Xs on the board to model subtraction while students use manipulatives.

- Tell a subtraction story.
- **Five ducks are swimming in a pond.** Have students place 5 buttons on their desks. Continue the story.
- **Two ducks fly away.** Instruct students to remove 2 buttons.
- **How many ducks are in the pond now?** 3

Intervention Strategy   Logical Learners

Using Counters   Relate subtraction to addition. Use 3 red counters and 2 yellow counters to model joining a set of 3 and a set of 2. Discuss what happens when sets are joined. Using the same counters, model 5 take away 3 and 5 take away 2. Compare what happens when sets are separated. Arrange the counters to show the sum of 4 and 1, and then have students show the related subtraction.

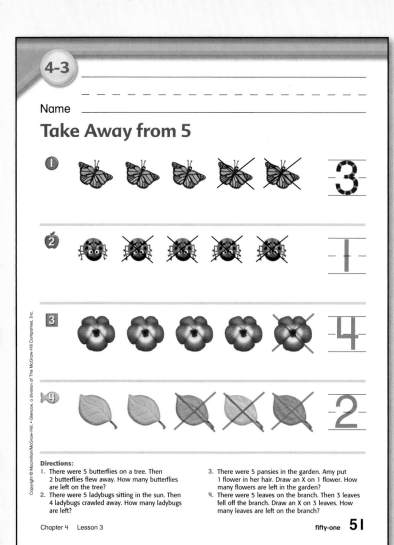

4-3

Name _____

Take Away from 5

① 🦋 🦋 🦋 🦋 🦋   3

② 🐞 🐞 🐞 🐞 🐞   1

③ 🌸 🌸 🌸 🌸 🌸   4

④ 🍃 🍃 🍃 🍃 🍃   2

Directions:

1. There were 5 butterflies on a tree. Then 2 butterflies flew away. How many butterflies are left on the tree?

2. There were 5 ladybugs sitting in the sun. Then 4 ladybugs crawled away. How many ladybugs are left?

3. There were 5 pansies in the garden. Amy put 1 flower in her hair. Draw an X on 1 flower. How many flowers are left in the garden?

4. There were 5 leaves on the branch. Then 3 leaves fell off the branch. Draw an X on 3 leaves. How many leaves are left on the branch?

Chapter 4　Lesson 3

fifty-one **51**

③ Practice

Direct students to page 51 in their student workbook. Read the directions at the bottom of the student page as they complete the exercise.

④ Assess

See It　Draw subtraction pictures to model subtracting from 5. Have students tell a subtraction story for the pictures.

Say It　Have students tell a subtraction story for 5 take away 2. Allow students to use manipulatives while they tell the story.

Do It　**Five birds were sitting on a tree branch. Three of the birds flew away. How many birds are left?** 2 Have students model 5 take away 3 using attribute buttons.

Write It　**You have 5 pennies. You give four of them to your friend. How many pennies do you have left?** 1 Have students draw a picture to show the subtraction problem, 5 take away 4.

English Learner Strategy

Singing a Song　Sing with students the following song: "There were 5 in the bed and the little one said, roll over, roll over. So, they all rolled over and 1 fell out. There were 4 in the bed and the little one said, roll over, roll over. So, they all rolled over and 1 fell out. There were 3 in the bed and the little one said, roll over, roll over. So, they all rolled over and 1 fell out. There were 2 in the bed and the little one said, roll over, roll over. So, they all rolled over and 1 fell out. There was 1 in the bed and the little one said, good night, sleep tight."

Math Coach Notes

Examples from Home　Be sure to emphasize the concept of separating sets when introducing subtraction. Help students think of things in their daily lives that involve the separating of sets or groups. For example, when a family member leaves the house to go to work or school, or when someone has 3 meatballs and then eats 1.

Take Away from 6

Lesson Planner

Objective
Learn how to subtract from 6.

Vocabulary

six

Other Resources

Materials
balls or eggs
colored paper
egg carton

Manipulatives
connecting cubes
pattern blocks

 **On-Hand Manipulatives**
paper clips
small objects for counting

CRM Chapter Resource Masters
Vocabulary and English Language Development (p. A95)
Skills Practice (p. A96)
Practice at Home (p. A97)

Teacher Tech Tools
TeacherWorks™ Plus
Math Online > macmillanmh.com
Advance Tracker

Student Tech Tools
StudentWorks™ Plus
Math Online > macmillanmh.com
eGlossary

Intervention Strategy

Naturalist   Another way to help students understand subtraction is to let them explore subtraction through nature. Have students collect natural items found outside the classroom, such as acorns, leaves, pine cones, pebbles, flowers, and leaves. Ask students to tell subtraction stories as they model the story with their collected items. If it is not possible to collect items outdoors, have students create and then narrate subtraction stories about items found in nature. Then have students draw pictures to illustrate their stories.

1 Introduce

- Ask 3 students to come to the front of the classroom. Ask the students to raise both their arms in the air.
- **How many arms are in the air?** 6
- Ask each student to put one arm behind his or her back.
- **How many arms were taken away?** 3
- **How many arms are raised?** 3
- **Six take away three is three.**

2 Teach

Key Concept

Foundational Skills and Concepts
- Cut the bottom of an egg carton in half so you have a row of 6 egg holders. Place a ball or other object in each egg holder.
- **How many balls do I have?** 6
- Remove 2 balls from the egg holder.
- **I had 6 balls. Then I took away 2. How many balls are left?** 4
- Refill the egg carton and repeat by taking away other amounts of balls.

Using Manipulatives

Connecting Cubes

- Provide each student with 6 connecting cubes.
- Display a 6-cube train and count the cubes with students.
- Remove 1 or more cubes. **How many cubes did I take away? How many cubes are left?** See students' work.
- Repeat until students have modeled all subtraction sentences to take away from 6 with their trains.

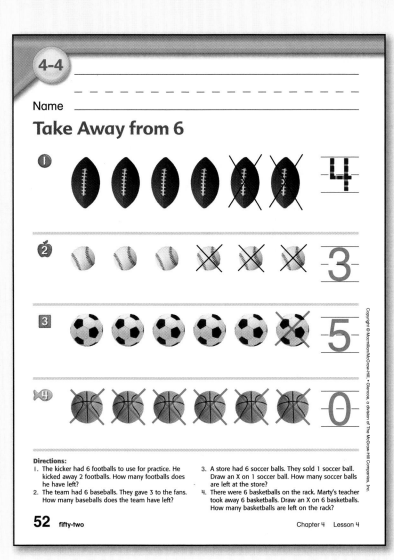

4-4

Name _____

Take Away from 6

① 🏈🏈🏈🏈❌❌   4

② ⚾⚾⚾✖✖✖   3

③ ⚽⚽⚽⚽⚽✖   5

④ ✖✖✖✖✖✖   0

Directions:

1. The kicker had 6 footballs to use for practice. He kicked away 2 footballs. How many footballs does he have left?
2. The team had 6 baseballs. They gave 3 to the fans. How many baseballs does the team have left?
3. A store had 6 soccer balls. They sold 1 soccer ball. Draw an X on 1 soccer ball. How many soccer balls are left at the store?
4. There were 6 basketballs on the rack. Marty's teacher took away 6 basketballs. Draw an X on 6 basketballs. How many basketballs are left on the rack?

52 fifty-two

Chapter 4   Lesson 4

Direct students to page 52 in their student workbook. Read the directions at the bottom of the student page as they complete the exercise.

③ Practice

Direct students to page 52 in their student workbook. Read the directions at the bottom of the student page as they complete the exercise.

For each exercise, students should count the total number of objects first. Then they trace the X or draw an X to show what is being taken away. Finally, students count the total remaining.

④ Assess

See It   Model subtraction using 6 blocks. Begin by showing students all the blocks. Then take away different numbers of blocks. Have students tell you how many blocks you took away each time.

Say It   Have students tell you how to model 6 minus 2 with their fingers.

Do It   Have students model subtraction sentences to take away from 6. Students will use connecting cubes.

Write It   Remove 1 or more cubes from a 6-cube train and have students draw a model of the subtraction.

⚠ Common Error Alert

Exercises 1–4   Sometimes students add instead of subtract. Explain that when you add to a set, the resulting set is larger than the original set, and when you take away from a set, or subtract, the resulting set is smaller than the original set. Model several "take away" examples, and point out how the answer to each problem is always less than the original number that you started with.

Math Coach Notes

Making Stories   Help students get involved in the exercises by encouraging them to make up stories to match the pictures in each exercise. Remind them to count the pictures that are not crossed out to find how many are left. Use with Exercises 1–2, page 52.

Progress Check 1

Formative Assessment

Use the Progress Check to assess students' mastery of the previous lessons. Have students review the lesson indicated for the problems they answered incorrectly.

 Common Error Alert

Subtracting Remind students that when we take away or subtract from a set it becomes smaller. Explain that the answer to a subtraction problem will always be a number that is less than the number of objects in the whole group.

Exercises 1 and 2 Have students cover the crossed-out objects to find how many are left.

Exercise 5 Make sure students count the items that are not crossed out to find the answer.

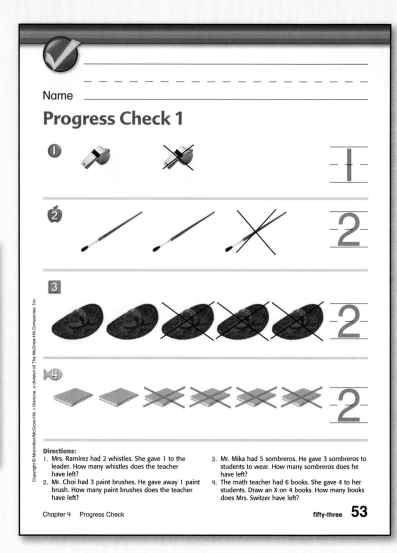

Name _____

Progress Check 1

Directions:
1. Mrs. Ramírez had 2 whistles. She gave 1 to the leader. How many whistles does the teacher have left?
2. Mr. Choi had 3 paint brushes. He gave away 1 paint brush. How many paint brushes does the teacher have left?
3. Mr. Mika had 5 sombreros. He gave 3 sombreros to students to wear. How many sombreros does he have left?
4. The math teacher had 6 books. She gave 4 to her students. Draw an X on 4 books. How many books does Mrs. Switzer have left?

Chapter 4   Progress Check   **fifty-three** **53**

Data-Driven Decision Making

Students missing Exercises . . .	Have trouble with . . .	Should review and practice . . .
1	taking away from 2.	TE Lesson 4-1, p. 49 CRM Skills Practice, p. A87
2	taking away from 3.	TE Lesson 4-2, p. 50 CRM Skills Practice, p. A90
3	taking away from 5.	TE Lesson 4-3, p. 51 CRM Skills Practice, p. A93
4	taking away from 6.	TE Lesson 4-4, p. 52 CRM Skills Practice, p. A96

Name _____

Replay

0 = blue, 1 = red, 2 = yellow, 3 = orange, 4 = black,
5 = white, 6 = green

Copyright © Macmillan/McGraw-Hill • Glencoe, a division of The McGraw-Hill Companies, Inc.

Directions:

1. Jimmy had 6 snowballs. He lost 1. How many does he have left? Color this number white.
2. Rob had 4 carrots. He ate 1. How many does he have left? Color this number orange.
3. There were 3 mittens in the closet. Marisol took 2 of them to wear. How many mittens are left? Color this number red.
4. Emma's snowman has 6 buttons. The wind made 0 buttons fall off. How many buttons are left? Color this number green.

5. There were 4 children playing in the snow. Then 2 children went home. How many children are still playing? Color this number yellow.
6. There were 5 icicles hanging from the tree. Then 1 icicle fell off. How many are left on the tree? Color this number black.
7. Andre's snowman had 2 scarves. Then 2 scarves blew away. How many are left on his snowman? Color this number blue.

54 fifty-four

Replay

Use the Replay activity to review and reinforce concepts and skills presented in Lessons 4-1, 4-2, 4-3, and 4-4.

Instructions

Explain to students that they should shade how many shapes are left after each step.

Student Technology

Students can use the following technology resources to reinforce chapter content.

StudentWorks™ Plus

Math Online macmillanmh.com

- eGames
- eGlossary

Take Away from 7

Lesson Planner

Objective
Learn how to subtract from 7.

Vocabulary
seven

Materials
paper
pencils
teacher-prepared picture
  cards (sets of 8 cards
  with 0 to 7 circles and
  the matching number
  on each card)

2   0   7

Manipulatives
color tiles
pennies
spinner
two-color counters

Other Resources

 On-Hand Manipulatives
buttons

CRM Chapter Resource Masters
Vocabulary and English Language
  Development (p. A98)
Skills Practice (p. A99)
Practice at Home (p. A100)

Teacher Tech Tools
TeacherWorks™ Plus
Math Online ▷ macmillanmh.com
Advance Tracker

Student Tech Tools
StudentWorks™ Plus
Math Online ▷ macmillanmh.com
eGlossary

Intervention Strategy
Interpersonal Learners

Subtraction Stories   One alternative way to learn to taking away from 7 is to have small groups of students work together to create subtraction stories that they can act out for the class. Encourage students to use their imaginations to create short plays about separating sets. Offer suggestions for story starters such as a family of bears that gets separated in the woods, or baby birds that grow up and leave the nest. Invite groups to use classroom items for props and/or costumes as needed.

1 Introduce

- Use eight students.
- Distribute one number card to each student.
- Ask the student with five circles to stand.
- **How many more circles are needed to make seven circles altogether?** 2
- Have students with two circles pair up with the students holding five circles.
- Continue with other addends of the sum seven until all students are paired up.

2 Teach

Key Concept

Foundational Skills and Concepts   Arrange seven students in a circle on the floor. Randomly distribute one color tile to each student. Place a spinner in the center of the circle.
- Choose a student to spin the spinner.
- Students with color tiles that match the color on the spinner move away from the circle.
- **How many students were in the circle?** 7
- **How many students moved away from the circle?** Responses will vary. **How many students are left in the circle?** Responses will vary.
- Repeat several times using different students. Distribute a new set of color tiles after two or three rounds.

Using Manipulatives

- Organize students into pairs, and give one partner 7 two-color counters.
- Ask the other partner to take away some counters.
- Then ask the pair to tell the subtraction story. For example:
- Partner 1: "I had 7 counters."
- Partner 2: "Then I took away 3 counters."
- Partner 1: "Now I have 4 counters left."
- Have students repeat this process several times.

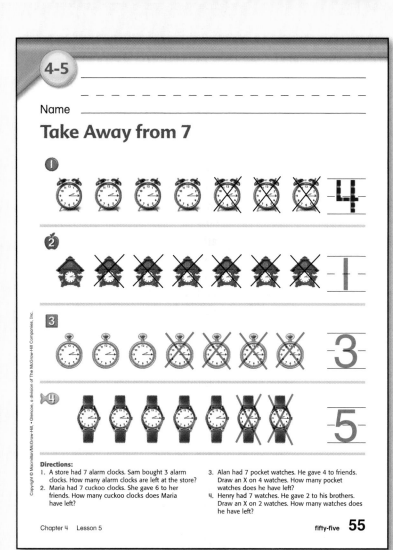

Name

Take Away from 7

1 4

2 1

3 3

4 5

Directions:
1. A store had 7 alarm clocks. Sam bought 3 alarm clocks. How many alarm clocks are left at the store?
2. Maria had 7 cuckoo clocks. She gave 6 to her friends. How many cuckoo clocks does Maria have left?
3. Alan had 7 pocket watches. He gave 4 to friends. Draw an X on 4 watches. How many pocket watches does he have left?
4. Henry had 7 watches. He gave 2 to his brothers. Draw an X on 2 watches. How many watches does he have left?

Chapter 4   Lesson 5

fifty-five **55**

③ Practice

Direct students to page 55 in their student workbook. Read the directions at the bottom of the student page as they complete the exercise.

Remind students that the objects with an X on them are the ones that have been "taken away." The objects without an X show what is left.

④ Assess

See It   Give students 7 pennies. Have them place 2 pennies in a paper bag. Have students use a subtraction story to explain what happened to the pennies.

Say It   Give students 7 counters. Have students say subtraction sentences beginning with 7.

Do It   Show students 7 counters. Have them take away counters and explain how many are left.

Write It   Say: **"Draw 7 circles. Draw an X on 3 circles to show you are taking 3 away. How many circles are left?"** 4

English Learner Strategy

Using Manipulatives   Help students review number names by saying a number and then having them make a group of that size using counters or other items found in the classroom, such as pencils, crayons, books, chairs, and so on. Then ask them to remove a specified number of objects and talk about how many are left. Emphasize number names and mathematical words and phrases such as *take away* and *how many* as you give instructions and discuss the process.

Take Away from 8

Lesson Planner

Objective
Learn how to subtract from 8.

Vocabulary
eight

Materials
crayons
paper
pencils
small bags

Manipulatives
two-color counters

On-Hand Manipulatives
buttons

Other Resources

CRM Chapter Resource Masters
Vocabulary and English Language
  Development (p. A101)
Skills Practice (p. A102)
Practice at Home (p. A103)

Teacher Tech Tools
TeacherWorks™ Plus
Math Online > macmillanmh.com
Advance Tracker

Student Tech Tools
StudentWorks™ Plus
Math Online > macmillanmh.com
eGlossary

1 Introduce

- Count out 8 pennies with the class.
- One at a time, drop the pennies into a jar and have students count off one, two, three, through eight.
- Remove two pennies from the group and repeat the exercise so students can see you have taken two away from eight.

2 Teach

Key Concept

Foundational Skills and Concepts Tape 8 large photos onto the chalkboard or wall.

- Ask a student to take away 2 photos. Tape these two photos on the board away from the original 8 photos. Ask the student to stand next to the 2 photos.
- Tell students you had 8 photos, and then 2 were taken away. Now you have 6 photos left.
- Move the 2 sheets of paper back to make 8 again. Repeat the activity using other numbers. Ask students to help you find out how many photos are left.

Using Manipulatives

Two-Color Counters Provide each student with a bag of 8 counters and a piece of paper. Fold the paper in half.

- Have students count the counters and tell how many. Have students place them back in the bag.
- Ask students to reach in the bag and pull out some counters and place them on the left section of their paper. This is the number of counters they are taking away.
- Ask students to place the remaining counters on the right half of their paper. This is the number of counters they have left.
- Help students use the paper to recite how many they started with, how many were taken away, and how many they have left. For example, 8 take away 5 is 3.

Intervention Strategy — Auditory Learners

Have students count up to find the total number of objects. Then have them count back as they cross out the objects to find how many are left.

Name

Take Away from 8

① 🐻🐻🐻🐻🐻🐻̷🐻̷🐻̷ 5

② 🐕🐕🐕🐕🐕🐕🐕̷🐕̷ 6

③ 🐴🐴🐴🐴🐴🐴̷🐴̷🐴̷ 5

④ 🐱🐱🐱🐱🐱̷🐱̷🐱̷🐱̷ 4

Directions:
1. There were 8 bears sleeping. Then 3 bears woke up. How many bears are left sleeping?
2. There were 8 dogs barking. Then 2 dogs stopped barking. How many dogs are left barking?
3. There were 8 horses in the barn. Then 3 horses went outside. Draw an X on 3 horses. How many horses are left in the barn?
4. There were 8 cats in the window. Then 4 cats ran away. Draw an X on 4 cats. How many cats are left in the window?

Chapter 4 Lesson 6

---

 ③ Practice

Direct students to page 56 in their student workbook. Read the directions at the bottom of the student page as they complete the exercise.

Tell students that the bears with an X on them are the ones that woke up. How many are left sleeping?

④ Assess

See It Display 8 objects. Take away 1 object. Have students look and tell how many are left.

Say It Show students 8 counters. Take 3 away. Have students describe this subtraction situation.

Do It Have students model 8 take away 6, using counters.

Write It Have students draw a picture to illustrate 8. Have them draw 5 Xs to take away 5. **How many are left?** 3

⚠ Common Error Alert

Exercises 3–4 Students may not understand the meaning of the two groups of objects. Explain to students that the group of objects on the left side is how many are being taken away. The objects on the right side show how many are left (or remain). Also, explain that they can draw pictures and use Xs to cross out how many objects are being taken away.

Take Away from 9

Lesson Planner

Objective
Learn how to subtract from 9.

Vocabulary
nine

Other Resources

Materials
index cards
pictures of puppies

Manipulatives
connecting cubes

 **On-Hand Manipulatives**
paper clips

CRM Chapter Resource Masters
Vocabulary and English Language
 Development (p. A104)
Skills Practice (p. A105)
Practice at Home (p. A106)

Teacher Tech Tools
TeacherWorks™ Plus
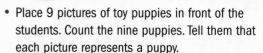 **Math Online** macmillanmh.com
Advance Tracker

Student Tech Tools
StudentWorks™ Plus
 **Math Online** macmillanmh.com
eGlossary

Intervention Strategy — Visual Learners

Using a Number Line   Have students use a number line as they practice subtraction. For example, for 9 take away 5 have students point to the 9 on the number line. Then have them count backward 5 spaces to model take away 5 and then say that means 4 are left. Explain that counting backward is the same as subtracting.

1 Introduce

- Place 9 pictures of toy puppies in front of the students. Count the nine puppies. Tell them that each picture represents a puppy.
- **My dog had 9 puppies. We gave away 3 puppies.**
- Remove 3.
- **How many puppies are left?** 6; count to verify the student responses
- Invite students to tell how they solved the problem.
- Continue the story until no puppies are left.

2 Teach

Key Concept

Foundational Skills and Concepts   Pass out 9 index cards to each student.
- Ask students to count how many index cards they have by having each student count 1, 2, 3 . . . 8, 9.
- Take away 1 or more index cards. Display a similar set of cards so the students will remember how many were taken away.
- Have the class count off again to find out how many index cards are left.
- Continue until there are no more index cards left. Then repeat the activity.

Using Manipulatives

Connecting Cubes   Give students 9 connecting cubes.
- Using connecting cubes, have students make a 9-cube train.
- Instruct students to separate their train into 2 sets.
- Call on students and have them show and describe how they separated their trains.
- **How many cubes did you have in your train?** 9
- **How many cubes did you take away when you separated your train?** 5
- **How many cubes are left in your train?** 4

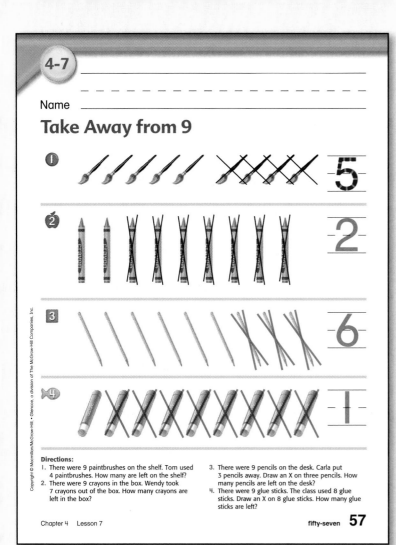

4-7

Name _____

Take Away from 9

① ///// XXXX $\underline{5}$

② crayons XXXXXXX $\underline{2}$

③ pencils XXX $\underline{6}$

④ XXXXXXXX | $\underline{|}$

Directions:
1. There were 9 paintbrushes on the shelf. Tom used 4 paintbrushes. How many are left on the shelf?
2. There were 9 crayons in the box. Wendy took 7 crayons out of the box. How many crayons are left in the box?
3. There were 9 pencils on the desk. Carla put 3 pencils away. Draw an X on three pencils. How many pencils are left on the desk?
4. There were 9 glue sticks. The class used 8 glue sticks. Draw an X on 8 glue sticks. How many glue sticks are left?

Chapter 4   Lesson 7   **fifty-seven 57**

Direct students to page 57 in their student workbook. Read the directions at the bottom of the student page as they complete the exercise.

See It   Have students solve 9 take away 3 using index cards.

Say It   Have students make up and solve a subtraction story problem that show 9 take away 2 is 7.

Do It   Have one student in a pair say a subtraction problem while the partner models the problem with connecting cubes. Allow students to switch roles.

Write It   Have students draw a subtraction story beginning with 9.

Progress Check 2

Formative Assessment

Use the Progress Check to assess students' mastery of the previous lessons. Have students review the lesson indicated for the problems they answered incorrectly.

 Common Error Alert

Subtracting Be sure students understand that when objects are taken away, the number that is left must be less than the original number. Remind them that to take away means "to separate a set into smaller sets."

Exercises 1 and 2 Remind students that the crossed-out items are the items that have been taken away from the set.

Exercises 2–4 Be sure students understand that items have already been crossed out. The number of items shown is the number of original items. The objects without the Xs show how many are left.

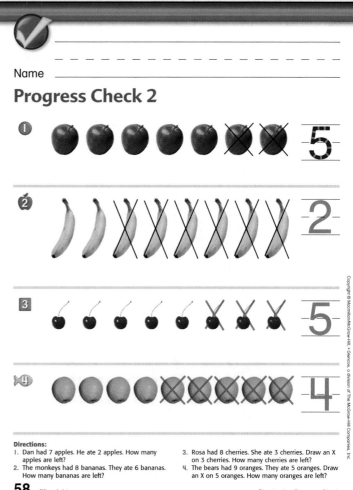

Directions:
1. Dan had 7 apples. He ate 2 apples. How many apples are left?
2. The monkeys had 8 bananas. They ate 6 bananas. How many bananas are left?
3. Rosa had 8 cherries. She ate 3 cherries. Draw an X on 3 cherries. How many cherries are left?
4. The bears had 9 oranges. They ate 5 oranges. Draw an X on 5 oranges. How many oranges are left?

58 fifty-eight

Chapter 4 Progress Check

Data-Driven Decision Making

Students missing Exercises . . .	Have trouble with . . .	Should review and practice . . .
1	taking away from 7.	TE Lesson 4-5, p. 55 CRM Skills Practice, p. A99
2-3	taking away from 8.	TE Lesson 4-6, p. 56 CRM Skills Practice, p. A102
4	taking away from 9.	TE Lesson 4-7, p. 57 CRM Skills Practice, p. A105

Intervention Strategies

Connecting Cube Groups

Materials: connecting cubes

Step 1   **Small Groups** Divide students into small groups. Give each group 10 connecting cubes.

Step 2   Draw several subtraction models on the board. For example:

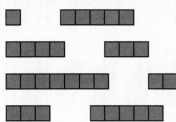

Step 3   Each group should model their connecting cubes to match the expression above.

Step 4   Instruct students that each group is to come up with another way to model their addition equation. They might use another form of manipulative, model the equation using students, or make their own drawing. Stress that groups should use different ways to find the answer.

Assign each group one of the expressions above.

Step 5   Have each group demonstrate their way of modeling the equation. Invite them to do this in front of the class.

Small Group Instruction

Walk around to each group as they model their equation using counters. Ask them specific questions that will help them relate addition to subtraction. Into what sets did you separate nine? If you wanted to join them back together, what two sets would you combine? What is the new set? What two numbers would you add to find the total?

Number Line Counts

Materials: none

Step 1   **Whole Class** Draw a number line on the chalkboard from 0 to 10.

Step 2   Tell the class: "We are going to count back together from 10 to 0." Lead the class in counting backward while pointing at each number on the number line. "Ten, nine, eight, seven..."

Step 3   Tell students that they can use a number line to count back any amount starting at any number. **Start at 10, and count back 3.** Ask a student to come to the chalkboard and model counting back by pointing at the numbers. To understand the concept of subtraction, the jumps should be labeled.

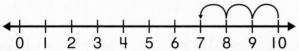

Step 4   Propose more examples for students to model. Invite a different student to the chalkboard for this problem.

Step 5   Tell the class that "counting back" is one way to subtract.

Time Management

Use this activity both before and after the chapter lessons. Monitor students' progress in the chapter by seeing how they react to the activity after completing all the lessons. Check to see if they are able to write the counting back examples offered earlier as subtraction problems.

Review

Vocabulary

Before beginning the exercises, review vocabulary introduced in the chapter. Refer to the page numbers to revisit vocabulary activities in the lessons.

eight (p. 56A)　　**six** (p. 52A)

five (p. 51A)　　**subtract** (p. 49A)

four (p. 50A)　　**take away** (p. 49A)

nine (p. 57A)　　**three** (p. 50A)

one (p. 49A)　　**two** (p. 49A)

seven (p. 55A)

Vocabulary Review Strategies

Write a list of the vocabulary words on the board and cover each word with a separate piece of construction paper. Create a riddle that corresponds with each word, and invite the students to guess the answer. When they guess correctly, remove the construction paper to reveal the word. For example, **I am a number that comes before eight. What is my name?** seven

Concept Review

The exercises in this section are grouped to cover content from each lesson in the chapter. The first exercise of each set is partially completed for the students in order to show them a method for solving the other exercise(s) in the set.

> **Exercises 1–2:** Lessons 4-1, 4-2, 4-3 (pp. 49–51)
> **Exercise 3:** Lessons 4-4, 4-5 (pp. 52, 55)
> **Exercise 4:** Lessons 4-6, 4-7 (pp. 56–57)

CRM Find Extra Practice for these concepts in the Practice Worksheets, pages A86–A106.

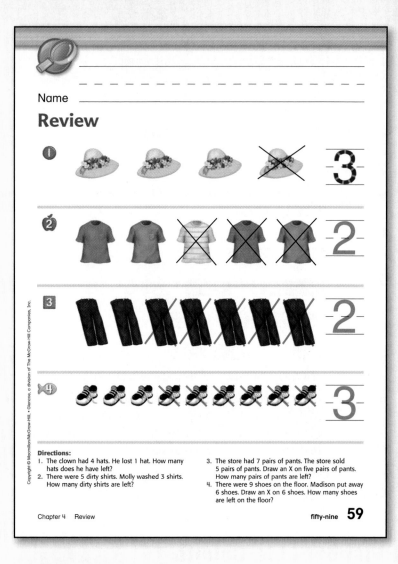

 **Dinah Zike's Foldables**

Have students use the Foldable they created at the beginning of the chapter to review and reinforce the concepts and skills they learned during the chapter. (See Chapter Resource Masters p. A82 for instructions.)

Intervention Strategy　Linguistic Learners

Describing Take-Away Pictures　One alternative method to help students is to have them describe each picture to you and then tell what to do to answer the question. It may be helpful to prompt students with questions, such as: "How many were in the group to begin with?" or "What does it mean when the items are crossed out?" Encourage students to tell as much as they can about the pictures.

Name _____

Test

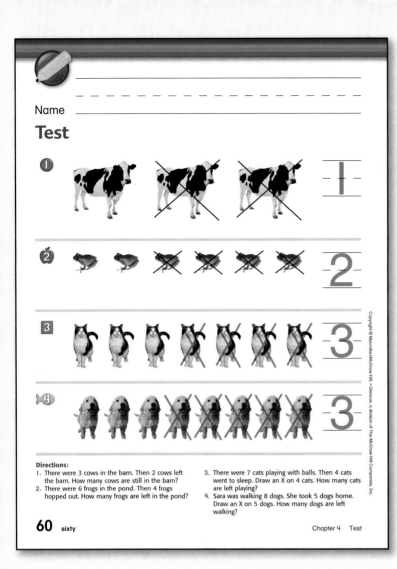

Directions:
1. There were 3 cows in the barn. Then 2 cows left the barn. How many cows are still in the barn?
2. There were 6 frogs in the pond. Then 4 frogs hopped out. How many frogs are left in the pond?
3. There were 7 cats playing with balls. Then 4 cats went to sleep. Draw an X on 4 cats. How many cats are left playing?
4. Sara was walking 8 dogs. She took 5 dogs home. Draw an X on 5 dogs. How many dogs are left walking?

60 sixty

Chapter 4 Test

Test

Chapter Resource Masters

Additional forms of the Chapter 4 Tests are available.

Test Format	Where to Find it
Chapter 4 Test	**Math Online** macmillanmh.com
Blackline Masters	Assessment Masters, pp. 48–49

Alternative Assessment

Model Subtraction Have students make up a subtraction story for 6, 7, 8, or 9. Ask them to use counters to model the subtraction story and then to write and solve the subtraction sentence for their story. You may want to change the numbers in their stories and have them repeat the activity for the new numbers.

Customize and create multiple versions of the chapter tests and their answer keys. All of these questions from the chapter tests are available on ExamView® Assessment Suite.

This online assessment tool allows teachers to track student progress with easily accessible, comprehensive reports available for every student. Assess students using any internet-ready computer.

Data-Driven Decision Making

Students missing Exercises . . .	Have trouble with . . .	Should review and practice . . .
1	taking away from 3.	TE Lesson 4-2, p. 50 CRM Skills Practice, p. A90
2	taking away from 6.	TE Lesson 4-4, p. 52 CRM Skills Practice, p. A96
3	taking away from 7.	TE Lesson 4-5, p. 55 CRM Skills Practice, p. A99
4	taking away from 8.	TE Lesson 4-6, p. 56 CRM Skills Practice, p. A102

Chapter Overview

Chapter-at-a-Glance

Lesson	Math Objective	State/Local Standards
5-1 Open or Closed Figures (pp. 63A–63)	Develop an understanding of open and closed figures.	
5-2 Curved or Straight (pp. 64A–64)	Develop an understanding of curved and straight lines.	
5-3 Circles (pp. 65A–65)	Develop an understanding of circles.	
5-4 Triangles (pp. 66A–66)	Develop an understanding of triangles.	
Progress Check 1 (p. 67)		
5-5 Rectangles (pp. 69A–69)	Develop an understanding of rectangles.	
5-6 Squares (pp. 70A–70)	Develop an understanding of squares.	
5-7 Create Two-Dimensional Figures (pp. 71A–71)	Develop an understanding of ways to make new shapes.	
Progress Check 2 (p. 72)		

Content-at-a-Glance

The diagram below summarizes and unpacks Chapter 5 content.

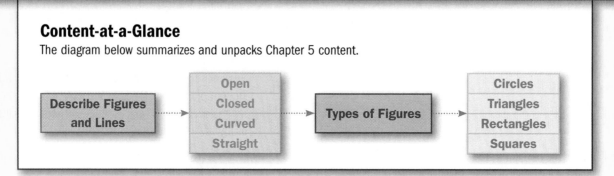

Chapter Assessment Manager

Diagnostic — Diagnose students' readiness.

	Student Study Guide/ Teacher Edition	Assessment Masters	Technology
Intensive Intervention Placement Test		1–4	ExamView® Assessment Suite
Section Pretest (Chapters 5–7)		42–43	ExamView® Assessment Suite
Chapter 5 Pretest		55–56	ExamView® Assessment Suite
Get Ready	SSG 62		Math Online macmillanmh.com StudentWorks™ Plus

Formative — Identify students' misconceptions of content knowledge.

	Student Study Guide/ Teacher Edition	Assessment Masters	Technology
Progress Checks	SSG 67, 72		Math Online macmillanmh.com StudentWorks™ Plus
Vocabulary Review	TE 73		Math Online macmillanmh.com
Lesson Assessments			ExamView® Assessment Suite

Summative — Determine student success in learning the concepts in the lesson, chapter, or section.

	Student Study Guide/ Teacher Edition	Assessment Masters	Technology
Chapter 5 Test	SSG 74	58–59	ExamView® Assessment Suite
Alternative Assessment	TE 74	53–54	ExamView® Assessment Suite
See It, Say It, Do It, Write It	TE 63, 64, 65, 66, 69, 70, 71		
Section Test (Chapters 5–7)		75–76	ExamView® Assessment Suite

Backmapping and Vertical Alignment **McGraw-Hill's** *Math Triumphs* intervention program was conceived and developed with the final result in mind: student success in grade-level mathematics, including Algebra 1 and beyond. The authors, using the **NCTM Focal Points and Focal Connections** as their guide, developed this brand-new series by backmapping from grade-level and Algebra 1 concepts, and vertically aligning the topics so that they build upon prior skills and concepts and serve as a foundation for future topics.

Chapter Resource Manager

	Lesson 5-1	**Lesson 5-2**	**Lesson 5-3**	**Lesson 5-4**
Concept	Open or Closed Figures	Curved or Straight	Circles	Triangles
Objective	Develop an understanding of open and closed figures.	Develop an understanding of curved and straight lines.	Develop an understanding of circles.	Develop an understanding of triangles.
Math Vocabulary	closed figure open shape	curved straight	circle	corner side triangle
Lesson Resources	**Materials** • balloon • bendable straws • paper • pencils • string or yarn **Manipulatives** • connecting cubes **Other Resources** CRM Vocabulary and English Language Development CRM Skills Practice CRM Practice at Home	**Materials** • boxes • crayons • cups • paper • pencils • pipe cleaners • scissors • straws **Manipulatives** • attribute buttons • geometric solids **Other Resources** CRM Vocabulary and English Language Development CRM Skills Practice CRM Practice at Home	**Materials** • boxes • cardboard clock • construction paper • crayons • cups • glue • magazines • pencils • scissors **Manipulatives** • attribute buttons **Other Resources** CRM Vocabulary and English Language Development CRM Skills Practice CRM Practice at Home	**Materials** • cardboard cut into triangle shapes • classroom objects • crayons • paper • rulers • sack or pillowcase • unsharpened pencils **Manipulatives** • attribute buttons • triangle pattern blocks **Other Resources** CRM Vocabulary and English Language Development CRM Skills Practice CRM Practice at Home
Technology	Math Online macmillanmh.com StudentWorks™ Plus 💿 ExamView® Assessment Suite	Math Online macmillanmh.com StudentWorks™ Plus 💿 ExamView® Assessment Suite	Math Online macmillanmh.com StudentWorks™ Plus 💿 ExamView® Assessment Suite	Math Online macmillanmh.com StudentWorks™ Plus 💿 ExamView® Assessment Suite

	Lesson 5-5	Lesson 5-6	Lesson 5-7	
Concept	Rectangles	Squares	Create Two-Dimensional Figures	
Objective	Develop an understanding of rectangles.	Develop an understanding of squares.	Develop an understanding of ways to make new shapes.	
Math Vocabulary	rectangle	square	apart together	
Lesson Resources	**Materials** • classroom objects • index cards • masking tape • paper • pencil • rulers • shoe box • square buttons	**Materials** • cardboard • cardboard squares • chalk • craft sticks • crayons • paper • scissors	**Materials** • cardboard • cardboard squares and triangles • construction paper cut into 6-inch squares • pencils • scissors	
	Manipulatives • connecting cubes	**Manipulatives** • pattern blocks	**Manipulatives** • pattern blocks	
	Other Resources **CRM** Vocabulary and English Language Development **CRM** Skills Practice **CRM** Practice at Home	**Other Resources** **CRM** Vocabulary and English Language Development **CRM** Skills Practice **CRM** Practice at Home	**Other Resources** **CRM** Vocabulary and English Language Development **CRM** Skills Practice **CRM** Practice at Home	
Technology	**Math Online ⟩** macmillanmh.com StudentWorks™ Plus 💿 ExamView® Assessment Suite	**Math Online ⟩** macmillanmh.com StudentWorks™ Plus 💿 ExamView® Assessment Suite	**Math Online ⟩** macmillanmh.com StudentWorks™ Plus 💿 ExamView® Assessment Suite	

Chapter Notes

Home Connection

- Read the Home Connection letter with students and have them write their names in the space below.
- Read and explain the activity under Help at Home. If time allows, complete a portion of the activity so students can introduce the activity to a parent or other caregiver.

Parent Communications As you progress through the chapter, take note of students who have trouble recognizing specific shapes. Send a note home to students' parents or other caregiver asking them to help reinforce the concept at home.

Shapes at Home You may suggest to students that they look around their homes for shapes. They are everywhere! Challenge students to draw pictures of at least three things at home that are the shape of a circle, a triangle, a rectangle, and a square.

Real-World Applications

- Make several cutouts of circles and squares. Place these shapes in a bag.
- Ask students to take a shape from the bag.
- Ask students to describe features of the shape, such as round, sides, corners.
- Students should then take the shape and match it to the shape of a two-dimensional classroom object, such as a poster. Be sure students differentiate between two- and three-dimensional objects.

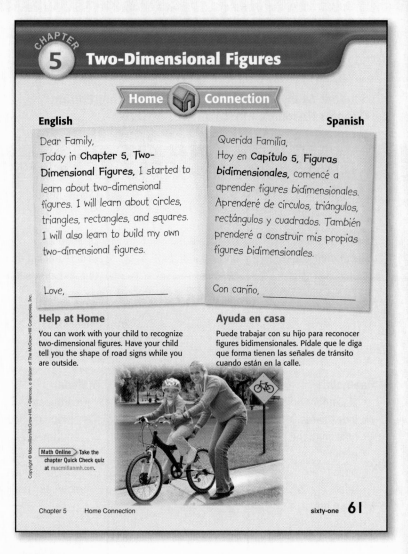

English **Spanish**

Dear Family,
Today in **Chapter 5, Two-Dimensional Figures**, I started to learn about two-dimensional figures. I will learn about circles, triangles, rectangles, and squares. I will also learn to build my own two-dimensional figures.

Love, _____

Querida Familia,
Hoy en **Capítulo 5, Figuras bidimensionales**, comencé a aprender figures bidimensionales. Aprenderé de circulos, triángulos, rectángulos y cuadrados. También prenderé a construir mis propias figures bidimensionales.

Con cariño, _____

Help at Home
You can work with your child to recognize two-dimensional figures. Have your child tell you the shape of road signs while you are outside.

Ayuda en casa
Puede trabajar con su hijo para reconocer figures bidimensionales. Pídale que le diga que forma tienen las señales de tránsito cuando están en la calle.

Math Online Take the chapter Quick Check quiz at macmillanmh.com.

Chapter 5   Home Connection   sixty-one **61**

Math Online
Visit macmillanmh.com for ongoing support of chapter content and instruction, including:
- Online Games
- Concepts in Motion

Key Vocabulary

Find interactive definitions in 13 languages in the **eGlossary** at macmillanmh.com.

English **Español** *Introduce the most important vocabulary terms from Chapter 5.*

circle círculo
a closed round figure (p. 65A)

square cuadrado
a rectangle that has four equal sides (p. 70A)

rectangle rectángulo
a shape with four sides and four corners (p. 69A)

triangle triángulo
a shape with three sides (p. 66A)

Name

Get Ready

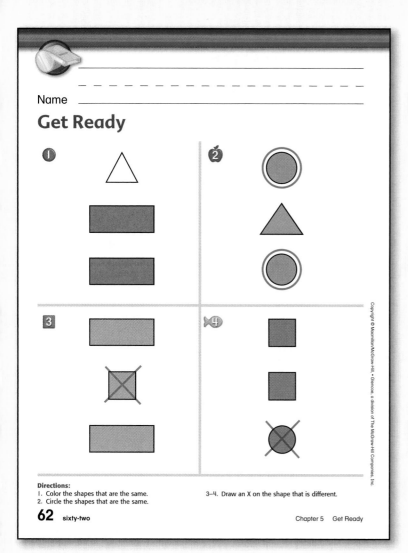

Directions:
1. Color the shapes that are the same.
2. Circle the shapes that are the same.

3–4. Draw an X on the shape that is different.

62 sixty-two

Chapter 5 Get Ready

Copyright © Macmillan/McGraw-Hill • Glencoe, a division of The McGraw-Hill Companies, Inc.

Get Ready

Diagnostic Assessment

Have students complete Get Ready to assess readiness for the chapter.

You may also assess student readiness with:

Assessment Masters: Chapter Pretest (pp. 55-56)

Math Online > macmillanmh.com
Online Readiness Quiz

Intervention Strategy

Step 1 Provide students with ten capital-letter alphabet cards (A through J).

Step 2 Students should sort the cards into three categories—letters with straight lines, letters with curved lines, and letters with both.

Step 3 Once students have sorted the cards, have them think of other ways to sort the cards, such as open or closed letters and letters that form circles and triangles.

Dinah Zike's Foldables

Guide students through the directions on p. A107 in the Chapter Resource Masters to create their own Foldables graphic organizer for use with this chapter.

Vocabulary Preview

- Introduce students to some of the vocabulary words they will learn in the chapter, including *open*, *straight*, *circle*, *square*, and *half*. Have students describe or tell the meaning of any words they may know.

- As the vocabulary words are presented in the chapter, have students decide on a way to represent the word. You may suggest that students work together to use their bodies to represent the word. For example, students can lie on the ground to form a triangle. You can take a picture of them, print it, label it, and display it to help students remember the meaning of *triangle*.

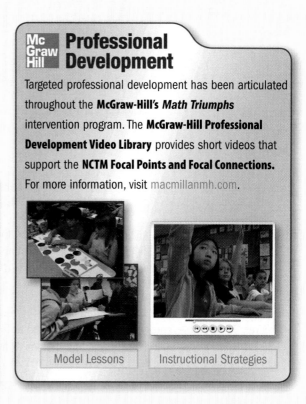

Professional Development

Targeted professional development has been articulated throughout the **McGraw-Hill's** *Math Triumphs* intervention program. The **McGraw-Hill Professional Development Video Library** provides short videos that support the **NCTM Focal Points and Focal Connections.** For more information, visit macmillanmh.com.

Model Lessons   Instructional Strategies

Open or Closed Figures

Lesson Planner

Objective
Develop an understanding of open and closed figures.

Vocabulary

closed

figure

open

shape

Other Resources

Materials
balloon
paper
pencils
string or yarn

Manipulatives
connecting cubes

 **On-Hand Manipulatives**
bendable straws

CRM **Chapter Resource Masters**
Vocabulary and English Language
    Development (p. A111)
Skills Practice (p. A112)
Practice at Home (p. A113)

Teacher Tech Tools
⊙ TeacherWorks™ Plus
[Math Online] macmillanmh.com
Advance Tracker

Student Tech Tools
⊙ StudentWorks™ Plus
[Math Online] macmillanmh.com
eGlossary

Intervention Strategy
Interpersonal/
Kinesthetic Learners

Body Figures   Have small groups of students use their bodies to make open and closed figures. For example, students may hold hands to form a closed figure, and then two students drop hands to make an open figure.

Have students use their own bodies to form open and closed figures. For example, students can touch their toes to form a closed figure or use their index fingers and thumbs to make a closed figure.

1 Introduce

Open the door and ask students whether it is open or closed.
• Close the door and repeat.
• Have students open and close backpacks and tell when they are open and closed.
• Use masking tape to make an open and closed figure on the floor. Have students go in the figure that is open.

2 Teach

Key Concept

Foundational Skills and Concepts   Extend your arms overhead to make a circle. Tell students you made a closed figure. Separate your arms.
• **How has the figure changed?**
• Explain to students that a figure is closed if there are no gaps between the parts. A figure is open if a part of the figure is missing. On the chalkboard, draw both open and closed figures, such as circles, squares, and triangles. With students, identify each as an open or closed figure.

Using Manipulatives

Connecting Cubes   Provide each student with a set of connecting cubes that connect to form a closed square.

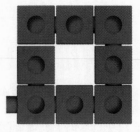

• **Is this figure open or closed?** closed
• Ask students to change the figure to an open figure.
• **How did you make your cubes into an open figure?** See students' work.
• Have students also use a piece of yarn (or 3–4 yarn pieces) to create open and closed figures and glue them to a piece of paper.

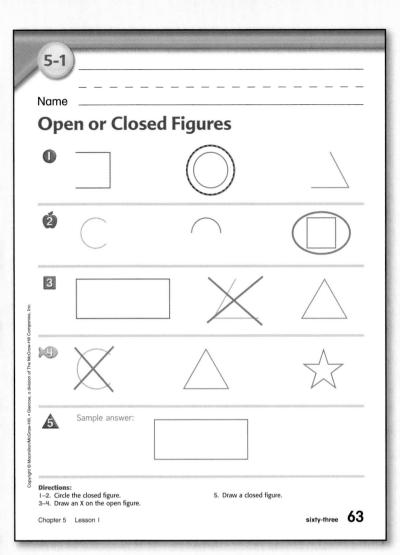

5-1

Name _____

Open or Closed Figures

Directions:
1–2. Circle the closed figure.
3–4. Draw an X on the open figure.

5. Draw a closed figure.

Chapter 5   Lesson I

sixty-three **63**

3 Practice

Direct students to page 63 of their student workbook. Read the directions at the bottom of the student page as they complete the exercises.

In Exercise 5, remind students that a figure is closed if there are no gaps between the parts.

4 Assess

See It   Draw open and closed figures on the chalkboard. Ask students to identify the open and closed figures.

Say It   Point to a figure on the chalkboard and have students say "open" or "closed."

Do It   Give students a 12-inch piece of yarn. Ask them to make a closed figure with the yarn. Repeat for an open figure.

Write It   Say "open" and have students draw an open figure. Repeat using the term closed.

Math Coach Notes

For this lesson, keep the focus on the terms *open figure* and *closed figure*. Students may identify shapes by name (closed circle or open square), but that is not necessary for understanding this lesson.

Curved or Straight

Lesson Planner

Objective
Develop an understanding of curved and straight lines.

Vocabulary
curved

straight

Other Resources

Materials
crayons
paper
pencils
pipe cleaners
straws

Manipulatives
attribute buttons
geometric solids

 **On-Hand Manipulatives**
boxes
cups
scissors

CRM **Chapter Resource Masters**
Vocabulary and English Language
  Development (p. A114)
Skills Practice (p. A115)
Practice at Home (p. A116)

Teacher Tech Tools
TeacherWorks™ Plus
Math Online > macmillanmh.com
Advance Tracker

Student Tech Tools
StudentWorks™ Plus
Math Online > macmillanmh.com
eGlossary

Intervention Strategy
Visual/Tactile Learners

Charts   Students may benefit from categorizing lines. Provide students with a two-column chart. For chart headings, have them draw a straight line on one side and a curved line on the other. Students can draw their own shapes in the chart or use manipulatives, letter tiles, or other appropriate objects.

Learning Centers   Set up a station with straws, pencils, and bent pipe cleaners. Have students pick up each object, feel its shape, and tell whether it is straight or curved. Set up a second station with paper and scissors. Tell students to cut some curved and straight shapes.

1 Introduce

- Ask students to stand up at their desks with their arms by their sides. Tell them their bodies are forming a straight line.
- Then ask students to hold out their arms and reach for the floor. Tell students their bodies are now bent or curved.

2 Teach

Key Concept

Foundational Skills and Concepts   Draw a straight horizontal line on the chalkboard.
- Using a different color, trace the line. Ask students to trace the line in the air with their fingers as you trace the line.
- Draw a curved line on the chalkboard. Using a different color, trace the line. Ask students to trace the line in the air with their fingers as you trace the line.
- **What is different about each line?** One line bends and one is straight.
- Using attribute blocks or buttons, show curved and straight with figures.

Using Manipulatives

Make Curved and Straight Lines   Provide students with pipe cleaners.
- Ask students to make a curved line with their pipe cleaner.
- Ask students to make a straight line with their pipe cleaner.
- Provide students with straws and repeat the process.

Name

Curved or Straight

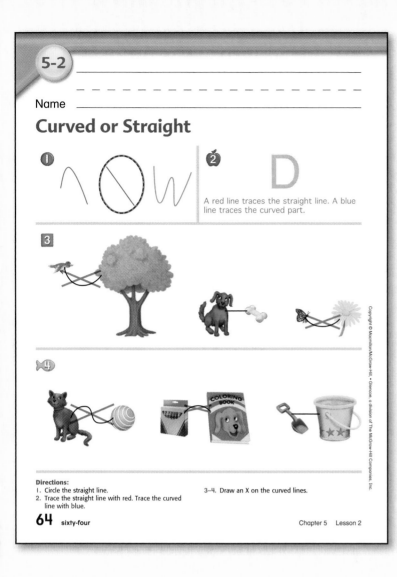

A red line traces the straight line. A blue line traces the curved part.

Directions:
1. Circle the straight line.
2. Trace the straight line with red. Trace the curved line with blue.

3–4. Draw an X on the curved lines.

64 sixty-four

Chapter 5   Lesson 2

③ Practice

Direct students to page 64 of their student workbook. Read the directions at the bottom of the student page as they complete the exercises.

For Exercise 5, students can name the letter. For extra practice, they can name other letters with straight and/or curved lines.

④ Assess

See It   Draw several curved and straight lines on the chalkboard. Have students circle the straight lines.

Say It   Draw a curved and a straight line. Point to each and have students identify it as straight or curved.

Do It   Give students yarn and a piece of paper. Have them make straight and curved lines with the yarn.

Write It   Have students use a red crayon to draw a straight line and a blue crayon to draw a curved line.

Circles

Lesson Planner

Objective
Develop an understanding of circles.

Vocabulary

circle

Materials
cardboard clock
construction paper
crayons
glue
magazines
pencils
scissors

Manipulatives
attribute buttons

 **On-Hand Manipulatives**
boxes
cups

Other Resources

CRM Chapter Resource Masters
Vocabulary and English Language
  Development (p. A117)
Skills Practice (p. A118)
Practice at Home (p. A119)

Teacher Tech Tools
TeacherWorks™ Plus
Math Online > macmillanmh.com
Advance Tracker

Student Tech Tools
StudentWorks™ Plus
Math Online > macmillanmh.com
eGlossary

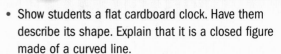
1 Introduce

- Show students a flat cardboard clock. Have them describe its shape. Explain that it is a closed figure made of a curved line.
- Ask students if they know the shape's name. Explain that it is a circle.
- Play "I Spy." Explain that everything you spy should be the shape of a circle. Note that objects should be flat, such as lids to cans, rugs, and so on.

2 Teach

Key Concept

Foundational Skills and Concepts   Draw a straight line, a curved line, a triangle, a square, and a circle on the chalkboard.
- Point to each item. Have students stop you when you point to the one with the same shape as the clock.
- When students identify the correct shape, remind them that it is called a circle. Have students repeat the word.
- **How many sides does a circle have?** none, zero

Using Manipulatives

Attribute Buttons   Provide students with a set of attribute buttons.

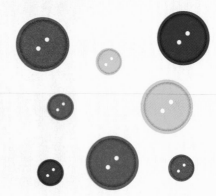

- Ask students to sort the buttons and to identify the circles.
- **How are the circles alike?** They are round.
- **How are the circles different?** They are different colors and sizes.

Intervention Strategy   Auditory Learners

Circle Rhymes   Students may benefit from learning or making up a rhyme about circles. For example, you may teach students to say, "No sides, one curved line, circles are all mighty fine!"

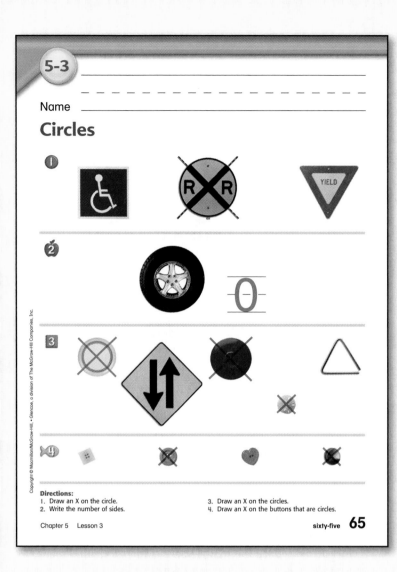

5-3

Name _____

Circles

Directions:
1. Draw an X on the circle.
2. Write the number of sides.
3. Draw an X on the circles.
4. Draw an X on the buttons that are circles.

Chapter 5   Lesson 3

sixty-five **65**

Practice

Direct students to page 65 of their student workbooks. Read the directions at the bottom of the student page as they complete the exercises.

Assess

See It   Draw several different shapes on the chalkboard. Ask students to point to the circles.

Say It   Show students a circle attribute button. Have them answer the following questions:
- **What is this shape?** circle
- **How many sides does a circle have?** none, zero
- **What kind of line is a circle made of?** curved

Do It   Have students name three objects in the room that have a circle shape.

Write It   Have students draw circles to make a picture.

⚠ Common Error Alert

No Sides   When discussing the attributes of circles, some students may think that a circle has one side. Remind students of the difference between straight and curved lines. Make sure students understand that since a circle has no straight lines, it has no sides. Instead, a circle has one curved line.

Triangles

Lesson Planner

Objective
Develop an understanding of triangles.

Vocabulary

corner

side

triangle

Other Resources

Materials
classroom objects
crayons
paper
rulers
sack or pillowcase
unsharpened pencils

Manipulatives
attribute buttons
triangle pattern blocks

**On-Hand
Manipulatives**
cardboard cut into triangle
shapes

CRM Chapter Resource Masters
Vocabulary and English Language
   Development (p. A120)
Skills Practice (p. A121)
Practice at Home (p. A122)

Teacher Tech Tools
TeacherWorks™ Plus
[Math Online] macmillanmh.com
Advance Tracker

Student Tech Tools
StudentWorks™ Plus
[Math Online] macmillanmh.com
eGlossary

Intervention Strategy

Kinesthetic
Learners

Mystery Bag Place circle, square, and triangle attribute
buttons in a sack or pillowcase. Have a student reach in and find
the triangle by feeling each shape. Students should describe each
shape they feel until they identify the triangle.

1 Introduce

- Have students use three unsharpened pencils to
  make a closed figure.
- Guide students to form a triangle. Tell them that
  each point where the pencils meet is called a corner.
- **What does the shape remind you of?** See students'
  work.
- **How is the shape different from a circle?** It has
  straight lines. It has three sides. It has three corners.

2 Teach

Key Concept

Foundational Skills and Concepts Draw a
large circle and a triangle on the chalkboard. Have
students identify the differences between the two
shapes. Point to each shape as you ask students
questions about the shape.

- **Does the circle have sides?** no
- **Does the triangle have sides?** yes **How many?** 3
- **Does the circle have corners?** no
- **Does the triangle have corners?** yes **How many?** 3
- Draw several more triangles of different shapes (such
  as equilateral, isoceles, or scalene), sizes, and
  orientations on the chalkboard. Explain to students
  that even though the shapes are different sizes and
  shapes, they are all triangles because they all have
  3 sides. Number and count the sides and corners
  with the students.

Using Manipulatives

Pattern Blocks Give students a triangle pattern
block. Have students use their fingertips to trace each
side of the pattern block.

- **How many sides does a triangle have?** 3
- Ask students to place the triangle on a sheet of
  paper and trace around the triangle.
- Ask students to draw another triangle inside the
  triangle they traced. Then ask students to draw a
  larger triangle outside the triangle they traced.
- Repeat the procedure with different-sized triangles.

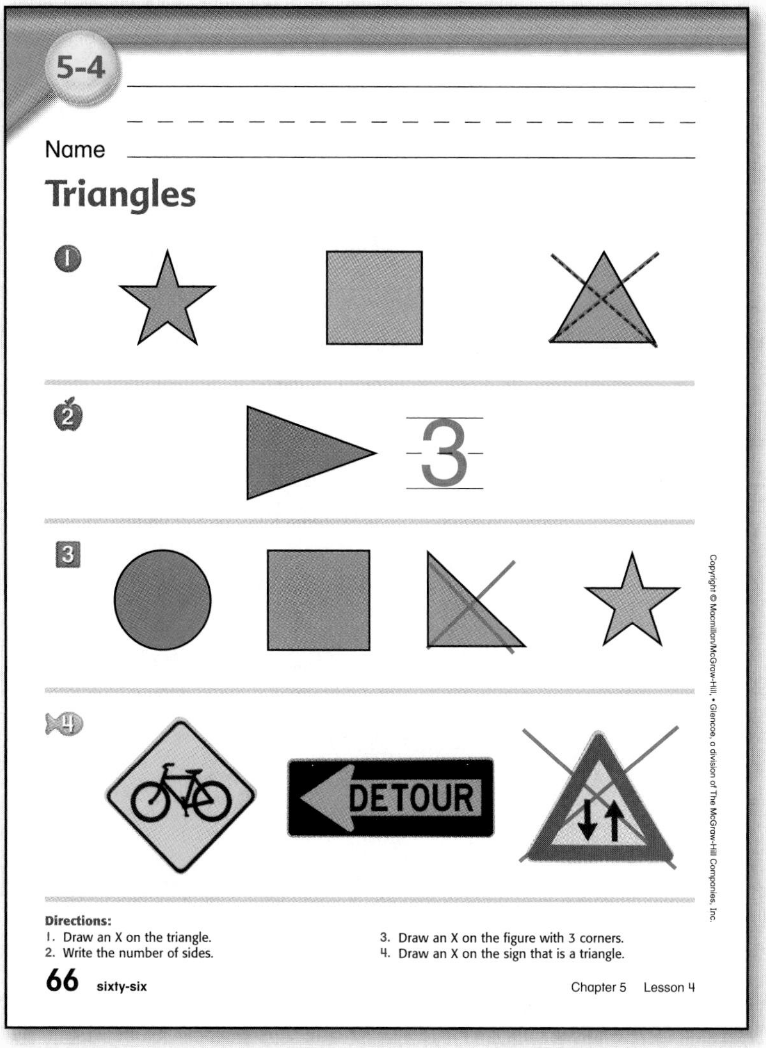
5-4

Name

Triangles

1

2 3

3

4

Copyright © Macmillan/McGraw-Hill, • Glencoe, a division of The McGraw-Hill Companies, Inc.

Directions:
1. Draw an X on the triangle.
2. Write the number of sides.
3. Draw an X on the figure with 3 corners.
4. Draw an X on the sign that is a triangle.

66 sixty-six Chapter 5 Lesson 4

3 Practice

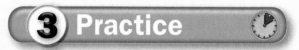

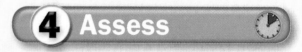

Direct students to page 66 of their student workbook. Read the directions at the bottom of the student page as they complete the exercises.

4 Assess

See It Draw several different shapes on the chalkboard. Ask students to point to the triangles.

Say It Show students a triangle attribute button. Have them answer the following questions:

- **What is this shape?** triangle
- **How many sides does a triangle have?** 3
- **How many corners does a triangle have?** 3

Do It Have students form a triangle using three objects, such as craft sticks, rulers, or markers. Ask them to trace the shape while they say the shape name.

Write It Have students use a ruler to make a triangle.

Common Error Alert

Exercise 2 Students may not recognize the triangle in Exercise 2. Students may associate a triangle with only one shape—that of an isosceles triangle with a corner at the top and two corners at the bottom. If students make this mistake, have them count the number of sides and the number of corners to make sure the shape is a triangle.

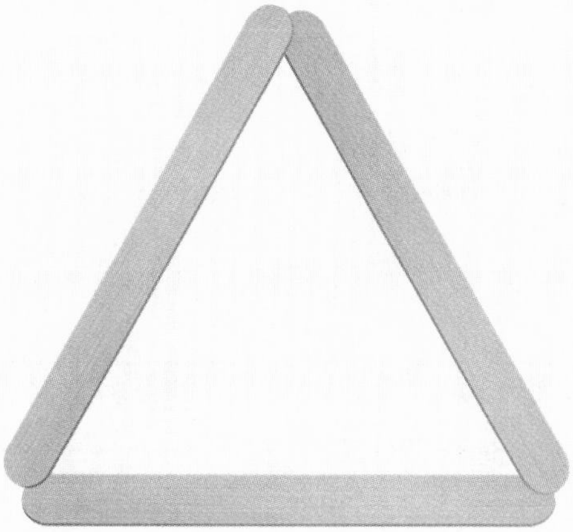

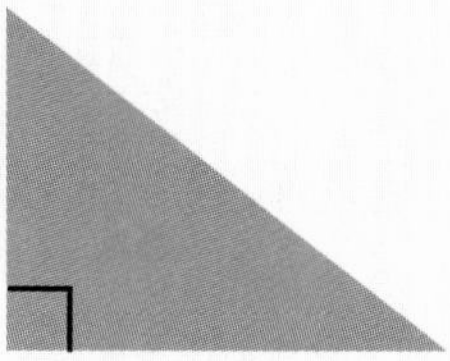

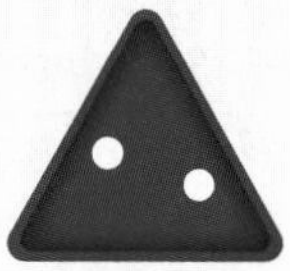

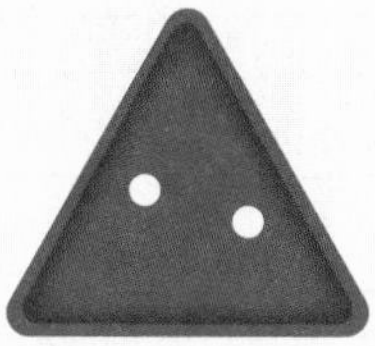

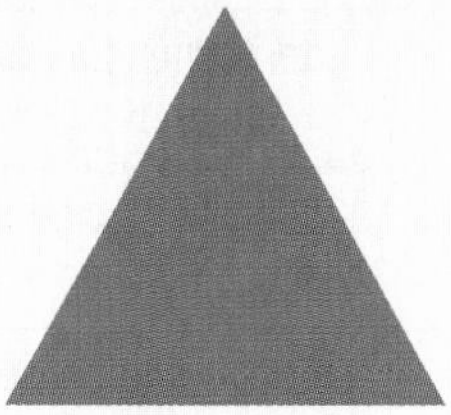

Progress Check 1

Formative Assessment

Use the Progress Check to assess students' mastery of the previous lessons. Have students review the lesson indicated for the problems they answered incorrectly.

 Common Error Alert

Figures In order to successfully complete the lesson, students must understand common math terms, including *figure, line,* and *circle.* If students are having difficulty, rephrase the directions. Then go back and clarify the terminology.

Exercise 1 Remind students that in an open figure, the lines do not all touch. In a closed figure, the sides touch.

Exercise 4 Students may be unsure of how to count the number of corners in the circle. Explain that zero can describe the number of corners.

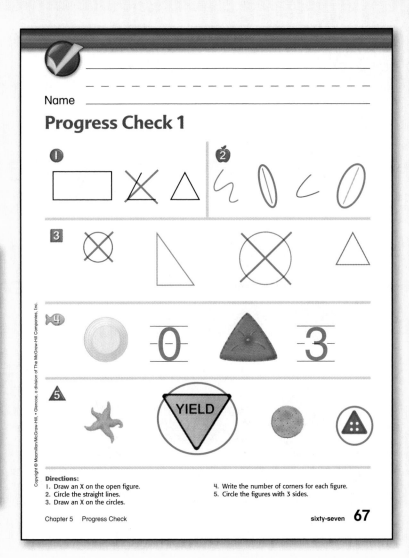

Data-Driven Decision Making

Students missing Exercises . . .	Have trouble with . . .	Should review and practice . . .
1	identifying open and closed figures.	TE Lesson 5-1, p. 63 CRM Skills Practice, p. A112
2	identifying curved and straight lines.	TE Lesson 5-2, p. 64 CRM Skills Practice, p. A115
3	recognizing circles.	TE Lesson 5-3, p. 65 CRM Skills Practice, p. A118
4	recognizing corners.	TE Lessons 5-3 and 5-4, pp. 65 and 66 CRM Skills Practice, pp. A118 and A121
5	understanding sides.	TE Lesson 5-4, p. 66 CRM Skills Practice, p. A121

Name _____

Replay

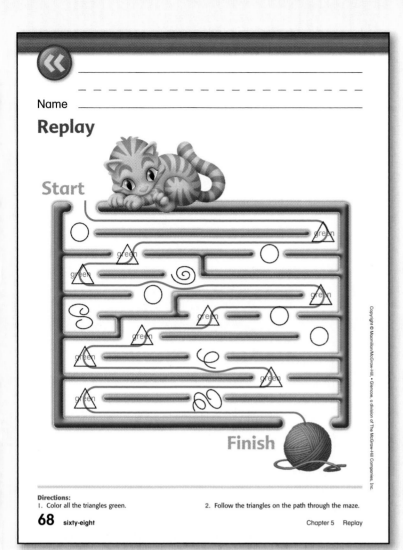

Start

Finish

Directions:
1. Color all the triangles green.

2. Follow the triangles on the path through the maze.

68 sixty-eight

Chapter 5 Replay

Replay

Use the Replay activity to review and reinforce concepts and skills presented in Lessons 5-1 through 5-4.

Instructions

Explain to students that they must get through the maze by passing only triangles.

Student Technology

Students can use the following technology resources to reinforce chapter content.

StudentWorks™ Plus

Math Online ▷ macmillanmh.com

• eGames
• eGlossary

Rectangles

Lesson Planner

Objective
Develop an understanding of rectangles.

Vocabulary
rectangle

Materials
classroom objects
index cards
masking tape
paper
pencil
rulers
shoe box

Manipulatives
connecting cubes

 **On-Hand Manipulatives**
square buttons

Other Resources

CRM Chapter Resource Masters
Vocabulary and English Language
 Development (p. A123)
Skills Practice (p. A124)
Practice at Home (p. A125)

Teacher Tech Tools
TeacherWorks™ Plus
Math Online > macmillanmh.com
Advance Tracker

Student Tech Tools
StudentWorks™ Plus
Math Online > macmillanmh.com
eGlossary

Intervention Strategy
Kinesthetic Learners

Walk the Lines Use masking tape to outline a rectangle on the floor. Students can walk the outline of the shape. As they walk on each line, students should count/number the sides. They can also jump on each corner to reinforce the concept that a corner is the place where two sides meet.

1 Introduce

Place circles, triangles, and rectangles in a shoe box. Show students the box lid. Talk about the shape. Replace the lid.
- Have students take a figure from the box and tell if it matches the shape of the lid.
- Encourage students to name shapes they know.

2 Teach

Key Concept

Foundational Skills and Concepts Draw a rectangle on the chalkboard. Name the shape.
- Lead students in counting the sides of the rectangle. Point to the two short sides of the rectangle.
- **How are these sides alike?** They are the same length (size).
- Repeat for the two long sides of the rectangle.
- Lead students in counting the corners. Number each corner as you point to it.
- Draw rectangles of various sizes and orientations. Have students count the number of sides and corners to verify that each shape is a rectangle.

Using Manipulatives

Connecting Cubes Provide each student with connecting cubes and an index card.

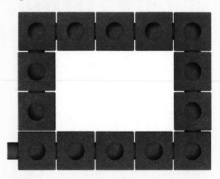

- **What shape is the index card?** rectangle
- Ask students to line the edges of the index card with connecting cubes. Ask students how many connecting cubes are on each side of the index card.
- Ask students to rearrange their cubes to make a rectangle that is longer than the index card.

Rectangles

Name _____

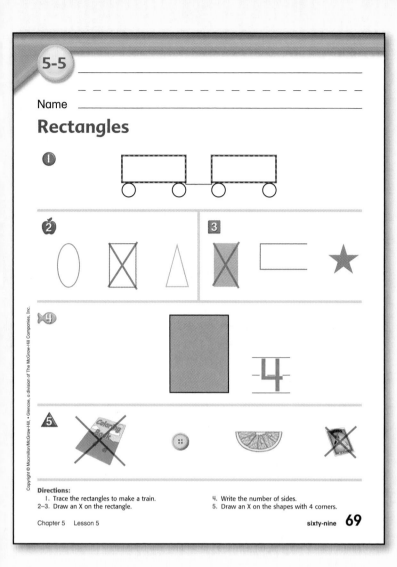

Directions:
1. Trace the rectangles to make a train.
2–3. Draw an X on the rectangle.
4. Write the number of sides.
5. Draw an X on the shapes with 4 corners.

Chapter 5   Lesson 5   sixty-nine **69**

③ Practice

Direct students to page 69 of their student workbook. Read the directions at the bottom of the student page as they complete the exercises.

④ Assess

See It   Show students classroom objects such as a dollar bill, a nickel, a piece of paper, a CD, and a ruler. Have students point to each object that is the shape of a rectangle.

Say It   Show students a rectangle. Have them answer the following questions:
- **What is this shape?** rectangle
- **How many sides does a rectangle have?** 4
- **How many corners does a rectangle have?** 4

Do It   Give students several circle, triangle, and rectangle pattern blocks, and tell them to use the blocks to make a picture. Students should identify the rectangles in their pictures.

Write It   Have students use rulers to make three rectangles of different sizes. Ask them to write the number of sides next to each rectangle.

Math Coach Notes

Quadrilaterals   A rectangle is a type of quadrilateral (shape with four sides). It is also a parallelogram. In order to be a rectangle, the four-sided figure must have four right angles (90°). While students do not need to be aware of the terms, if they identify a rhombus or kite as a rectangle, you can point out the differences between the angles of the corners.

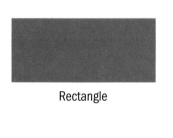

Rectangle

Rhombus

Squares

Lesson Planner

Objective
Develop an understanding of squares.

Vocabulary

square

Other Resources

Materials
cardboard
chalk
craft sticks
crayons
paper
scissors

Manipulatives
pattern blocks

On-Hand Manipulatives
cardboard squares

CRM Chapter Resource Masters
Vocabulary and English Language
   Development (p. A126)
Skills Practice (p. A127)
Practice at Home (p. A128)

Teacher Tech Tools
⊙ TeacherWorks™ Plus
[Math Online] macmillanmh.com
Advance Tracker

Student Tech Tools
⊙ StudentWorks™ Plus
[Math Online] macmillanmh.com
eGlossary

Intervention Strategy   Naturalist Learners

Nature Walk   Take students on a nature walk or a walk around the school. Students can take a journal or clipboard on the walk and draw objects they see with a square shape.

1 Introduce

- Give each student two square attribute blocks of the same color and one rectangle attribute block of a different color.
- Review the characteristics of the rectangle.
- Tell students to use the two squares to cover the rectangle.
- Explain to students that they are going to learn about squares.

2 Teach

Key Concept

Foundational Skills and Concepts   Show students a sheet of $8\frac{1}{2} \times 11$-inch paper.
- **What makes this a rectangle?** It has four sides and four corners.
- Turn the paper into a square. Fold the top-left corner down toward the right edge, forming a triangle. Cut off the bottom portion. Open the paper to reveal a square.
- Count the sides and corners.
- **How is the square different from the rectangle?** All 4 sides of the square are the same length.
- Have students identify objects in the classroom that are in the shape of a square.

Using Manipulatives

Pattern Blocks   Trace a square pattern block onto sheets of paper. Provide students with a square pattern block and a sheet of paper with the traced square.
- **How many sides does the pattern block have?** 4
- Ask students to place the block inside the square on the paper.
- Ask student to turn the block.
- **Does the block still fit inside the traced square?** yes
- Continue turning the block. Explain to students that the block fits inside the square because all 4 sides of the square are the same size.
- Have students practice making crayon rubbings of the square pattern block.

Name

Squares

1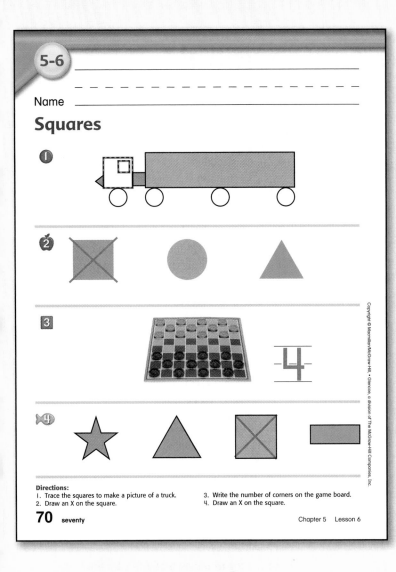

2

3

4

Directions:
1. Trace the squares to make a picture of a truck.
2. Draw an X on the square.
3. Write the number of corners on the game board.
4. Draw an X on the square.

Chapter 5 Lesson 6

---

③ Practice

Direct students to page 70 of their student workbook. Read the directions at the bottom of the student page as they complete the exercises.

④ Assess

See It Show students flat objects in the classroom such as a rug or poster, and have them identify the squares.

Say It Show students a square. Have them answer the following questions:
- **What is this shape?** square
- **How many sides does a square have?** 4
- **How many corners does a rectangle have?** 4
- **How is a square different from a rectangle?**
  A square is a rectangle with all 4 sides the same length.

Do It Give students 4 craft sticks or other objects of the same length. Have them use the sticks to make a square.

Write It Give students different attribute blocks. Have them select a square and trace it. Students who have difficulty tracing can make a crayon rubbing of the shape.

⚠ Common Error Alert

Exercise 4 Students may incorrectly assume that if a square is a rectangle, then a rectangle is a square. They may not understand that the sides of a square are equal. Give the students 4 pipe cleaners of equal length.
- **What shape can you make?** a square
- Give students 2 pipe cleaners of equal length, and 2 more pipe cleaners of another equal length shorter than the first 2.
- **What shape can you make?** a rectangle

Create Two-Dimensional Figures

Lesson Planner

Objective
Develop an understanding of ways to make new shapes.

Vocabulary
apart

together

Other Resources

Materials
cardboard
construction paper cut into
  6-inch squares
pencils
scissors

Manipulatives
pattern blocks

 **On-Hand Manipulatives**
cardboard squares and
  triangles

CRM Chapter Resource Masters
Vocabulary and English Language
  Development (p. A129)
Skills Practice (p. A130)
Practice at Home (p. A131)

Teacher Tech Tools
⊙ TeacherWorks™ Plus
Math Online > macmillanmh.com
Advance Tracker

Student Tech Tools
⊙ StudentWorks™ Plus
Math Online > macmillanmh.com
eGlossary

Intervention Strategy
Interpersonal Learners

Cardboard Cutouts   Make cardboard cutouts of squares, triangles, and rectangles, making sure shapes of the same type are the same dimensions. Give each student a cutout. Instruct students to find classmates who have the same shape. Encourage pairs or groups to put their shapes together to make at least one larger shape.

① Introduce

- Have two students hold cardboard squares. Ask the class to name the shapes. Instruct the students to put the pieces of cardboard together. Point out that the 2 squares have made a rectangle.
- Have two more students hold same-size, right triangle, cardboard triangles. Ask the class to name the shapes. Instruct the students to put the pieces of cardboard together to make a square. Provide assistance if needed.

② Teach

Key Concept

Foundational Skills and Concepts   Show students a 6-inch square piece of construction paper.
- **What is this shape?** square
- Fold the square in half by taking the top-left corner to the bottom-right corner, forming a triangle.
- **Now what shape do I have?** triangle
- Open the paper, cut on the crease, making two triangles.
- **How many triangles made the square?** 2
- Repeat the activity but fold the square paper in half twice to make 4 smaller squares.
- Pass out construction paper and scissors. Repeat the activity.

Using Manipulatives

Pattern Blocks   Provide students with square pattern blocks. Provide two equal-sized objects that are right triangles.
- Have students separate the squares and the triangles into separate piles. Ask students to try to put the square blocks together to make different shapes. Repeat with the right triangle blocks.
- **What shape can you make from 2 squares?** rectangle
- **What shapes can you make from 4 squares?** rectangle and square
- **What shape can you make from 2 triangles?** square

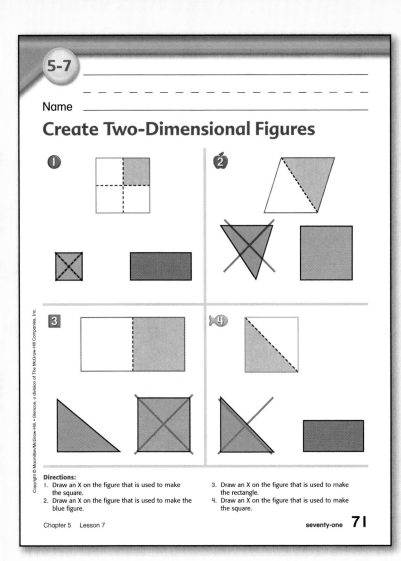

5-7

Name _____

Create Two-Dimensional Figures

Directions:
1. Draw an X on the figure that is used to make the square.
2. Draw an X on the figure that is used to make the blue figure.
3. Draw an X on the figure that is used to make the rectangle.
4. Draw an X on the figure that is used to make the square.

Chapter 5 Lesson 7

seventy-one **71**

Direct students to page 71 of their student workbook. Read the directions at the bottom of the student page as they complete the exercises.

For Exercises 3 and 4, students should place pattern blocks on the shape so that the combination of pattern blocks forms the exact shape on the page. If students have difficulty, suggest the shape of pattern blocks they should use.

See It   Show students a rectangle divided into 2 squares. Have students name the rectangle and use a finger to outline the figure. Have students name the squares that make the rectangle. Have them outline the shape of each square.

Say It   Draw a large triangle on the board and divide it into 4 smaller triangles. Ask students to identify each shape.

Do It   Draw a large square on the board. Ask students to direct you to draw lines inside the square to make other shapes. Provide students with construction paper. Have them fold the paper and identify the shapes they made.

Write It   Have students use pattern blocks to make new shapes. Have them draw or trace the new shapes.

Math Coach Notes

Strategies
• Young children have a lot of prior knowledge of shapes that they acquire through play, such as sorting, fitting blocks together, and experimenting with objects that roll. Draw upon this prior knowledge as you work with shapes.
• When beginning to teach geometry, rely on familiar objects. As students gain more familiarity, they will develop appropriate vocabulary and build upon their understanding.
• Working with shapes helps develop students' spatial ability, which is necessary in everyday life.

Progress Check 2

Formative Assessment

Use the Progress Check to assess students' mastery of the previous lessons. Have students review the lesson indicated for the problems they answered incorrectly.

 Common Error Alert

Confusing Squares and Rectangles
Because rectangles and squares are similar, some students may have difficulty differentiating between the two. Remind students that only squares have four sides that are the same length.

Exercise 1   If students have difficulty with Exercise 1, remind them that a corner is the point where two sides meet. Students who are having difficulty with corners can place a counter on each corner and count the number of counters.

Exercise 2   Make sure students understand that they will draw an X on more than one shape. Read the directions again, emphasizing the plural ending in *squares*.

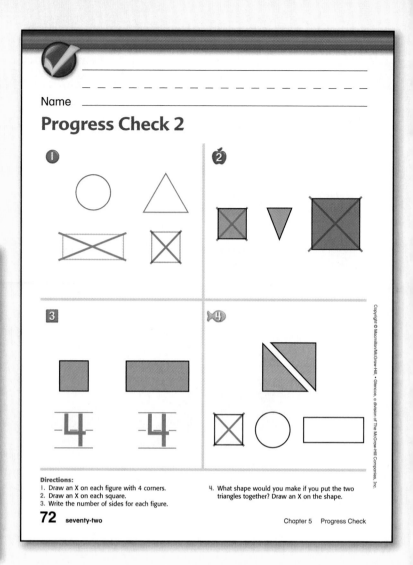

Data-Driven Decision Making

Students missing Exercises . . .	Have trouble with . . .	Should review and practice . . .
1	recognizing corners.	**TE** Lessons 5-5 and 5-6, pp. 69 and 70 **CRM** Skills Practice, pp. A124 and A127
2	identifying squares.	**TE** Lesson 5-6, p. 70 **CRM** Skills Practice, p. A127
3	identifying rectangles and squares.	**TE** Lessons 5-5 and 5-6, pp. 69 and 70 **CRM** Skills Practice, pp. A124 and A127
4	composing two-dimensional figures.	**TE** Lesson 5-7, p. 71 **CRM** Skills Practice, p. A130

Intervention Strategies

Visual

Materials: chalk, classroom objects

Step 1 **Whole Class** Tell students that in this chapter, they will be learning about lines and shapes. Draw a circle on the board, and say the word *circle* to the class. Ask students to give examples of places where they have seen this shape at home, such as the sun, a tire, a smiley face, and a pizza.

Step 2 Ask students whose first language is not English to say the word for a circle in their native language. Then have them repeat the word *circle*. Assist them with pronunciation if necessary.

Step 3 Direct each student to look around the classroom for other examples of circles. Ask students to point to circular objects or objects made of circles as they see them, such as the clock, a ball, a globe, and counters.

Step 4 Follow the same steps for other shapes students encounter in this chapter: square, triangle, rectangle.

Step 5 After students have finished learning about each of the shapes, say each shape name slowly to the class. Ask students to identify classroom objects that are comprised of those shapes.

Kinesthetic

Materials: cardboard shapes (circles, triangles, squares, and rectangles), glue, construction paper

Step 1 **Whole Class** Cut out a number of large cardboard shapes and a number of smaller shapes (circles, triangles, squares, and rectangles).

Step 2 Explain to the class that they are going to make a piece of art using basic shapes. Construct your own art before class as an example (such as the rocket ship with triangle for nose, rectangle for body, and circles for windows; or a truck with rectangles for cab and body, circles for wheels).

Step 3 Allow students to pick out their shapes and begin their construction. Monitor their activity.

Step 4 When they have finished, have students come to the front of the classroom and present their art. Have them describe what they created and tell what shapes they used for each part. You may model this by giving your example. **I built a rocket ship. I made the body of the ship from a rectangle. The nose is made with a triangle. And the windows are made from circles.**

Teaching Strategies

Depending upon the number of non-native speakers in the class, devote additional time on saying and pronouncing the shapes with those students to improve their language skills.

Time Management

Have the shapes prepared before students arrive, and have additional construction paper and scissors in case more shapes are needed. Include additional time if students need help applying glue.

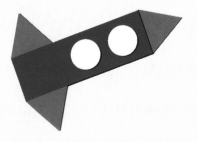

Review

Vocabulary

Before beginning the exercises, review vocabulary introduced in the chapter. Refer to the page numbers to revisit vocabulary activities in the lessons.

apart (p. 71A)   **rectangle** (p. 69A)

circle (p. 65A)   **shape** (p. 63A)

closed (p. 63A)   **side** (p. 66A)

corner (p. 66A)   **square** (p. 70A)

curved (p. 64A)   **straight** (p. 64A)

figure (p. 63A)   **together** (p. 71A)

open (p. 63A)   **triangle** (p. 66A)

Vocabulary Review Strategies

Focus on the meaning of the word. Provide students with opportunities to use the vocabulary words in context. For example, show students a rectangle and have them identify the shape in a sentence. Lead them to say, "That is a **rectangle.** It has four **sides** and four **corners.** It has **four** straight lines."

Concepts

The exercises in this section are grouped to cover content from each lesson in the chapter.

Exercise 1: Lesson 5-1 (p. 63)
Exercise 2: Lesson 5-2 (p. 64)
Exercise 3: Lesson 5-6 (p. 70)
Exercise 4: Lessons 5-3, 5-5, and 5-6 (pp. 65, 69, 70)
Exercise 5: Lesson 5-7 (p. 71)

CRM Find Extra Practice for these concepts in the Practice Worksheets, pages A111–A131.

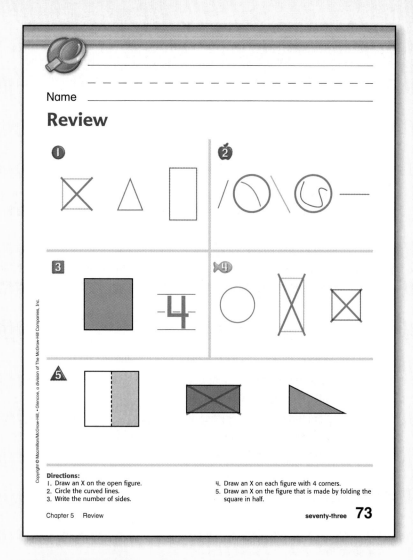

FOLDABLES **Study Organizer** ## Dinah Zike's Foldables

Have students use the Foldables they created at the beginning of the chapter to review and reinforce the concepts and skills they learned during the chapter. (See Chapter Resource Master p. A107 for instructions.)

Intervention Strategy   Linguistic Learners

Word Similarities   Say the words *rectangle* and *triangle* and write them both on the chalkboard. Ask students if they recognize any similarities between the two words. Explain that an angle is like a corner. Below the words on the chalkboard, draw a rectangle and a triangle. Have students circle all the corners on each shape. Ask the students to count the corners and say the numbers aloud.

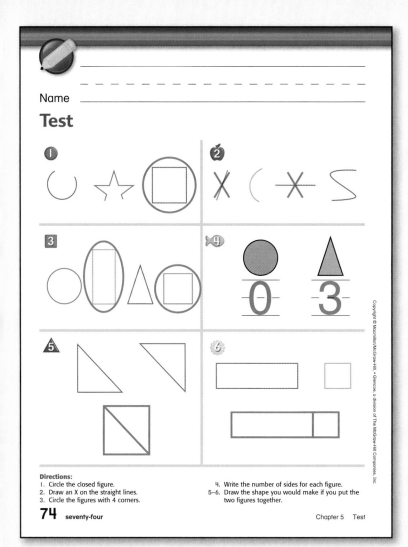

Name _____

Test

Directions:
1. Circle the closed figure.
2. Draw an X on the straight lines.
3. Circle the figures with 4 corners.
4. Write the number of sides for each figure.
5–6. Draw the shape you would make if you put the two figures together.

74 seventy-four

Chapter 5 Test

Test

Chapter Resource Masters

Additional forms of the Chapter 5 Tests are available.

Test Format	Where to Find it
Chapter 5 Test	**Math Online** macmillanmh.com
Blackline Masters	Assessment Masters, pp. 58–59

Alternative Assessment

Create a Shapes Portfolio   Have students draw each of the shapes they have learned about on a separate sheet of paper. Keep all the pages together in a portfolio. Ask students questions about each of the shapes. **How many corners does the shape have? How many sides? Does the shape have straight or curved lines?**

ExamView®
Assessment Suite

Customize and create multiple versions of the chapter tests and their answer keys. All of these questions from the chapter tests are available on ExamView® Assessment Suite.

Advance TRACKER

This online assessment tool allows teachers to track student progress with easily accessible, comprehensive reports available for every student. Assess students using any Internet-ready computer.

Data-Driven Decision Making

Students missing Exercises . . .	Have trouble with . . .	Should review and practice . . .
1	identifying open and closed figures.	**TE** Lesson 5-1, p. 63 **CRM** Skills Practice, p. A112
2	identifying curved and straight lines.	**TE** Lesson 5-2, p. 64 **CRM** Skills Practice, p. A115
3	recognizing rectangles and squares.	**TE** Lessons 5-5 and 5-6, pp. 69 and 70 **CRM** Skills Practice, pp. A124 and A127
4	recognizing circles and triangles.	**TE** Lessons 5-3 and 5-4, pp. 65 and 66 **CRM** Skills Practice, pp. A118 and A121
5-6	making new shapes.	**TE** Lesson 5-7, p. 71 **CRM** Skills Practice, p. A130

Chapter-at-a-Glance

Lesson	Math Objective	State/Local Standards
6-1 Introduce Three-Dimensional Figures (pp. 77A–77)	Compare and explore three-dimensional figures with two-dimensional figures.	
6-2 Roll and Stack (pp. 78A–78)	Determine if three-dimensional figures will roll and/or stack.	
6-3 Spheres (pp. 79A–79)	Identify and describe spheres.	
6-4 Cylinders (pp. 80A–80)	Identify and describe cylinders.	
Progress Check 1 (p. 81)		
6-5 Rectangular Prisms (pp. 83A–83)	Identify and describe rectangular prisms.	
6-6 Cubes (pp. 84A–84)	Identify and describe cubes.	
6-7 Create Three-Dimensional Figures (pp. 85A–85)	Compose and decompose three-dimensional figures.	
Progress Check 2 (p. 86)		

Content-at-a-Glance

The diagram below summarizes and unpacks Chapter 6 content.

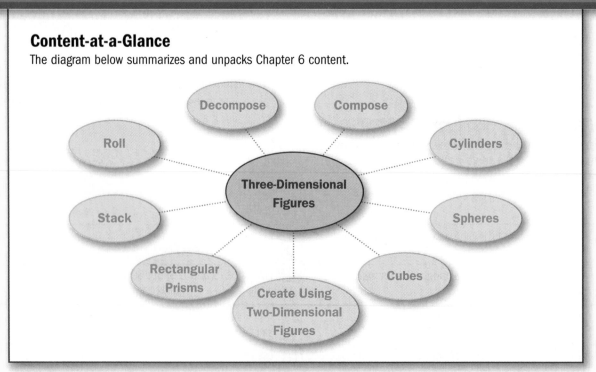

Chapter Assessment Manager

Diagnostic Diagnose students' readiness.

	Student Study Guide/ Teacher Edition	Assessment Masters	Technology
Intensive Intervention Placement Test		1–4	ExamView® Assessment Suite
Section Pretest (Chapters 5–7)		42–43	ExamView® Assessment Suite
Chapter 6 Pretest		65–66	ExamView® Assessment Suite
Get Ready	SSG 76		Math Online ▷ macmillanmh.com StudentWorks™ Plus

Formative Identify students' misconceptions of content knowledge.

	Student Study Guide/ Teacher Edition	Assessment Masters	Technology
Progress Checks	SSG 81, 86		Math Online ▷ macmillanmh.com StudentWorks™ Plus
Vocabulary Review	TE 87		Math Online ▷ macmillanmh.com
Lesson Assessments			ExamView® Assessment Suite

Summative Determine student success in learning the concepts in the lesson, chapter, or section.

	Student Study Guide/ Teacher Edition	Assessment Masters	Technology
Chapter 6 Test	SSG 88	68–69	ExamView® Assessment Suite
Alternative Assessment	TE 88	73–74	ExamView® Assessment Suite
See It, Say It, Do It, Write It	TE 77, 78, 79, 80, 83, 84, 85		
Section Test (Chapters 5–7)		75–76	ExamView® Assessment Suite

Backmapping and Vertical Alignment McGraw-Hill's *Math Triumphs* intervention program was conceived and developed with the final result in mind: student success in grade-level mathematics, including Algebra 1 and beyond. The authors, using the **NCTM Focal Points and Focal Connections** as their guide, developed this brand-new series by backmapping from grade-level and Algebra 1 concepts, and vertically aligning the topics so that they build upon prior skills and concepts and serve as a foundation for future topics.

Chapter Resource Manager

All-In-One Planner and Resource Center

	Lesson 6-1	Lesson 6-2	Lesson 6-3	Lesson 6-4
Concept	Introduce Three-Dimensional Figures	Roll and Stack	Spheres	Cylinders
Objective	Compare and explore three-dimensional figures with two-dimensional figures.	Determine if three-dimensional figures will roll and/or stack.	Identify and describe spheres.	Identify and describe cylinders.
Math Vocabulary	face shape side solid	roll stack	sphere	circle cylinder rectangle
Lesson Resources	**Materials** • paper shapes • soup can • paper towel tube • rectangular tissue box • tape **Manipulatives** • geometric solids **Other Resources** [CRM] Vocabulary and English Language Development [CRM] Skills Practice [CRM] Practice at Home	**Materials** • 3 shape pictures • crayons • oatmeal container **Manipulatives** • geometric solids **Other Resources** [CRM] Vocabulary and English Language Development [CRM] Skills Practice [CRM] Practice at Home	**Materials** • large ball • stapler • textbook **Manipulatives** • geometric solids **Other Resources** [CRM] Vocabulary and English Language Development [CRM] Skills Practice [CRM] Practice at Home	**Materials** • cans of various sizes • paper towel tubes • blocks • ball • white construction paper **Manipulatives** • geometric solids **Other Resources** [CRM] Vocabulary and English Language Development [CRM] Skills Practice [CRM] Practice at Home
Technology	**Math Online** › macmillanmh.com StudentWorks™ Plus ⊙ ExamView® Assessment Suite	**Math Online** › macmillanmh.com StudentWorks™ Plus ⊙ ExamView® Assessment Suite	**Math Online** › macmillanmh.com StudentWorks™ Plus ⊙ ExamView® Assessment Suite	**Math Online** › macmillanmh.com StudentWorks™ Plus ⊙ ExamView® Assessment Suite

Lesson 6-5	Lesson 6-6	Lesson 6-7	
Rectangular Prisms	Cubes	Create Three-Dimensional Figures	**Concept**
Identify and describe rectangular prisms.	Identify and describe cubes.	Compose and decompose three-dimensional figures.	**Objective**
face rectangle rectangular prism	cube face side square	figure net	**Math Vocabulary**
Materials • book • box of paper clips • shoebox • box of crayons **Manipulatives** • geometric solids **Other Resources** **CRM** Vocabulary and English Language Development **CRM** Skills Practice **CRM** Practice at Home	**Materials** • construction paper • book • blocks • scissors **Manipulatives** • geometric solids • number cubes **Other Resources** **CRM** Vocabulary and English Language Development **CRM** Skills Practice **CRM** Practice at Home	**Materials** • construction paper • tape • nets for cubes and rectangular prisms **Manipulatives** • geometric solids • number cubes **Other Resources** **CRM** Vocabulary and English Language Development **CRM** Skills Practice **CRM** Practice at Home	**Lesson Resources**

Math Online ▷
macmillanmh.com
StudentWorks™ Plus
◉ ExamView®
  Assessment Suite
	Math Online ▷
	macmillanmh.com
	StudentWorks™ Plus
	◉ ExamView®
	  Assessment Suite
		Math Online ▷
		macmillanmh.com
		StudentWorks™ Plus
		◉ ExamView®
		  Assessment Suite
			Technology

Chapter Notes

Home Connection

- Read the Home Connection letter with students and have them write their names in the space below.
- Read and explain the activity under Help at Home. If time allows, complete a portion of the activity so students can introduce the activity to a parent or other caregiver.

Real-World Applications

- Have students bring in (or have available) three-dimensional shapes from home: sphere, cube, rectangular prism, and cylinder. (They can use commonly available sources, such as oatmeal boxes, beach balls, shoe boxes, and corrugated cardboard boxes.)
- Have students use glue, clear packaging tape, yarn, paper, plastic scraps, and other such decorating items to turn their three-dimensional shapes into heads with faces.
- Have students describe how decorating a cylinder is different/more challenging than decorating a rectangular prism. (The cylinder rolls.)
- Place the heads on display in the classroom with the most prominent positions changing to feature the shapes students are studying in the different lessons.

Math Online

Visit macmillanmh.com for ongoing support of chapter content and instruction, including:
- Online Games
- Concepts in Motion

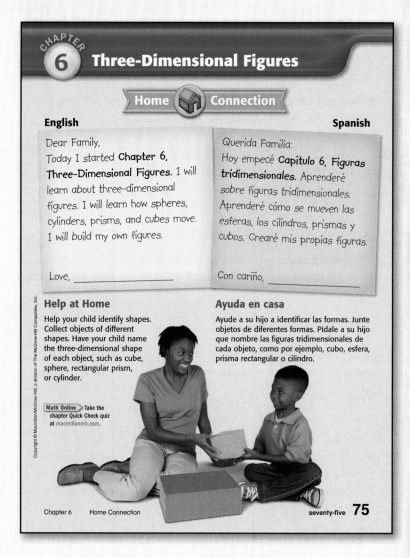

Home Connection

English   **Spanish**

Dear Family,
Today I started **Chapter 6, Three-Dimensional Figures.** I will learn about three-dimensional figures. I will learn how spheres, cylinders, prisms, and cubes move. I will build my own figures.

Love, _____

Querida Familia:
Hoy empecé **Capítulo 6, Figuras tridimensionales.** Aprenderé sobre figuras tridimensionales. Aprenderé cómo se mueven las esferas, los cilindros, prismas y cubos. Crearé mis propias figuras.

Con cariño, _____

Help at Home

Help your child identify shapes. Collect objects of different shapes. Have your child name the three-dimensional shape of each object, such as cube, sphere, rectangular prism, or cylinder.

Math Online Take the chapter Quick Check quiz at macmillanmh.com.

Ayuda en casa

Ayude a su hijo a identificar las formas. Junte objetos de diferentes formas. Pídale a su hijo que nombre las figuras tridimensionales de cada objeto, como por ejemplo, cubo, esfera, prisma rectangular o cilindro.

Chapter 6   Home Connection   seventy-five **75**

Key Vocabulary

Find interactive definitions in 13 languages in the **eGlossary** at macmillanmh.com.

English   Español *Introduce the most important vocabulary terms from Chapter 6.*

cube   cubo
a square block (p. 84A)

rectangular prism   prisma rectangular
a three-dimensional shape (p. 83A)

cylinder   cilindro
a solid figure shaped like a can (p. 80A)

sphere   esfera
a solid shape that has the shape of a round ball (p. 79A)

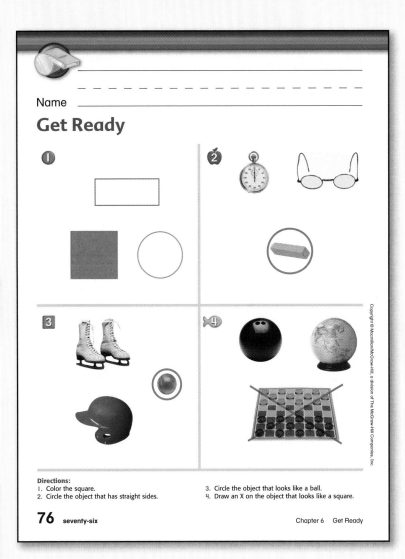

Name _____

Get Ready

①

②

③

④

Copyright © Macmillan/McGraw-Hill, a division of The McGraw-Hill Companies, Inc.

Directions:
1. Color the square.
2. Circle the object that has straight sides.
3. Circle the object that looks like a ball.
4. Draw an X on the object that looks like a square.

76 seventy-six

Chapter 6 Get Ready

Get Ready

Diagnostic Assessment

Have students complete the Get Ready exercises to assess readiness. Refer to the lessons below for support for prerequisite skills.

Exercises 1–4: Grade K, Chapter 5, Lessons 3–6 (pp. 65–70)

You may also assess student readiness with:
Assessment Masters: Chapter Pretest (pp. 65–66)

Math Online ⟩ macmillanmh.com
Online Readiness Quiz

Intervention Strategy

Divide the class into groups of three. Give each group construction paper and the following solids: cylinder, rectangular prism, and cube. Ask the members in each group to take one shape and trace the sides of their shape on construction paper. Have students discuss the different shapes that make the solids with their groups. Have the groups share the shapes they found for each solid.

Dinah Zike's Foldables

Guide students through the directions on p. A132 in the Chapter Resource Masters to create their own Foldable graphic organizer for use with this chapter.

Vocabulary Preview

- Before students begin the chapter, write a list of the vocabulary words from the chapter on the board.
- Make a vocabulary book with students.
- On each page of the book, write a vocabulary word from the chapter.
- If students are familiar with the word, have them tell you about it. Have them find a picture of it in a magazine or store advertisement to represent each term.
- As students proceed through the chapter, they can refer back to their books and insert other pictures.

McGraw Hill Professional Development

Targeted professional development has been articulated throughout **McGraw-Hill's Math Triumphs** intervention program. The **McGraw-Hill Professional Development Video Library** provides short videos that support the **NCTM Focal Points and Focal Connections.** For more information, visit macmillanmh.com.

Model Lessons   Instructional Strategies

Introduce Three-Dimensional Figures

Lesson Planner

Objective
Compare and explore three-dimensional figures with two-dimensional figures.

Vocabulary

face	**side**
shape	**solid**

Other Resources

Materials
paper squares, circles, and rectangles the same sizes as the models
paper towel tube
rectangular tissue box
soup can
tape

Manipulatives
geometric solids

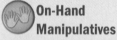 **On-Hand Manipulatives**
number or puzzle cube
rectangular tissue box
tomato juice can

CRM Chapter Resource Masters
Vocabulary and English Language Development (p. A136)
Skills Practice (p. A137)
Practice at Home (p. A138)

Teacher Tech Tools
TeacherWorks™ Plus
Math Online ▷ macmillanmh.com
Advance Tracker

Student Tech Tools
StudentWorks™ Plus
Math Online ▷ macmillanmh.com
eGlossary

English Learner Strategy

Vocabulary Give students six square pieces of paper. Have students number each square. Ask them to write "square" in English and their native language on each piece of paper. Give students a cube, a rectangular prism, and a cylinder. Have them match the square to the solid with square faces. Have students name the solid in English and their native language.

---

1 Introduce

- Give students paper squares. Show students one square.
- **What shape is this?** square
- Show students a cube. Point to its faces.
- **How are these two different?** Sample answer: The square is flat, and the other is solid.

2 Teach

Key Concept

Foundational Skills and Concepts Say: "We can use squares, circles, and rectangles to make some solids." Explain that solids will have height while shapes are flat like drawings on paper.

- Show students a paper towel tube. Hold the tube up so students can see one end. Trace the base on the board.
- **What shape did I draw?** circle **What shape does the paper towel tube have on its end face?** circle
- Show students a rectangular tissue box. Trace the side on the board.
- **What shape did I draw?** rectangle
- Show students a large number cube. Trace one of the sides on the board.
- **What shape did I draw?** square

Using Manipulatives

Geometric Solids Make sure every student has paper cutouts of the square, circle, and rectangle. Give small groups a cube, cylinder, rectangular prism and tape.

- Have students explore the solids and group the paper cutouts with the matching faces of the solids.
- **Show me the solid that has a circle on one face.** Students show the cylinder.
- Repeat for the rectangle and square.

Name

Introduce Three-Dimensional Figures

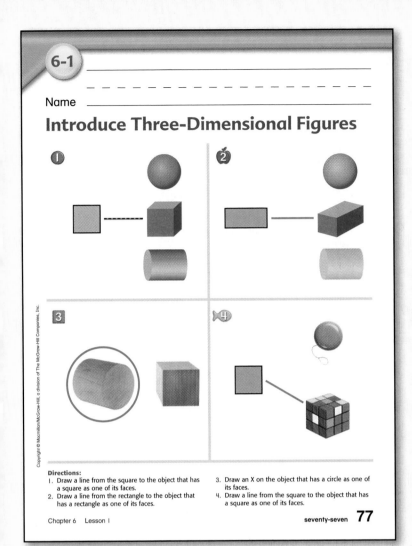

Directions:

1. Draw a line from the square to the object that has a square as one of its faces.
2. Draw a line from the rectangle to the object that has a rectangle as one of its faces.
3. Draw an X on the object that has a circle as one of its faces.
4. Draw a line from the square to the object that has a square as one of its faces.

Chapter 6   Lesson 1

seventy-seven **77**

Direct students to page 77 of their student workbooks. Read the directions at the bottom of the student page as they complete the exercises.

Remind students to use the solids and paper cutouts to remember which figures are made with the different shapes.

See It   Draw a square on the board. Have students find one solid with a square face.

Say It   Have students recite: "Cubes, cylinders, and rectangular prisms are solids. I can make them with squares, circles, and rectangles."

Do It   Give students a paper cutout of a circle, square, or a rectangle. Have students match the shape with the side of a solid.

Write It   Show students a solid. Have students trace and say the name of one face.

Math Coach Notes

Interchangeable Terms   The terms *shape* and *two-dimensional figure* as well as *solid* and *three-dimensional figure* are often used interchangeably. Help students make the connection between these terms, as they are used in the basal program.

Roll and Stack

Lesson Planner

Objective
Determine if three-dimensional figures will roll and/or stack.

Vocabulary
roll

stack

Other Resources

Materials
3 pictures: a ball (labeled roll), a book (labeled stack), a can (labeled both) (one set per student pair)
crayons
oatmeal container

Manipulatives
geometric solids

 **On-Hand Manipulatives**
3 dictionaries or other books that are the same size
a can
number blocks
tennis balls

CRM Chapter Resource Masters
Vocabulary and English Language Development (p. A139)
Skills Practice (p. A140)
Practice at Home (p. A141)

Teacher Tech Tools
🖸 TeacherWorks™ Plus
Math Online > macmillanmh.com
Advance Tracker

Student Tech Tools
🖸 StudentWorks™ Plus
Math Online > macmillanmh.com
eGlossary

1 Introduce

- Show the three tennis balls. Roll one ball to a student.
- **What is the ball doing?** rolling
- Show students 3 blocks.
- **Can you roll the blocks?** no
- **Why not?** The blocks have flat faces.
- Stack the cubes.
- **Can I stack the balls?** no
- **Why not?** The balls are round.

2 Teach

Key Concept
Foundational Skills and Concepts   Explain to students that solids can be compared by their ability to roll or stack.
- **Name an object that will stack or make a tower.** Sample answers: block, book, or cube
- **Name an object that will not stack.** a ball
- **Will a ball roll across the room?** yes
- **Why do you think so?** I have rolled a ball before.
- **Can I roll a cube across the room?** no
- **Why do you think so?** It is not round. It will tumble.

Using Manipulatives

Geometric Solids   Give student pairs the labeled pictures, two rectangular prisms, two cubes, two spheres, and two cylinders.

roll	stack	both

- Have students Think, Pair, Share with their partner which solids will roll, stack, or roll and stack.
- Have students explore the solids.
- Encourage students to test which solids will roll and stack.
- Tell students one shape will roll *and* stack.
- Have students sort their shapes and place the shapes on the papers with the correct attributes.
- Check students' work.

Intervention Strategy   Tactile Learners

Physical Attributes   Have students close their eyes. Give them each a cube. Have students say what they feel as they touch the shape. (Sample answer: The faces are flat.) Have students say if they think the shape will stack, roll, or stack and roll. Then have students open their eyes and use another cube to see if they are correct. Repeat with a cylinder, a sphere and a rectangular prism.

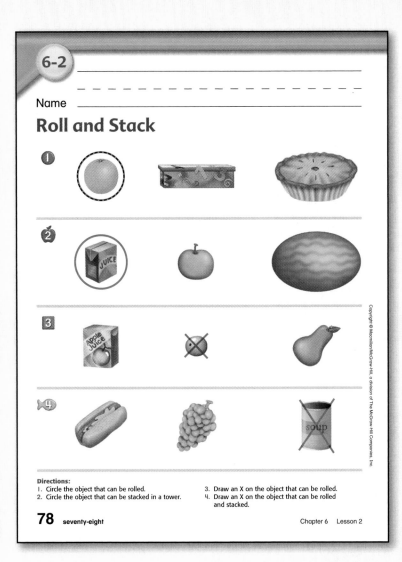

6-2

Name _____

Roll and Stack

① ⚫ [orange] [box] [pie]

② 🍎 [juice box] [apple] [melon]

③ ▪ [apple juice box] [⊗] [pear]

🐟④ [hot dog bun] [grapes] [soup can ⊗]

Directions:
1. Circle the object that can be rolled.
2. Circle the object that can be stacked in a tower.
3. Draw an X on the object that can be rolled.
4. Draw an X on the object that can be rolled and stacked.

78 seventy-eight

Chapter 6 Lesson 2

③ Practice

Direct students to page 78 of their student workbooks. Read the directions at the bottom of the student page as they complete the exercises.

Remind students to use their solids to test which objects roll, stack, or do both.

④ Assess

See It   Show students a sphere, cylinder, cube, or rectangular prism. Have students say if the object will roll, stack, or do both.

Say It   Have students describe objects they see in the classroom. Have them explain which can be rolled, which objects can be stacked, and which can be both rolled and stacked.

Do It   Have students use geometric solids to show which objects can be stacked and rolled.

Write It   Have students find pictures from a magazine or store advertisement of objects that can be rolled, stacked, or both.

Math Coach Notes

Everyday Solids   Have students use the corresponding geometric solids (spheres, cubes, and rectangular prisms) as well as the common everyday objects as they learn which shapes can be stacked and which can be rolled. When presenting rectangular prisms be certain that none of the faces are squares.

Spheres

Lesson Planner

Objective
Identify and describe spheres.

Vocabulary

sphere

Other Resources

Materials
large ball, such as a
   basketball
stapler
textbook

Manipulatives
geometric solids

 **On-Hand
   Manipulatives**
large ball
textbook

CRM Chapter Resource Masters
Vocabulary and English Language
   Development (p. A142)
Skills Practice (p. A143)
Practice at Home (p. A144)

Teacher Tech Tools
⊙ TeacherWorks™ Plus
| Math Online | macmillanmh.com
Advance Tracker

Student Tech Tools
⊙ StudentWorks™ Plus
| Math Online | macmillanmh.com
eGlossary

① Introduce

- Show the class a ball.
- **What is this?** a ball
- Say: "Describe the ball." It is round.
- Say: "A solid that is shaped like a ball is called a sphere."
- **Can you roll a ball?** yes
- **Do you think you can roll a sphere?** yes

② Teach

Key Concept

Foundational Skills and Concepts Show students the geometric solid of a sphere. Remind students that solid figures are also called three-dimensional figures.

- Say: "This is a sphere."
- **What object is the same shape as a sphere?** a ball
- Show students different-sized balls and other spheres, such as marbles. Say: "These are also spheres."
- **Does a ball or sphere roll or stack?** roll

Using Manipulatives

Geometric Solids Give student pairs geometric solids and real-world objects (various boxes and balls).

- Have pairs look at the objects and make a group of spheres and a group of other solids.
- Have students test the solids by trying to stack and roll them.
- **Can you stack two spheres?** no
- **Can you roll spheres?** yes
- Have students look at their groups and explain why each solid is a sphere or not a sphere.
- Have students describe what a sphere looks like. Sample answers: Spheres look like balls. Spheres are round. Spheres roll.

Intervention Strategy
Auditory/Kinesthetic Learners

Mnemonics Create a mnemonic for students to use to remember the meaning of the word "sphere." Write "sphere" and "snowman" on the board, making one S for the two initial S's and writing the two words at right angles to each other. Then draw a snowman next to the words. Allow students to make a sphere snowman using clay or Styrofoam® balls.

S p h e r e
n
o
w
m
a
n

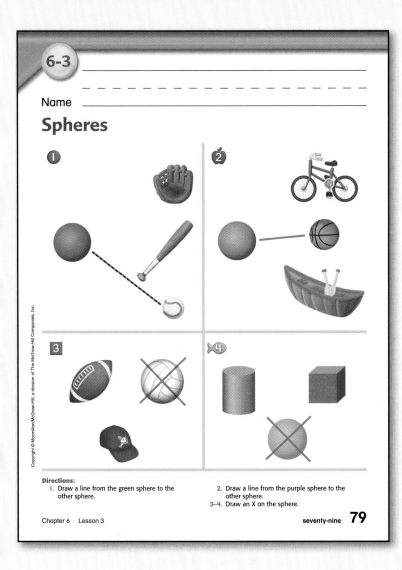

Name _____

Spheres

①

②

③

④

Directions:
1. Draw a line from the green sphere to the other sphere.

2. Draw a line from the purple sphere to the other sphere.
3–4. Draw an X on the sphere.

Chapter 6   Lesson 3

seventy-nine **79**

Practice ③

Direct students to page 79 of their student workbooks. Read the directions at the bottom of the student page as they complete the exercises.

Remind students that a sphere is shaped like a ball.

Assess ④

See It   Show students a basketball, a stapler, and a math textbook. Have students say which object is a sphere.

Say It   Have students say, "I had a ball learning about spheres."

Do It   Have students use clay to make a sphere. Have students show how their spheres roll but do not stack.

Write It   Have students draw and name three examples of spheres.

Math Coach Notes

Spherical Reminders   Encourage students to draw examples of round objects they are familiar with from their homes and from school. Remind students that a sphere has the shape of a round ball.

English Learner Strategy

Letter Sounds   Write the word *sphere* on the board. Say the word aloud and invite students to repeat it. Point out how the "ph" makes the "f" sound in this word.

Invite students to say the word for sphere in their native language and if possible write that word on the board as well.

Cylinders

Lesson Planner

Objective
Identify and describe cylinders.

Vocabulary

circle

cylinder

rectangle

Other Resources

Materials
ball
blocks
cans of various sizes
paper towel tubes
white construction paper

Manipulatives
geometric solids

 **On-Hand Manipulatives**
oatmeal container
tennis ball package

CRM **Chapter Resource Masters**
Vocabulary and English Language
   Development (p. A145)
Skills Practice (p. A146)
Practice at Home (p. A147)

Teacher Tech Tools
TeacherWorks™ Plus
Math Online > macmillanmh.com
Advance Tracker

Student Tech Tools
StudentWorks™ Plus
Math Online > macmillanmh.com
eGlossary

Intervention Strategy   Visual Learners

Mnemonics   Create a mnemonic for
students to remember the meaning of the word
"cylinder." Write "cylinder" and "cans" on the
board, making one C for the two initial C's and
writing the two words at right angles to each
other. Then draw a can of soup next to the
words. Say: **A cylinder is like a soup can.**

c y l i n d e r
a
n

1 Introduce

- Give small groups 3 cans of different sizes.
- Say: "Describe a can." It has circles on each end.
- Say: "Cans are cylinders."
- **Can you roll a can?** yes
- Have students roll the cans to each other.
- **Can you stack cans?** yes
- Have students stack the cans.

2 Teach

Key Concept

Foundational Skills and Concepts   Remind
students that solid figures are also called three-
dimensional figures. Show students a paper roll and
say: "This is a cylinder." Show how a cylinder is curved
but also has flat sides unlike a sphere.

- **Look at the end of this cylinder. What is the
shape?** a circle
- Cut the length of the tube and unroll it.
- **What shape is this?** rectangle
- Explain to students that a cylinder is made from
2 circles and 1 rectangle.
- Repeat with a soup can, showing students the ends,
then remove the label to show the rectangle.

Using Manipulatives

Geometric Solids   Give student pairs a variety
of cylinders (different-sized soup cans, coffee cans,
paper towel rolls, and so on).

- Have students trace the ends of their cylinders and
name the shape.
- Have students explain how the cylinders are alike.
Their ends are all circles.
- Ask how they are different. They are different sizes.
- **Can you stack your cylinders?** yes
- **Can you roll your cylinders?** yes
- Hold up the following three-dimensional figures:
a cylinder and a cube. Have students point to
the cylinder.

Name _____

Cylinders

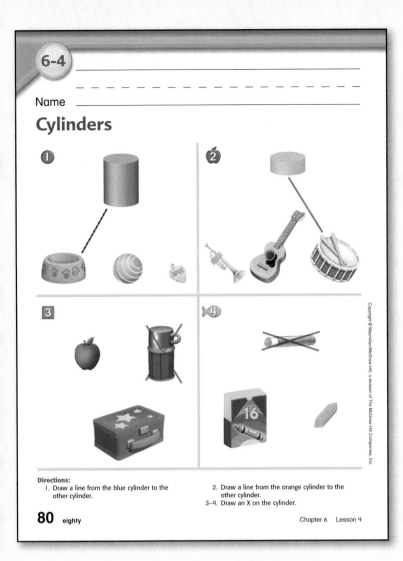

Directions:
1. Draw a line from the blue cylinder to the other cylinder.
2. Draw a line from the orange cylinder to the other cylinder.
3–4. Draw an X on the cylinder.

80 eighty

Chapter 6   Lesson 4

Copyright © Macmillan/McGraw-Hill, a division of The McGraw-Hill Companies, Inc.

Practice

Direct students to page 80 of their student workbooks. Read the directions at the bottom of the student page as they complete the exercises.

Remind students that cylinders are like cans or tubes of paper. Guide students to roll a sheet of paper to make a model of a cylinder.

Assess

See It   Show students a can, a block, and a ball. Have students identify the cylinder.

Say It   Have students say, "A cylinder can be stacked and rolled. A cylinder looks like a can I can hold."

Do It   Have students make a cylinder with a sheet of paper and describe the ends of the cylinder and its ability to stack and roll.

Write It   Have students trace the ends of a cylinder. Have students say what they know about the ends of the cylinder and the cylinder's ability to stack and roll.

Math Coach Notes

Ends and Bases   The ends of the cylinder will be called the *bases* in later grades. You may wish to use the term *base* with students as you describe the cylinder.

Progress Check 1

Formative Assessment

Use the Progress Check to assess students' mastery of the previous lessons. Have students review the lesson indicated for the problems they answered incorrectly.

 Common Error Alert

Three-Dimensional Figures If students are having trouble differentiating between two-dimensional shapes and three-dimensional figures, allow students to use geometric solids and flat cutouts of different shapes to help them.

Exercise 2 Be sure students know that round objects with curved sides and faces such as cans and balls can be rolled, and objects like blocks and books cannot be rolled, but they can be stacked.

Exercise 4 Be sure students know that a cylinder is a three-dimensional figure that is shaped like a can.

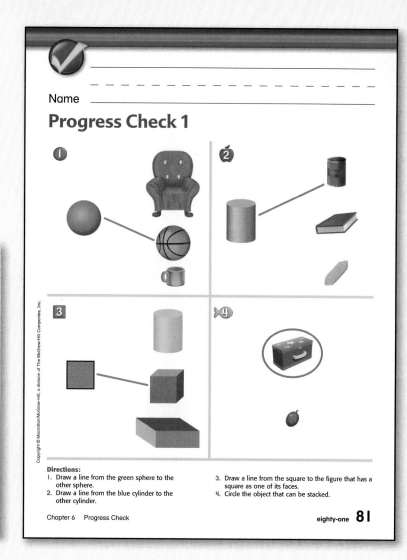

Data-Driven Decision Making

Students missing Exercises . . .	Have trouble with . . .	Should review and practice . . .
1	identifying the three-dimensional figure that can be created from the two-dimensional shape shown.	TE Lesson 6-1, p. 77 CRM Skills Practice, p. A137
2	identifying the object that can be stacked.	TE Lesson 6-2, p. 78 CRM Skills Practice, p. A140
3	matching spheres.	TE Lesson 6-3, p. 79 CRM Skills Practice, p. A143
4	matching cylinders.	TE Lesson 6-4, p. 80 CRM Skills Practice, p. A146

Name _____

Replay

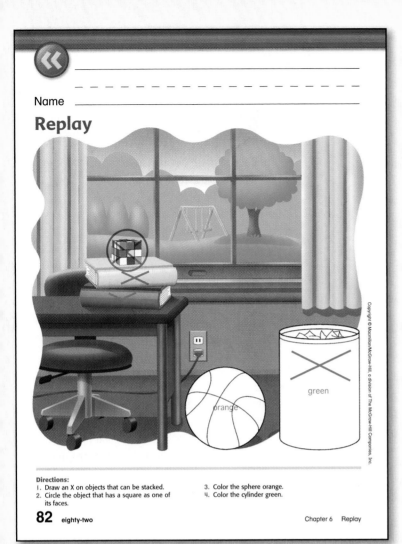

Directions:
1. Draw an X on objects that can be stacked.
2. Circle the object that has a square as one of its faces.
3. Color the sphere orange.
4. Color the cylinder green.

82 eighty-two   Chapter 6   Replay

Replay

Use the Replay activity to review and reinforce concepts and skills presented in lessons 6-1 through 6-4.

Instructions

Remind students of the difference between spheres and cylinders and which objects stack. Have students look for one type of three-dimensional figure at a time.

Student Technology

Students can use the following technology resources to reinforce chapter content.

StudentWorks™ Plus

Math Online > macmillanmh.com

- eGames
- eGlossary

Copyright © Macmillan/McGraw-Hill, a division of The McGraw-Hill Companies, Inc.

orange

Rectangular Prisms

Lesson Planner

Objective
Identify and describe rectangular prisms.

Vocabulary

face

rectangle

rectangular prism

Other Resources

Materials
book
box of crayons
box of paper clips
shoe box

Manipulatives
geometric solids

 **On-Hand Manipulatives**
book
box of chalk
box of crayons
box of paper clips
shoe box

CRM Chapter Resource Masters
Vocabulary and English Language
  Development (p. A148)
Skills Practice (p. A149)
Practice at Home (p. A150)

Teacher Tech Tools
◎ TeacherWorks™ Plus
Math Online > macmillanmh.com
Advance Tracker

Student Tech Tools
◎ StudentWorks™ Plus
Math Online > macmillanmh.com
eGlossary

① Introduce

- Give each student two rectangular prisms (boxes).
- Have students describe the boxes.
- **Are these solid objects?** yes
- **Do you think you can stack them?** yes
- Have students stack the boxes.
- **Do you think they will roll?** no
- Have students try rolling them.

② Teach

Key Concept

Foundational Skills and Concepts   Remind students that solids are three-dimensional figures. Show students a rectangular prism so they see one side at a time. Compare the rectangular prism to a sphere and a cylinder. Point out all the faces are flat on the rectangular prism.

- **What shape is each face?** rectangle
- Say: "An object that is solid and has faces that are rectangles is called a rectangular prism."
- **How many faces does a rectangular prism have?** 6
- **Can you find and name rectangular prisms in the classroom?** Sample answers: board eraser, book, box, and building blocks

Using Manipulatives

Geometric Solids Visual   Have examples of rectangular prisms visible around the classroom so students can see that rectangular prisms are made with rectangles. Give student pairs a variety of solids: rectangular prisms, cylinders, and spheres.

- Have pairs sort their solids into groups of rectangular prisms and other solids.
- Have students trace the faces of each solid with their fingers.
- Start with the rectangular prisms. Have students explain how they know the name of the solid.
- **What shape is each face?** a rectangle
- **How do you know these are rectangular prisms?** Each face is a rectangle. You can stack them, but they do not roll.
- Have students name the other solids.

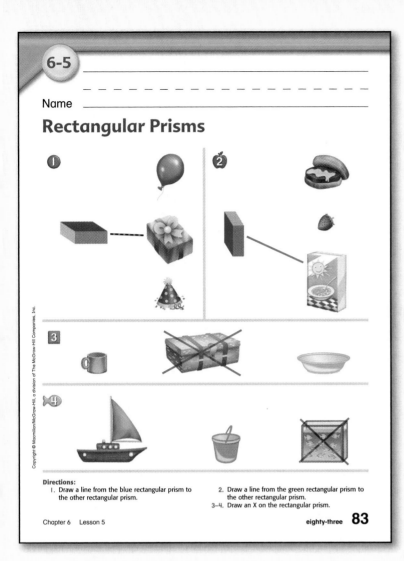

Name _____

Rectangular Prisms

Directions:
1. Draw a line from the blue rectangular prism to the other rectangular prism.
2. Draw a line from the green rectangular prism to the other rectangular prism.
3–4. Draw an X on the rectangular prism.

Chapter 6   Lesson 5

eighty-three **83**

③ Practice

Direct students to page 83 of their student workbooks. Read the directions at the bottom of the page as they complete the exercises.

Remind students that rectangular prisms are like boxes; they can be stacked but not rolled. Encourage students to use a box as a model when they work through the exercises.

④ Assess

See It Have students identify the rectangular prism among a group of geometric solids.

Say It Have students recite, "A rectangular prism is a solid made with rectangles."

Do It Have students tape rectangles to the faces of a rectangular prism. Then have students name the shape of each side and the shape of the solid.

Write It Have students trace each face of a rectangular prism and identify the shape of each face and the shape of the solid.

Math Coach Notes

Solid Imprints Allow students to explore solids by making imprints in sand or clay. Have them describe the imprinted shapes they see.

Intervention Strategy   Kinesthetic Learners

Real-World Examples Give students self-stick notes labeled "rectangular prism." Have students hunt for rectangular prisms and then stick the labels on them. Students show the class which rectangular prisms they labeled and explain why they are rectangular prisms.

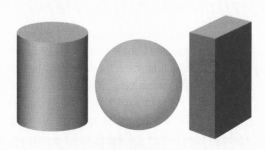

Cubes

Lesson Planner

Objective
Identify and describe cubes.

Vocabulary

cube	side
face	square

Other Resources

Materials
blocks
book
construction paper
scissors

Manipulatives
geometric solids
number cubes

 **On-Hand Manipulatives**
wooden cube blocks

CRM Chapter Resource Masters
Vocabulary and English Language
Development (p. A151)
Skills Practice (p. A152)
Practice at Home (p. A153)

Teacher Tech Tools
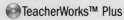 TeacherWorks™ Plus
Math Online ▷ macmillanmh.com
Advance Tracker

Student Tech Tools
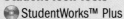 StudentWorks™ Plus
Math Online ▷ macmillanmh.com
eGlossary

English Learner Strategy

Math Manipulatives Using flat square blocks (for example, hundreds squares from a base-ten set), determine the number of square blocks that make a cube when stacked. Have them stack the blocks to form a cube. Have students use an extra block to check the shape of each side of their cube. Have students say: "The faces of a cube are all square and they are the same size."

1 Introduce

- Draw a square on the board.
- **What is this shape?** square
- **How many sides does it have?** 4
- Count and label each side.
- **What is special about a square?** All the sides are equal in length.

2 Teach

Key Concept

Foundational Skills and Concepts Show students a cube. Count the sides aloud with the class. Say: "This is a cube, and it has six sides." Compare and contrast the cube and a rectangular prism. Have students count the sides of each. Remind students that the faces of a rectangular prism are rectangles.

- **What shape are the faces of this cube?** square
- **Are the squares of equal size?** yes
- **What can you tell me about the faces of a cube?** A cube has 6 faces. The faces are squares and equal in size.

Using Manipulatives

Geometric Solids Give student pairs a variety of cubes (number cubes, blocks, storage containers, boxes).

- Have students experiment with their cubes.
- **Can you stack your cubes?** yes
- **Can you roll your cubes?** yes
- Have students trace each face of a cube.
- Have students label and cut out their squares.
- **How many faces does the cube have?** six
- **Are the faces of the cube the same size?** yes

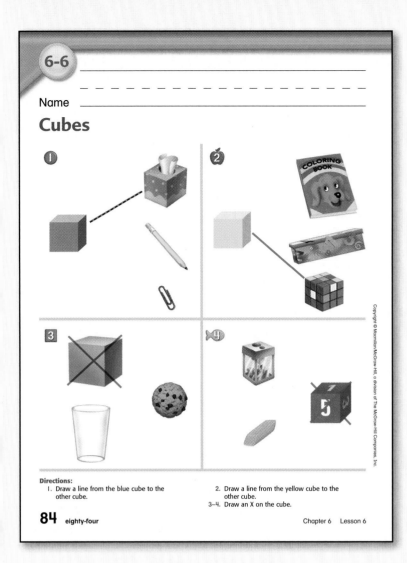

6-6

Name _____

Cubes

1.

2.

3.

4.

Directions:
1. Draw a line from the blue cube to the other cube.
2. Draw a line from the yellow cube to the other cube.
3–4. Draw an X on the cube.

③ Practice

Direct students to page 84 of their student workbooks. Read the directions at the bottom of the page as they complete the exercises.

Remind students that each side of a cube is a square. Encourage students to look at and hold a model cube as they complete the exercises.

④ Assess

See It   Show students a square piece of construction paper (equal in size to one face of the square block), a book, and a square block. Have students identify which object is a cube.

Say It   Have students recite, "A cube has six sides. Each side is a square."

Do It   Give students a cube and six self-stick notes. Have students label each side of the cube with a self-stick note. Have students count and label the sides of the cube.

Write It   Have students trace the sides of a cube. Have students count and label the sides they traced.

⚠ Common Error Alert

Cubes and Rectangular Prisms   Students may confuse the rectangular prism and the cube. Encourage students to look at a cube, an eraser, a number cube, and a box of crayons to help them compare and see the differences in the objects. Direct them to focus on how a cube is made from squares that are all the same size. Make a list with students and have them give examples of both rectangular prisms and cubes.

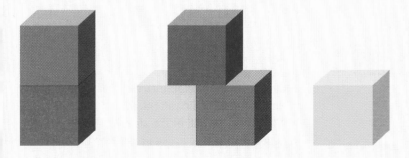

Create Three-Dimensional Figures

Lesson Planner

Objective
Compose and decompose three-dimensional figures.

Vocabulary
figure

net

Other Resources

Materials
construction paper
nets for cubes and
  rectangular prisms made
  from geometric solids used
  in this lesson
tape

Manipulatives
geometric solids
number cubes

 **On-Hand Manipulatives**
boxes (cubes)
paper towel tube
rectangular tissue box

CRM Chapter Resource Masters
Vocabulary and English Language
  Development (p. A154)
Skills Practice (p. A155)
Practice at Home (p. A156)

Teacher Tech Tools
TeacherWorks™ Plus
Math Online > macmillanmh.com
Advance Tracker

Student Tech Tools
StudentWorks™ Plus
Math Online > macmillanmh.com
eGlossary

1 Introduce

- Give students two boxes: a cube and a rectangular prism.
- Have students identify each solid.
- **Which box has faces that are rectangles?** rectangular prism
- Have students point to the rectangles.
- **Which box has faces that are squares?** cube
- Have students point to the squares.

2 Teach

Key Concept
Foundational Skills and Concepts Show students a square and a rectangular box. Disassemble the boxes to show the "folds." Repeat with a paper towel tube. Tell students that a net is flat and shows the faces of a solid figure.
- Give each student a paper tube.
- **What shape are the end faces of the tube?** circle
- Say: "Our tubes are open. We need to trace the ends of the tubes to see the circles."
- Have students trace the ends of the tube.
- Cut the tube and unroll it.
- **What other shape is a cylinder made from?** rectangle
- Have students cut and unroll their tubes.

Using Manipulatives
Geometric Solids Give students a cube, a rectangular prism, a cylinder, and construction paper.

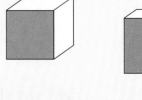

- Have students trace each face of their cube.
- **How many sides did you trace?** 6
- **What shape are all of the sides?** square
- Repeat with the rectangular prism and the cylinder.

Intervention Strategy
Kinesthetic/Visual Learners

Making Figures Give students a net for a cube. Have students color each square a different color. Have student assemble their cubes and share the number of colors they used to create their cubes.

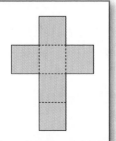

Name _____

Create Three-Dimensional Figures

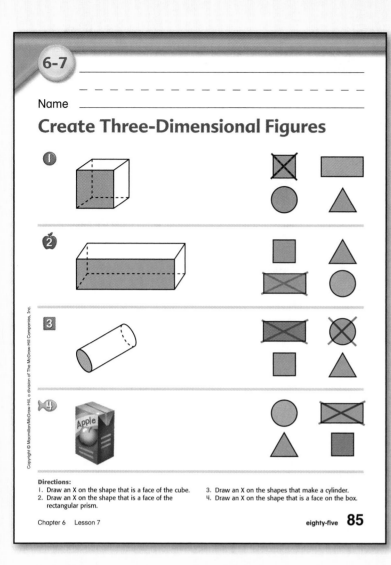

Directions:
1. Draw an X on the shape that is a face of the cube.
2. Draw an X on the shape that is a face of the rectangular prism.
3. Draw an X on the shapes that make a cylinder.
4. Draw an X on the shape that is a face on the box.

Chapter 6   Lesson 7

eighty-five **85**

Direct students to page 85 of their student workbooks. Read the directions at the bottom of the student page as they complete the exercises.

Guide students to use their unfolded boxes and paper tubes as they complete the exercises. Encourage students to fold and unfold their boxes and tubes.

See It   Show students cards with a circle, a rectangle, a square, a cube, a rectangular prism, and a cylinder. Have students match the shapes with the solids.

Say It   Have students recite, "Solids have flat faces that are circles, rectangles, and squares."

Do It   Have students imprint faces of a solid in sand or clay and identify the shape and the solid.

Write It   Show students a cube, a rectangular prism, or a cylinder and have students write and name the shapes of the faces.

> ⚠️ **Common Error Alert**
>
> **Cubes and Rectangular Prisms**   Students may confuse cubes and rectangular prisms. Allow them to use paper to trace and wrap each side of the cube and rectangular prism. Then have students unwrap their figures to see the shapes of the sides.

Intervention Strategy

Visual/Logical Learners

Treasure Hunt
- Place geometric solids and objects they represent (such as a soup can) around the room in half-hidden places.
- On two large pieces of construction paper, write the vocabulary terms *rectangular prism* and *cube.*
- Review the vocabulary terms with students. Ask them to go on a treasure hunt for the objects. When students find an object, have them place it on the construction paper with the correct term.
- When all objects have been found, review each of the vocabulary terms and discuss the properties they represent. For example, a cube's sides are all square.
- Ask students to recall which objects can be stacked and which can be rolled, and which can be both stacked and rolled.
- Allow students time to stack and roll the objects.

Progress Check 2

Formative Assessment

Use the Progress Check to assess students' mastery of the previous lessons. Have students review the lesson indicated for the problems they answered incorrectly.

 Common Error Alert

Figure Students may have trouble identifying three-dimensional figures. Encourage students to use geometric solids to help them.

Exercise 1 Be sure students know the difference between a rectangular prism and a cube. Provide students with cubes and rectangular prisms to look at so they can compare the two figures.

Exercises 3 and 4 Be sure students understand what is meant by the word *net* and understand how to use a net. Remind students that cubes are made up of all squares, and rectangular prisms are made up of squares and rectangles.

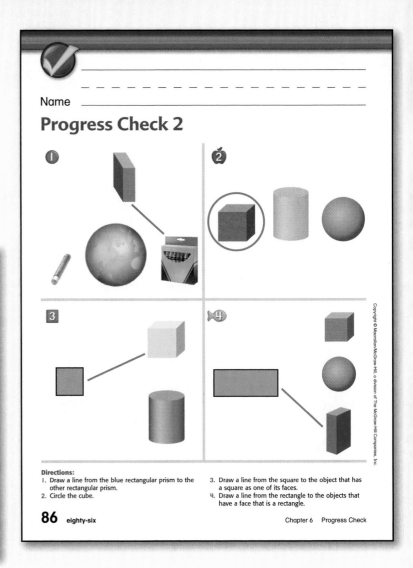

Name _____

Progress Check 2

Directions:
1. Draw a line from the blue rectangular prism to the other rectangular prism.
2. Circle the cube.
3. Draw a line from the square to the object that has a square as one of its faces.
4. Draw a line from the rectangle to the objects that have a face that is a rectangle.

86 eighty-six

Chapter 6   Progress Check

Copyright © Macmillan/McGraw-Hill, a division of The McGraw-Hill Companies, Inc.

Data-Driven Decision Making

Students missing Exercises . . .	Have trouble with . . .	Should review and practice . . .
1	matching the rectangular prism to the object it looks like.	TE Lesson 6-5, p. 83 CRM Skills Practice, p. A149
2	identifying a cube.	TE Lesson 6-6, p. 84 CRM Skills Practice, p. A152
3–4	identifying the figure formed by the net.	TE Lesson 6-7, p. 85 CRM Skills Practice, p. A155

Intervention Strategies

Compare Two- and Three-Dimensional Objects

Materials: Each group will need small cardboard boxes (about 4"W × 6"L × 1" H), cardboard rectangles about the same size as the bottom of the box, an empty cylindrical canister (potato chip canister or tennis ball container), and cardboard circles about the same size as the bottom of the canister.

Step 1 Divide the class into small groups. Give each group a rectangle.

Step 2 Ask the groups to each put the rectangle in a book and close the book.

Step 3 Discuss that the rectangle is two-dimensional so the book can close flat on it.

Step 4 Give each group a rectangular box. Ask each group to put the box in a book and close the book without bending the box or the book.

Step 5 Discuss that the box is three-dimensional, so it is not flat, and the book cannot close on it.

Step 6 Give each group a circle.

Step 7 Have one group member sit on the circle.

Step 8 **How tall is the circle?** It has no height.

Step 9 Give each group a cylindrical canister.

Step 10 **Is the canister flat?** no
Ask students to describe the height of the canister.

Step 11 Explain that the canister is a three-dimensional object because it has height.

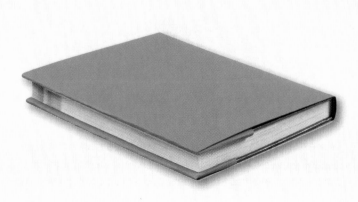

Review

Vocabulary

Before beginning the exercises, review vocabulary introduced in the chapter. Refer to the page numbers to revisit vocabulary activities in the lessons.

circle (p. 80A)   **roll** (p. 78A)

cube (p. 84A)   **shape** (p. 77A)

cylinder (p. 80A)   **side** (p. 77A)

face (p. 77A)   **solid** (p. 77A)

figure (p. 85A)   **sphere** (p. 79A)

net (p. 85A)   **square** (p. 84A)

rectangle (p. 80A)   **stack** (p. 78A)

rectangular prism (p. 83A)

Vocabulary Review Strategies

Assess Vocabulary Show students real-life objects that show the following three-dimensional figures: sphere, cylinder, rectangular prism, cube. For example, show a ball, a shoe box, and a can of paint. Have students identify the objects using the vocabulary words *sphere, cylinder, rectangular prism* and *cube*.

Concepts

The exercises in this section are grouped to cover content from each lesson in the chapter.

    Exercise 1: Lessons 6-1, 6-7 (pp. 77, 85)
    Exercise 2: Lesson 6-2 (p. 78)
    Exercise 3: Lesson 6-3 (p. 79)
    Exercise 4: Lesson 6-6 (p. 84)

CRM Find Extra Practice for these concepts in the Practice Worksheets, pages A132–A152.

 **Dinah Zike's Foldables**

Have students use the Foldable they created at the beginning of the chapter to review and reinforce the concepts and skills they learned during the chapter. (See Chapter Resource Masters p. A132 for instructions.)

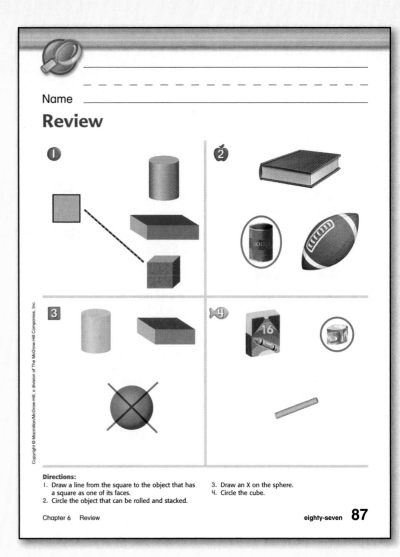

Directions:
1. Draw a line from the square to the object that has a square as one of its faces.
2. Circle the object that can be rolled and stacked.
3. Draw an X on the sphere.
4. Circle the cube.

Chapter 6 Review

⚠ Common Error Alert

Three-Dimensional Figures If students are having trouble identifying three-dimensional figures, remind students that a three-dimensional figure has height and a two-dimensional figure is flat.

Exercise 2 Be sure students know that they are looking for the object that can be both rolled and stacked.

Exercise 4 Be sure students remember that a cube has a square on each of its faces. They may confuse the rectangular prism with the cube.

Name

Chapter Test

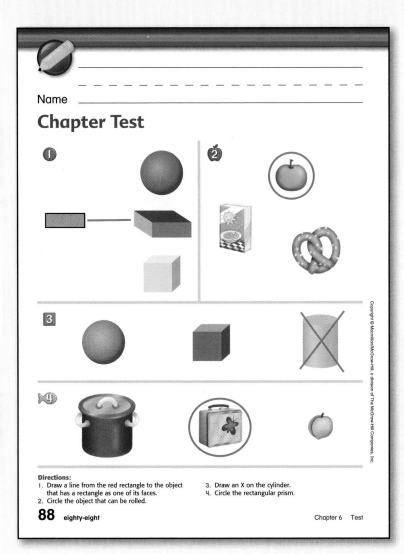

①

④

Directions:
1. Draw a line from the red rectangle to the object that has a rectangle as one of its faces.
2. Circle the object that can be rolled.
3. Draw an X on the cylinder.
4. Circle the rectangular prism.

88 eighty-eight

Test

Chapter Resource Masters

Additional forms of the Chapter 6 Tests are available.

Test Format	Where to Find it
Chapter 6 Test	**Math Online** macmillanmh.com
Blackline Masters	Assessment Masters, pp. 68–69

Alternative Assessment

Have students create a mobile with paper models of spheres, cylinders, cubes and rectangular prisms. Encourage students to separate the models based on their abilities to roll and stack. Students might start with the cylinder on top since the cylinder both rolls and stacks. They may then have two branches—one with the sphere, and the other with the rectangular prism and the cube. Once students have completed the mobile, ask students to identify the different shapes and display the mobiles throughout the classroom.

ExamView®
Assessment Suite

Customize and create multiple versions of your chapter tests and their answer keys. All of these questions from the chapter tests are available on ExamView® Assessment Suite.

Advance TRACKER

This online assessment tool allows teachers to track student progress with easily accessible, comprehensive reports available for every student. Assess students using any internet-ready computer.

Data-Driven Decision Making

Students missing Exercises . . .	Have trouble with . . .	Should review and practice . . .
1	distinguishing between two-dimensional and three-dimensional figures and identifying rectangular prisms.	**TE** Lessons 6-1 and 6-5, pp. 77 and 83 **CRM** Skills Practice, pp. A137 and A149
2	defining rolling and stacking.	**TE** Lesson 6-2, p. 78 **CRM** Skills Practice, p. A140
3	identifying cylinders.	**TE** Lesson 6-4, p. 80 **CRM** Skills Practice, p. A146
4	distinguishing between sphere, cylinders, and rectangular prisms.	**TE** Lessons 6-3, 6-4 and 6-5, pp. 79, 80, and 83 **CRM** Skills Practice, pp. A143, A146, and A149

Chapter Overview

Chapter-at-a-Glance

Lesson	Math Objective	State/Local Standards
7-1 Before or After (pp. 91A–91)	Develop an understanding of *before* and *after* as position words.	
7-2 Above or Below (pp. 92A–92)	Develop an understanding of *above* and *below* as position words.	
7-3 Top, Middle, or Bottom (pp. 93A–93)	Develop an understanding of *top*, *middle*, and *bottom* as position words.	
7-4 Left or Right (pp. 94A–94) **Progress Check 1** (p. 95)	Develop an understanding of *left* and *right*.	
7-5 Front or Back (pp. 97A–97)	Develop an understanding of *front* and *back*.	
7-6 Inside or Outside (pp. 98A–98)	Develop an understanding of *inside* and *outside* as position words.	
7-7 Solve Puzzles (pp. 99A–99) **Progress Check 2** (p. 100)	Develop problem-solving skills by fitting figures to a given space.	

Content-at-a-Glance

The diagram below summarizes and unpacks Chapter 7 content.

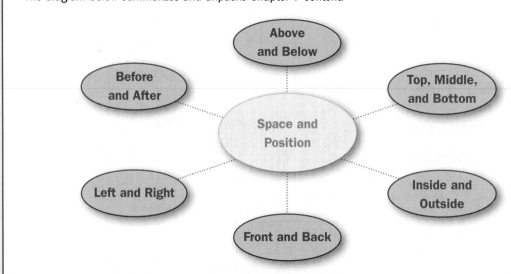

Chapter Assessment Manager

Diagnostic Diagnose students' readiness.

	Student Study Guide/ Teacher Edition	Assessment Masters	Technology
Intensive Intervention Placement Test		1–4	💿 ExamView® Assessment Suite
Section Pretest (Chapters 5–7)		78–79	💿 ExamView® Assessment Suite
Chapter 7 Pretest		81–82	💿 ExamView® Assessment Suite
Get Ready	〔SSG〕 90		Math Online ▸ macmillanmh.com StudentWorks™ Plus

Formative Identify students' misconceptions of content knowledge.

	Student Study Guide/ Teacher Edition	Assessment Masters	Technology
Progress Checks	〔SSG〕 95, 100		Math Online ▸ macmillanmh.com StudentWorks™ Plus
Vocabulary Review	〔TE〕 101		Math Online ▸ macmillanmh.com
Lesson Assessments			💿 ExamView® Assessment Suite

Summative Determine student success in learning the concepts in the lesson, chapter, or section.

	Student Study Guide/ Teacher Edition	Assessment Masters	Technology
Chapter 7 Test	〔SSG〕 102	84–85	💿 ExamView® Assessment Suite
Alternative Assessment	〔TE〕 102	73–74	💿 ExamView® Assessment Suite
See It, Say It, Do It, Write It	〔TE〕 91, 92, 93, 94, 97, 98, 99		
Section Test (Chapters 5–7)		121–122	💿 ExamView® Assessment Suite

Backmapping and Vertical Alignment McGraw-Hill's *Math Triumphs* intervention program was conceived and developed with the final result in mind: student success in grade-level mathematics, including Algebra 1 and beyond. The authors, using the **NCTM Focal Points and Focal Connections** as their guide, developed this brand-new series by backmapping from grade-level and Algebra 1 concepts, and vertically aligning the topics so that they build upon prior skills and concepts and serve as a foundation for future topics.

Chapter Resource Manager

	Lesson 7-1	**Lesson 7-2**	**Lesson 7-3**	**Lesson 7-4**
Concept	Before or After	Above or Below	Top, Middle, or Bottom	Left or Right
Objective	Develop an understanding of *before* and *after* as position words.	Develop an understanding of *above* and *below* as position words.	Develop an understanding of *top*, *middle*, and *bottom* as position words.	Develop an understanding of *left* and *right*.
Math Vocabulary	after before	above below	bottom middle top	left right
Lesson Resources	**Materials** • crayons • different-colored construction-paper squares • paper **Manipulatives** • connecting cubes • color tiles **Other Resources** CRM Vocabulary and English Language Development CRM Skills Practice CRM Practice at Home	**Materials** • books • crayons **Manipulatives** • connecting cubes • pattern blocks **Other Resources** CRM Vocabulary and English Language Development CRM Skills Practice CRM Practice at Home	**Materials** • action figure • blocks • books • plate • sliced cheese • slices of bread • toy car **Manipulatives** • pattern blocks • connecting cubes **Other Resources** CRM Vocabulary and English Language Development CRM Skills Practice CRM Practice at Home	**Materials** • different-colored construction-paper figures • drawing paper • masking tape **Manipulatives** • pattern blocks **Other Resources** CRM Vocabulary and English Language Development CRM Skills Practice CRM Practice at Home
Technology	**Math Online** › macmillanmh.com StudentWorks™ Plus ExamView® Assessment Suite	**Math Online** › macmillanmh.com StudentWorks™ Plus ExamView® Assessment Suite	**Math Online** › macmillanmh.com StudentWorks™ Plus ExamView® Assessment Suite	**Math Online** › macmillanmh.com StudentWorks™ Plus ExamView® Assessment Suite

Lesson 7-5	Lesson 7-6	Lesson 7-7	
Front or Back	Inside or Outside	Solve Puzzles	**Concept**
Develop an understanding of *front* and *back*.	Develop an understanding of *inside* and *outside* as position words.	Develop problem-solving skills by fitting figures to a given space.	**Objective**
back front	inside outside	space	**Math Vocabulary**
Materials • classroom objects with obvious fronts and backs • drawing paper • picture book • teddy bear	**Materials** • crayons • drawing paper • open boxes • paper clips	**Materials** • construction-paper figures in colors to match pattern blocks • four-piece puzzles • small bags or cups	**Lesson Resources**
Manipulatives • clock • spinner • pattern blocks	**Manipulatives** • attribute buttons • connecting cubes	**Manipulatives** • pattern blocks	
Other Resources **CRM** Vocabulary and English Language Development **CRM** Skills Practice **CRM** Practice at Home	**Other Resources** **CRM** Vocabulary and English Language Development **CRM** Skills Practice **CRM** Practice at Home	**Other Resources** **CRM** Vocabulary and English Language Development **CRM** Skills Practice **CRM** Practice at Home	
Math Online ▷ macmillanmh.com StudentWorks™ Plus ⊙ ExamView® Assessment Suite	**Math Online** ▷ macmillanmh.com StudentWorks™ Plus ⊙ ExamView® Assessment Suite	**Math Online** ▷ macmillanmh.com StudentWorks™ Plus ⊙ ExamView® Assessment Suite	**Technology**

Chapter Notes

Home Connection

- Read the Home Connection letter with students and have them write their name in the space below.
- Read and explain the activity under Help at Home. If time allows, complete a portion of the activity so students can introduce the activity to a parent or other caregiver.

Real-World Applications

- At the end of the class, have students explain where objects belong as they put them away: "Blocks belong inside the box." "Markers belong to the right of the coats."
- Have students explain where objects belong at home. "Socks belong in the middle drawer." "The mailbox is in front of the house."
- If verbal explanations are too advanced, have them draw and label objects: "Top" or "T," "Right" or "R," "Front" or "F."

Math Online

Visit macmillanmh.com for ongoing support of chapter content and instruction, including:
- Online Games
- Concepts in Motion

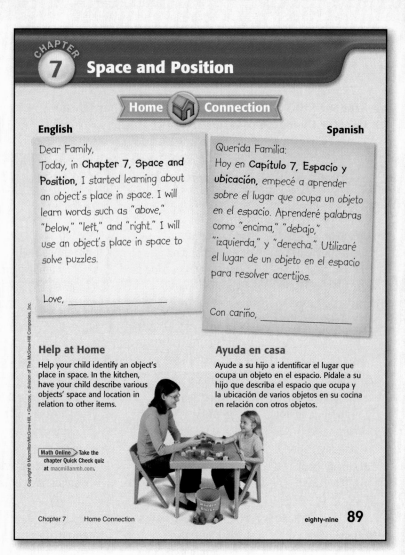

CHAPTER
7 **Space and Position**

Home Connection

English   **Spanish**

Dear Family,
Today, in **Chapter 7, Space and Position**, I started learning about an object's place in space. I will learn words such as "above," "below," "left," and "right." I will use an object's place in space to solve puzzles.

Love, _____

Querida Familia:
Hoy en **Capítulo 7, Espacio y ubicación**, empecé a aprender sobre el lugar que ocupa un objeto en el espacio. Aprenderé palabras como "encima," "debajo," "izquierda," y "derecha." Utilizaré el lugar de un objeto en el espacio para resolver acertijos.

Con cariño, _____

Help at Home
Help your child identify an object's place in space. In the kitchen, have your child describe various objects' space and location in relation to other items.

Ayuda en casa
Ayude a su hijo a identificar el lugar que ocupa un objeto en el espacio. Pídale a su hijo que describa el espacio que ocupa y la ubicación de varios objetos en su cocina en relación con otros objetos.

Math Online ▷ Take the chapter Quick Check quiz at macmillanmh.com.

Chapter 7   Home Connection   eighty-nine **89**

Key Vocabulary

Find interactive definitions in 13 languages in the **eGlossary** at macmillanmh.com.

English   Español *Introduce the most important vocabulary terms from Chapter 7.*

after   después
to follow in place or time (p. 91A)   6 is just after 5.

before   antes
to precede in place or time (p. 91A)   6 is just before 7.

above   más arriba
in a higher position (p. 92A)

below   abajo
in a lower position (p. 92A)

bottom   fondo
the lowest postion (p. 93A)

middle   medio
positioned in between, equal distance from each side (p. 93A)

top   además de
the highest position (p. 93A)

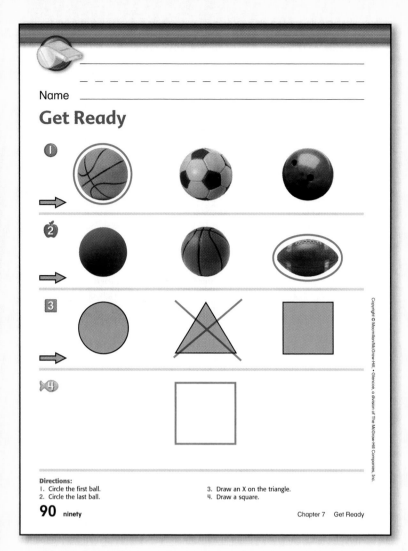

Name _____

Get Ready

① ➡️

② ➡️

③ ➡️

④

Directions:
1. Circle the first ball.
2. Circle the last ball.
3. Draw an X on the triangle.
4. Draw a square.

90 ninety

Chapter 7 Get Ready

Get Ready

Diagnostic Assessment

Have students complete the Get Ready exercises to assess readiness. Refer to the lessons below for support for prerequisite skills.

Exercises 1–4: Grade K, Chapter 2, Lessons 1–4 (pp. 19-22)

You may also assess student readiness with:
Assessment Masters: Chapter Pretest (pp. 81–82)

Math Online ⟩ macmillanmh.com
Online Readiness Quiz

Intervention Strategy

Step 1 On the board, draw 9 circles in 3 rows of 3.

Step 2 Have a student point to the center circle. Describe the position of the circle without using the word *middle*. For example, "The circle is in the second row."

Step 3 Have students point to a circle and describe its position in words they know.

 **Dinah Zike's Foldables**

Guide students through the directions on p. A157 in the Chapter Resource Masters to create their own Foldable graphic organizer for use with this chapter.

Vocabulary Preview

- Before students begin the chapter, have them practice using important terms throughout the chapter.
- Provide students with three plastic counters that have a front and back, such as bears; one sheet of construction paper, and a paper cup.
- Give students directions, using key vocabulary words, where to place the bears. Say: "Put a bear inside the cup," or "Put a bear at the top of the paper."

Professional Development

Targeted professional development has been articulated throughout **McGraw-Hill's Math Triumphs** intervention program. The **McGraw-Hill Professional Development Video Library** provides short videos that support the **NCTM Focal Points and Focal Connections.** For more information, visit macmillanmh.com.

Model Lessons   Instructional Strategies

Before or After

Lesson Planner

Objective
Develop an understanding of *before* and *after* as position words.

Vocabulary
after

before

Other Resources

Materials
different-colored
  construction-paper
  squares

Manipulatives
color tiles
connecting cubes

 **On-Hand
Manipulatives**

crayons
paper

CRM Chapter Resource Masters
Vocabulary and English Language
  Development (p. A161)
Skills Practice (p. A162)
Practice at Home (p. A163)

Teacher Tech Tools
TeacherWorks™ Plus
Math Online > macmillanmh.com
Advance Tracker

Student Tech Tools
StudentWorks™ Plus
Math Online > macmillanmh.com
eGlossary

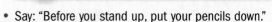

Intervention Strategy

Kinesthetic Learners

Games Make a marching game to practice before and after. Ask students to line up in front of you, marching in place. Have the second student from the front say, in time with the march, his or her name and who is before and after him or her. Then have the first student in line march to the end of the line, giving the new second student a turn to state his or her information. Clap in time with the march. Repeat until every student has had a chance to speak.

① Introduce

- Say: "Before you stand up, put your pencils down."
- Say: "After you stand up, line up at the door."
- Stand at the back of the line and ask who is standing just before you.
- Move to the front of the line and ask who is standing just after you.

② Teach

Key Concept

Foundational Skills and Concepts Explain that before and after can represent either time or position. Tell students the following story.

- Draw 3 circles in a row. Label the circles "Alan," "Beth," and "Carlo," in order.
- Say: "To get to school, Alan, Beth, and Carlo ride the school bus."
- Point to each circle as you say the names.
- Say: "Before they can board the bus, they stand in line. Beth stands before Carlo." Draw a bus to the left of Alan.
- Point to the middle and last circles (middle and right).
- Say: "She also stands after Alan."
- Point to the first circle and middle circles (left and middle).
- Say: "After their bus ride, Alan, Beth, and Carlo go to their classroom to learn with their friends."

Using Manipulatives

Connecting Cubes Give students one of each color of connecting cube.

- Say: "Before the purple cube, connect the orange cube. Attach the red cube before the orange cube."
- Say: "After the purple cube, connect the yellow cube. Attach the green cube after the yellow cube."
- **Which color is after the orange cube?** purple
- **Which color is before the orange cube?** red
- Continue to ask questions about the location of other cubes.

Name _____

Before or After

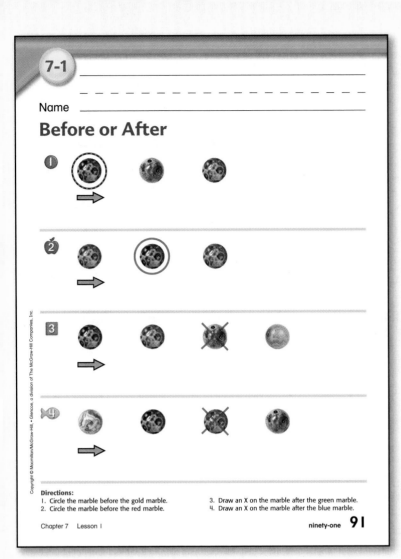

Directions:
1. Circle the marble before the gold marble.
2. Circle the marble before the red marble.
3. Draw an X on the marble after the green marble.
4. Draw an X on the marble after the blue marble.

Chapter 7   Lesson 1

ninety-one **91**

③ Practice

Direct students to page 91 of their student workbook. Read the directions at the bottom of the student page as they complete the exercises.

Explain to students that location is from left to right unless the directions give a different starting point. Remind students of Alan, Beth, and Carlo and how they lined up for the bus.

④ Assess

See It   Using a row of different-color tiles, point to the left-most tile to remind students to begin on the left. Have students point to the tile before or after a specified color tile.

Say It   Draw four figures, with an arrow over the left-most shape to remind students where to start. Point to figures and have students name their positions *before* or *after.*

Do It   Have students start with a white connecting cube and attach a different color cube to each side of the white cube. Ask students which color comes before and after the white cube.

Write It   Have students draw 3 circles, and underline the left-most circle to remind themselves where to begin. Have them color the center circle red. Then have them color the circle before the red circle blue and the circle after the red circle green.

English Learner Strategy

Words in Other Languages   Invite students speaking English as a second language to share the words for *before* and *after* in their native language. Have groups of three students stand in line, facing one direction. Ask the middle student in each line to point to the student before him or her and say "before," both in English and in his or her native language. Repeat for "after."

Lesson 7-2 — Above or Below

Lesson Planner

Objective
Develop an understanding of *above* and *below* as position words.

Vocabulary
above

below

Other Resources

Materials
3 different objects, such as a ball, a box, and a toy

Manipulatives
connecting cubes
pattern blocks

 **On-Hand Manipulatives**
books
crayons

CRM Chapter Resource Masters
Vocabulary and English Language Development (p. A164)
Skills Practice (p. A165)
Practice at Home (p. A166)

Teacher Tech Tools
TeacherWorks™ Plus
Math Online ▷ macmillanmh.com
Advance Tracker

Student Tech Tools
StudentWorks™ Plus
Math Online ▷ macmillanmh.com
eGlossary

Intervention Strategy
Kinesthetic Learners

Movements Use index cards with the words *above* and *below*. Tell students to copy your motion if what you say matches the word on the card you move. For example, students would put their "below" card under their chair if you move your "below" card and at the same time say, "Put your 'below' card below your chair." Students would not copy your action if you move your "below" card while you say, "Put your 'above' card above your head."

1 Introduce

- Place the ball on a middle shelf of the classroom bookcase. Place the box on the shelf above.
- Have students tell where the box is, using the words *above* or *below*. above the ball
- Place the toy below the ball.
- Have students say where the toy is, using the words *above* or *below*.

2 Teach

Key Concept

Foundational Skills and Concepts On the board, draw a horizontal line. Draw a circle above the line and a square below the line. Explain that the circle is *above* the line, and the square is *below* the line.
- Write "above" next to the circle and "below" next to the square.
- Have students come to the board and draw Xs above or below the line.

Using Manipulatives

Connecting Cubes Give students one of each color of connecting cube and tell students they will be stacking their cubes up and down.
- Have students place the red cube on their desks. Show and tell students to connect their purple cube above the red cube. Then have students connect the orange cube and then the green cube.
- **Which color is above the orange cube?** green
- **Which color is below the orange cube?** purple
- **Which colors are above the purple cube?** orange and green
- Continue to ask which cubes are above and below the other cubes.
- Extend the activity using different colors of cubes.

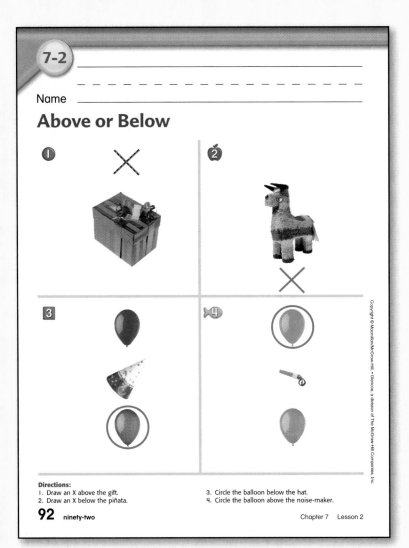

7-2

Name

Above or Below

Directions:
1. Draw an X above the gift.
2. Draw an X below the piñata.

3. Circle the balloon below the hat.
4. Circle the balloon above the noise-maker.

92 ninety-two

Chapter 7 Lesson 2

Copyright © Macmillan/McGraw-Hill • Glencoe, a division of The McGraw-Hill Companies, Inc.

③ Practice

Direct students to page 92 of their student workbook. Read the directions at the bottom of the student page as they complete the exercise.

Encourage students to draw a line on their paper with a circle above and a square below to help them remember *above* and *below.*

④ Assess

See It   Place 3 different recognizable books on 3 different shelves of the classroom bookshelf. Have students identify the position of each book as above or below another.

Say It   Point to objects on the walls. Ask students to describe the position of an object in relation to another object using *above* or *below.*

Do It   Draw a simple picture on the board. Have students draw an X as directed above or below objects in the picture.

Write It   Have students fold a sheet of paper in half. Have students draw a green circle below the fold and a red circle above the fold.

Intervention Strategy
Interpersonal Learners

Pattern Blocks   Organize students into pairs. Give each pair a set of pattern blocks. Tell pairs to take turns performing your instruction. Begin by telling pairs to put the square above the circle. Then tell them to put the triangle above the square. Finally, tell students to put another triangle below the circle. Check to make sure each pair has the blocks organized the same way.

Top, Middle, or Bottom

Lesson Planner

Objective
Develop an understanding of *top*, *middle*, and *bottom* as position words.

Vocabulary

bottom

middle

top

Materials
action figure
blocks
plate
sliced cheese
slices of bread
toy car

Manipulatives
connecting cubes
pattern blocks

 **On-Hand Manipulatives**
books

Other Resources

CRM Chapter Resource Masters
Vocabulary and English Language
  Development (p. A167)
Skills Practice (p. A168)
Practice at Home (p. A169)

Teacher Tech Tools
TeacherWorks™ Plus
Math Online macmillanmh.com
Advance Tracker

Student Tech Tools
StudentWorks™ Plus
Math Online macmillanmh.com
eGlossary

Intervention Strategy
Kinesthetic Learners

Stretches Have students stand by their desks. Tell them they will be stretching to practice *top, middle* and *bottom.* When you say "top," have them put their hands on top of their heads. When you say "middle," have them put their hands on their middle (waist). When you say "bottom," have them touch the bottom of their feet.

① Introduce

- Show a plate, sliced cheese, and two slices of bread. Tell students you want to make a cheese sandwich.
- Have students tell you exactly how to make the sandwich.
- **What goes on the plate first?** bread
- **What goes next?** cheese
- **What goes next?** bread
- **What's on the top?** bread
- **What's on the bottom?** bread
- **Where is the cheese?** in the middle of the sandwich

② Teach

Key Concept

Foundational Skills and Concepts Explain that you will build a tower with a top, a middle, and a bottom.
- Put a block on the table. Say: "bottom."
- Put a second block on the first. Say: "top."
- **If I want a middle block, where would it need to be?** the middle of the tower
- Put the third block between the two blocks. Say: "middle."
- Have students think of the classroom in terms of top, middle, and bottom.
- **The lights are above our heads, are they in the top, middle or bottom of the room?** top
- Repeat with the people and the floor.

Using Manipulatives

Attribute Blocks Give students a circle, square, and triangle attribute block.
- Have students make an attribute block "sandwich" with the triangle in the middle.
- Have students them make a "sandwich" with the circle on top and the square on the bottom.
- Repeat with different placements for the attribute blocks.

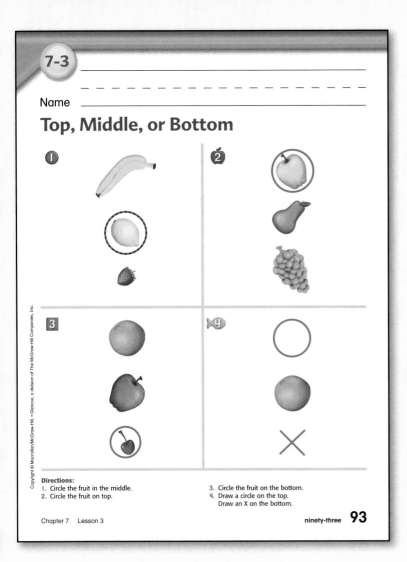

7-3

Name

Top, Middle, or Bottom

①

②

③

④

Directions:
1. Circle the fruit in the middle.
2. Circle the fruit on top.

3. Circle the fruit on the bottom.
4. Draw a circle on the top.
   Draw an X on the bottom.

Chapter 7   Lesson 3

ninety-three   **93**

Copyright © Macmillan/McGraw-Hill • Glencoe, a division of The McGraw-Hill Companies, Inc.

③ Practice

Direct students to page 93 of their student workbook.

Have students use cubes or pattern blocks to create a visual to remind them of position for top, middle, and bottom.

④ Assess

See It   Show students a toy car. Have students identify the top, middle, and bottom of the car.

Say It   Stand an action figure on the table. Point to the top of its head, its middle, and the bottom of its feet and have students say if you are pointing to the top, middle, or bottom.

Do It   Have students make a connecting cube sandwich with a red top, green middle, and yellow top.

Write It   Have students draw a picture of a tree. Have them draw a sun on top of the tree, a bird hole in the middle of the tree, and some grass at the bottom of the tree.

⚠ Common Error Alert

Position Words   Some students can identify positions kinesthetically, but have difficulty using vocabulary to describe or identify positions. To make sure students have a firm grasp of *top, middle,* and *bottom,* always use these words when physically demonstrating the positions. Conversely, gesture to a position when verbally naming it.

Lesson 7-3 Top, Middle, or Bottom   **93**

Left or Right

Lesson Planner

Objective
Develop an understanding of *left* and *right*.

Vocabulary
left

right

Other Resources

Materials
drawing paper
masking tape

Manipulatives
pattern blocks

 **On-Hand Manipulatives**
different-colored
   construction-paper shapes

CRM Chapter Resource Masters
Vocabulary and English Language
   Development (p. A170)
Skills Practice (p. A171)
Practice at Home (p. A172)

Teacher Tech Tools
◉ TeacherWorks™ Plus
Math Online ▷ macmillanmh.com
Advance Tracker

Student Tech Tools
◉ StudentWorks™ Plus
Math Online ▷ macmillanmh.com
eGlossary

Intervention Strategy
Kinesthetic Learners

Labels   Have the class gather at one side of the classroom and face the door. Put tape on the floor in the middle of the classroom. Explain that one side of the tape is left and one side is right. Put "left" and "right" labels on the walls. Make sure that your instructions and labels match students' left and right. Have students walk to the right side of the classroom and then walk to the left side of the classroom.

1 Introduce

Label the board "left" and "right." Draw a flower, with the right side red and the left side blue.
- **What color is the flower?** red and blue
- Have students describe which side is red and which is blue. They may say the side closest to you is one color, or the side next to an object in the room is one color.
- Explain that they could say the *right* side is red and the *left* side is blue.

2 Teach

Key Concept

Foundational Skills and Concepts   Label the board or wall at the front of the classroom "left" and "right." Have students play "Teacher Says" by following your directions, as you face the front of the room.
- Raise your right hand and say: "Teacher says, raise your right hand."
- Touch your ear with your left hand and say: "Teacher says, touch your ear with your left hand."
- Continue modeling different actions with left and right.

Using Manipulatives

Pattern Blocks   Divide each student's desk or table into left and right sides with masking tape. Give students one of each pattern block.

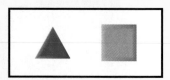

- Say: "Put the green triangle on the left side of your desk."
- Say: "Put the orange square on the right side of your desk."
- Repeat with other shapes and colors.

Name

Left or Right

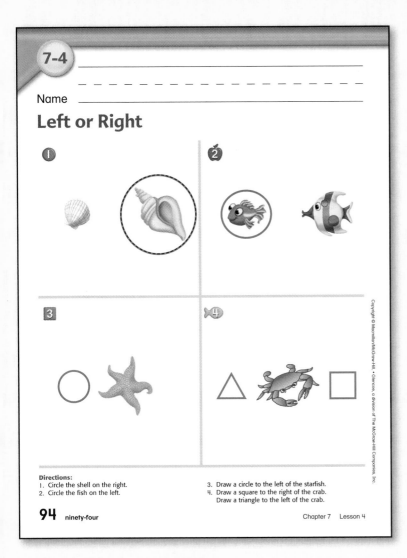

Directions:
1. Circle the shell on the right.
2. Circle the fish on the left.

3. Draw a circle to the left of the starfish.
4. Draw a square to the right of the crab.
   Draw a triangle to the left of the crab.

94 ninety-four

Chapter 7 Lesson 4

③ Practice

Direct students to page 94 of their student workbook. Read the directions at the bottom of the student page as they complete the exercises.

Encourage students to label the sides of their paper with an "L" and an "R" to remember their left and right as they work through the exercises.

④ Assess

See It   Have students identify an object in the classroom that is to the right of the door. For example, the flag is to the right of the door.

Say It   Point to an object in the classroom and have students say if it is to the right or left of the windows. For example, "The sink is to the left of the windows."

Do It   Ask students to pick up a domino in their right hand. Ask students to count the dots on the left side of the domino.

Write It   Have students draw a butterfly on a sheet of paper. Ask students to color the right side of the butterfly green and the left side orange.

Math Coach Notes

Left and Right   Have students hold up the hand they use to draw. For each student, trace his or her hand and have them tell whether it is "right" or "left." Repeat the process for the other hand. Have students copy "R" and "L" to label each hand correctly. Tape the drawings to their workspace to use as they learn.

Progress Check 1

Formative Assessment

Use the Progress Check to assess students' mastery of the previous lessons. Have students review the lesson indicated for the problems they answered incorrectly.

 Common Error Alert

Positions If students have difficulty with the concept of positions, have them use themselves as a central figure. Have students practice identifying what is above and below them, and to their left and right. Suggest that they consider their heads as top, their stomachs as middle, and their legs and feet as bottom.

Exercise 1 Be sure students view the images from left to right. The image on the left is the first and comes before the others. The middle image comes after the first, and the last image comes after the second image.

Exercise 5 Have students think of their heads as their *top*. Explain that their head is the top of their body and their feet are at the bottom. There is nothing higher than their head, or their *top*.

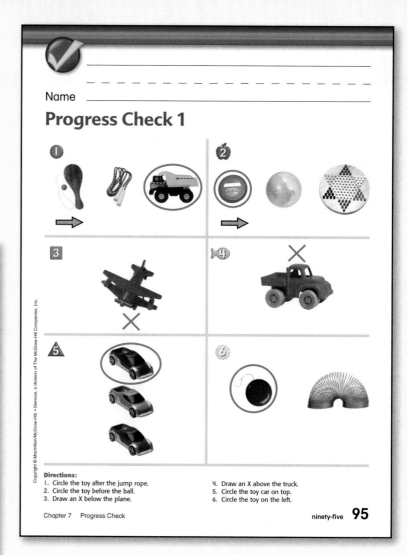

Data-Driven Decision Making

Students missing Exercises . . .	Have trouble with . . .	Should review and practice . . .
1–2	before and after.	TE Lesson 7-1, p. 91 CRM Skills Practice, p. A162
3–4	above and below.	TE Lesson 7-2, p. 92 CRM Skills Practice, p. A165
5	top, middle, and bottom.	TE Lesson 7-3, p. 93 CRM Skills Practice, p. A168
6	left and right.	TE Lesson 7-4, p. 94 CRM Skills Practice, p. A171

Name _____

Replay

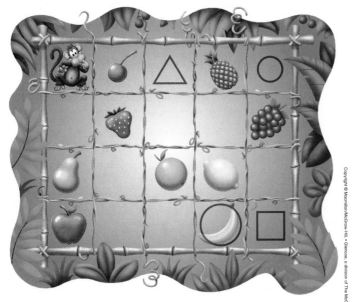

Directions:
Mr. Monkey is hungry! Follow the directions to move Mr. Monkey to his dinner.

1. Move Mr. Monkey to 1 space to the right of the cherry. Draw a triangle in this space.
2. Move Mr. Monkey 2 spaces to the right of your triangle. Draw a circle in this space.

3. Move Mr. Monkey 3 spaces below your circle. Draw a square in this space.
4. Move Mr. Monkey 1 space to the left of your square.
5. Circle the food Mr. Monkey wants to eat.

96 ninety-six

Chapter 7   Replay

Copyright © Macmillan/McGraw-Hill • Glencoe, a division of The McGraw-Hill Companies, Inc.

Replay

Use the Replay activity to review and reinforce concepts and skills presented in Lessons 7-1, 7-2, and 7-4.

Instructions

Make sure that students mark the location of the monkey after each step. Explain to students that the new location of the monkey is the starting point for the next step.

Student Technology

Students can use the following technology resources to reinforce chapter content.

StudentWorks™ Plus

Math Online ⟩ macmillanmh.com
- eGames
- eGlossary

Front or Back

Lesson Planner

Objective
Develop an understanding of *front* and *back*.

Vocabulary

back

front

Other Resources

Materials
drawing paper
teddy bear

Manipulatives
clock
pattern blocks
spinner

 **On-Hand Manipulatives**

classroom objects with
obvious fronts and backs:
clock, book, chair, and
so on
picture book

CRM Chapter Resource Masters
Vocabulary and English Language
  Development (p. A173)
Skills Practice (p. A174)
Practice at Home (p. A175)

Teacher Tech Tools
TeacherWorks™ Plus
Math Online ▷ macmillanmh.com
Advance Tracker

Student Tech Tools
StudentWorks™ Plus
Math Online ▷ macmillanmh.com
eGlossary

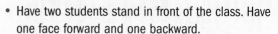 **1 Introduce**

- Have two students stand in front of the class. Have one face forward and one backward.
- **Which is front and which is back?** Students should identify the front and back correctly.
- Repeat with a teddy bear. Point out that the front side of an object is usually "prettier" and more interesting than the back of an object.

 **2 Teach**

Key Concept

Foundational Skills and Concepts   Give students drawing paper and pick classroom objects with obvious fronts and backs, for example, a clock, a book, and a chair. Show the front and back of each.

- Have students indicate the front and back of each object. **Point to the front of the book. Show me the back of the box.**
- Have students draw the front and back of a book. Have them label the front "F" and back "B."

Using Manipulatives

Clock, Spinner, and Pattern Blocks   Give each student a clock, a spinner, and pattern blocks.

- Have students lay their clock on their desks, face up.
- **Which side of the clock do you see on everyone's desks?** the side with hands
- Tell students the hands are on the *front* of the clock. The *back* of the clock does not show the time.
- Have students pick up a pattern block.
- **Does the block have a front and a back?** no
- **Why not?** The sides are the same.
- Repeat this activity with the spinner, first asking students to spin their spinner.

English Learner Strategy

Using Objects   Using the objects from Foundational Skills and Concepts, have students hold the objects and explain what they are showing. Be sure they use the words *front* and *back* in their explanations, for example, "This is the front of the desk/the back of the box." If students have difficulty, have them say "front" and "back," or use labels as they indicate what they are showing.

Name _____

Front or Back

Directions:
1. Circle the picture of the front of the monkey.
2. Circle the picture of the back of the duck.
3. Draw an X on the back of the bunny.
4. Draw an X on the front of the giraffe.
5. Circle the pictures that show the back of a bear.

Chapter 7   Lesson 5   **ninety-seven 97**

③ Practice

Direct students to page 97 of their student workbook. Read the directions at the bottom of the student page as they complete the exercises.

④ Assess

See It Give students a picture book. Ask them to show the front.

Say It Turn so you face students. Ask: "Which part of me do you see?" Turn around. Repeat.

Do It Have students point to the back of their heads. Have them show the front of a book.

Write It Show students a simple drawing of the front and back of a pig with *front* and *back* under each picture. Have have students circle the correct word for each picture.

Math Coach Notes

The concept of *front* and *back* will be difficult for students at first. Be patient and repeat the Introduce activity and Foundational Skills and Concepts section if necessary. When choosing classroom objects for the Foundational Skills and Concepts section, be careful not to pick items that have no definable front or back, such as a globe or a cube-shaped block. Items that are difficult to show, such as the back of a writing board or a cabinet, should also be avoided. However, smaller items, such as dominoes, rulers, and flash cards are ideal examples.

Inside or Outside

Lesson Planner

Objective
Develop an understanding of *inside* and *outside* as position words.

Vocabulary
inside

outside

Other Resources

Materials
drawing paper
open boxes

Manipulatives
attribute buttons
connecting cubes

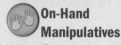 **On-Hand Manipulatives**
paper clips
crayons

CRM Chapter Resource Masters
Vocabulary and English Language
  Development (p. A176)
Skills Practice (p. A177)
Practice at Home (p. A178)

Teacher Tech Tools
TeacherWorks™ Plus
Math Online ⟩ macmillanmh.com
Advance Tracker

Student Tech Tools
StudentWorks™ Plus
Math Online ⟩ macmillanmh.com
eGlossary

1 Introduce

- Have students sit in a circle.
- Have one student stand in the center of the circle while the class sings and plays "The Farmer in the Dell."
- As students pick other students with the game, have the new students stand inside the circle.
- Explain that the new students are *inside* the circle.

2 Teach

Key Concept

Foundational Skills and Concepts   Point to objects and ask if they are inside or outside the classroom. Point to objects outside a window or cabinet and ask the same question. Then have students think of a refrigerator.

- **What objects can you name that are inside a refrigerator?** milk, fruit, meat
- **What objects can you name that are outside a refrigerator?** table, clothes, sink

Using Manipulatives

Attribute Buttons   Give students a box and 3 of each color attribute button.

- Have students put their red buttons in the box.
- **How many buttons are inside the box?** 3
- **How many buttons are outside the box?** 9
- Repeat with different numbers of buttons inside and outside the box.

⚠ **Common Error Alert**

Inside and Outside   If students confuse *inside* and *outside,* show the positions with an open box and a connecting cube. Repeat the words as you show the positions *inside* and *outside.* Have the students repeat them with you. Then have the students place the cube in the same positions, while saying the words aloud.

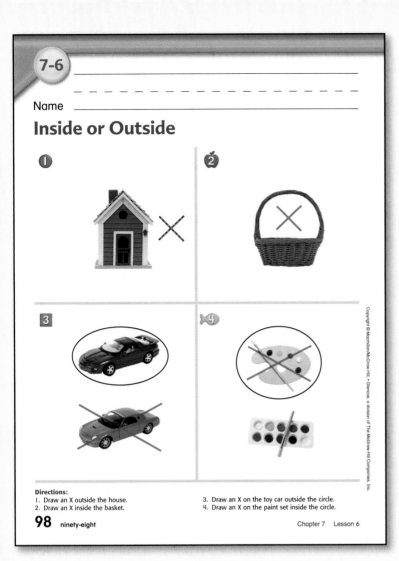

Inside or Outside

Directions:
1. Draw an X outside the house.
2. Draw an X inside the basket.
3. Draw an X on the toy car outside the circle.
4. Draw an X on the paint set inside the circle.

98 ninety-eight

Chapter 7   Lesson 6

③ Practice

Direct students to page 98 of their student workbook. Read the directions at the bottom of the student page as they complete the exercises.

④ Assess

See It   Draw a square on the board. Draw a smiling face inside it and a frowning face outside it. Ask: "Which face is inside?"

Say It   Place a marble outside a jar. Ask: "Is the marble inside or outside?" Place the marble inside. Repeat.

Do It   Ask students to place two connecting cubes inside their closed hand. Ask them to place the connecting tubes outside their hand.

Write It   Have students draw objects inside and outside a circle.

Math Coach Notes

In your descriptions, be sure to use the words *inside* and *outside*. During the Introduce activity, guide students quietly as they follow your directions. For English learners, say *inside* and *outside* in their own language, as well as in English, during the Teach stage for the first few questions (if possible).

Solve Puzzles

Lesson Planner

Objective
Develop problem-solving skills by fitting figures to a given space.

Vocabulary
space

Other Resources

Materials
four-piece puzzles
small bags or cups

Manipulatives
pattern blocks

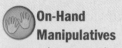 **On-Hand Manipulatives**
construction-paper shapes
in colors to match
pattern blocks

CRM Chapter Resource Masters
Vocabulary and English Language
  Development (p. A179)
Skills Practice (p. A180)
Practice at Home (p. A181)

Teacher Tech Tools
TeacherWorks™ Plus
Math Online > macmillanmh.com
Advance Tracker

Student Tech Tools
StudentWorks™ Plus
Math Online > macmillanmh.com
eGlossary

1 Introduce

- Give students pattern blocks and a small bag or cup.
- **How many blocks fit inside your bag?** Answers will vary, depending on the size of the container.
- Explain to students that some puzzles have shapes fitting into other shapes or objects.

2 Teach

Key Concept

Foundational Skills and Concepts   On the board, draw a square to be used as the base of a house. At the side, draw these figures in sizes to fit the house: circle (doorknob), rectangle (door), and triangle (roof). Tell students you will use the shapes to make a house.

- **Which shape would make a good roof for the house?** triangle
- Draw the triangle above the square.
- **Which shape would fit in the house as a door?** rectangle
- Draw the rectangle inside the square as a door.
- **Which shape would fit in the door to make a doorknob?** circle
- Draw the doorknob.

Using Manipulatives

Pattern Blocks   Give student pairs pattern blocks. Show students how two green triangles fit on a blue rhombus.

- **How many green pieces fit on a blue piece?** 2
- Have students experiment with their pieces to see what pieces cover other pieces.
- **How many green pieces fit on a red piece?** 3
- Repeat with the different pieces.

 Common Error Alert

If students need help distinguishing shapes, use pattern blocks to show four of the same shapes in a row. Have students pick a block different from the others in the row. To focus on differences in shape only, use patterns blocks that are all the same color.

Name _____

Solve Puzzles

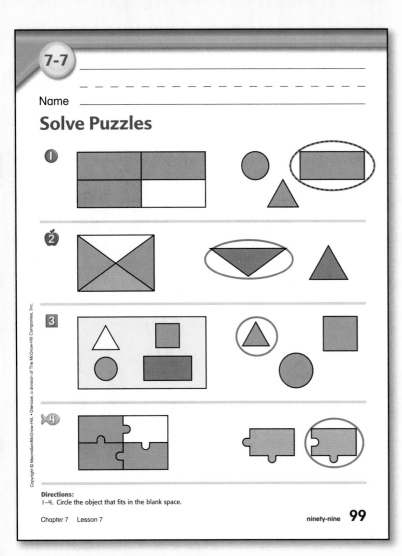

①

②

③

④

Directions:
1–4. Circle the object that fits in the blank space.

Chapter 7   Lesson 7

ninety-nine **99**

③ Practice

Direct students to page 99 of their student workbook. Read the directions at the bottom of the student page as they complete the exercises.

④ Assess

See It   Show students a yellow pattern block with four green triangles on top. Have students find the pattern block that would fill the space. blue rhombus

Say It   Have students use pattern blocks and say as they demonstrate, "Two red pieces fit on one yellow piece."

Do It   Give students a yellow hexagon block and green triangle blocks. Have students arrange six triangles to match the yellow piece.

Write It   Give students a yellow and red pattern block. Have students trace the yellow block then draw the red block to fit inside the yellow block.

Math Coach Notes

Guide students quietly during the Introduce activity. Watch for students who are having trouble and use the Common Error Alert exercises to help. During the Foundational Skills and Concepts, have the square, circle, rectangle, and triangle drawn before class begins. If simple puzzles are available, such as four-piece puzzles, use them for the Introduce activity instead of pattern blocks.

Progress Check 2

Formative Assessment

Use the Progress Check to assess students' mastery of the previous lessons. Have students review the lesson indicated for the problems they answered incorrectly.

 Common Error Alert

Some students may have difficulty deciding which side of an object is the front and which is the back. Encourage students to think of the front as the "face" of an object or the side that is turned up. The back of an object might be the side that you might not always see, for example, a student cannot easily view his or her own back.

Exercises 1–2 If students have trouble remembering left and right, have them point both index fingers and extend both thumbs. Looking at the backs of their hands, students should see that the two fingers on their left hand make the letter "L." Encourage them to remember that L is the first sound in "Left."

Exercise 4 Tell students to think of themselves as inside when they are in the classroom. Tell them to think of themselves as outside when they are on the playground. This can help them identify objects as inside and outside.

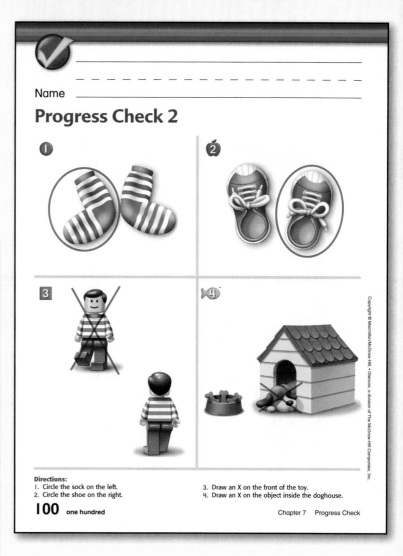

Directions:
1. Circle the sock on the left.
2. Circle the shoe on the right.
3. Draw an X on the front of the toy.
4. Draw an X on the object inside the doghouse.

100 one hundred

Chapter 7 Progress Check

Data-Driven Decision Making

Students missing Exercises . . .	Have trouble with . . .	Should review and practice . . .
1–2	left and right.	TE Lesson 7-4, p. 94 CRM Skills Practice, p. A171
3	front and back.	TE Lesson 7-5, p. 95 CRM Skills Practice, p. A174
4	inside and outside.	TE Lesson 7-6, p. 96 CRM Skills Practice, p. A177

Intervention Strategies

Drawing Vocabulary

Materials: crayons or markers, glue, magazines and store advertisements, paper, and scissors

Vocabulary: before, after, above, below, top, middle, bottom, left, right, front, back, inside, outside

Step 1 Divide the class into small groups. Give each a large piece of paper and a vocabulary word.

Step 2 Explain that each group is responsible for making a drawing (or finding pictures) on a separate sheet of paper for each word. This drawing should accurately represent the position word. Monitor students as they create these drawings. Make sure they are accurate, clear, and neatly done so that others can interpret them.

Step 3 Collect all the drawings, write the word at the top that it depicts, and tape the pages to a giant sheet of poster board. Display this poster board at the front of the class throughout the chapter so that students have an additional reference in case they are confused.

Step 4 Give each group a rectangular box. Ask each group to put the box in a book and close the book without bending the box or the book.

Using Bodies for Space and Position Relations

Materials: masking tape

Step 1 Instruct all students to stand up in a line, front to back. Tell students that they should follow your instructions as you call them out.

Step 2 Say: "If you are in line after [say a student's name], put both your arms in the air." Say: "If you are in line before [say a student's name], clap once."

Step 3 Make a large square out of masking tape on the floor in the center of the classroom. Tell students that this square represents a box. Say: "Reach inside the box." Then, one at a time, bring students up to the box. Say: "Step inside the box. Now, step back outside the box."

Review

Vocabulary

Before beginning the exercises, review vocabulary introduced in the chapter. Refer to the page numbers to revisit vocabulary activities in the lessons.

above (p. 92A)	**inside** (p. 98A)
after (p. 91A)	**left** (p. 94A)
back (p. 97A)	**middle** (p. 93A)
before (p. 91A)	**outside** (p. 98A)
below (p. 92A)	**right** (p. 94A)
bottom (p. 93A)	**space** (p. 99A)
front (p. 97A)	**top** (p. 93A)

Vocabulary Review Strategies

Practice with Objects On separate sheets of paper or cardboard, write the following vocabulary words: *left, right, front, back, inside, outside, before, after, above, below, top, bottom, middle.* Mix up the papers and place them face down. Place a box with a lid, such as a shoe box on your desk or on the floor. Ask a student to pick a paper. Tell him or her the word that is on the paper and ask him or her to show the word, using the box and a block. Ask the rest of the class, "Where is the block?" (inside, left, back) Quietly coach as necessary. Have students take turns.

Concepts

The exercises in this section are grouped to cover content from each lesson in the chapter.

> **Exercise 1:** Lesson 7-1 (p. 91)
> **Exercise 2:** Lesson 7-2 (p. 92)
> **Exercise 3:** Lesson 7-3 (p. 93)
> **Exercise 4:** Lesson 7-4 (p. 94)
> **Exercise 5:** Lesson 7-6 (p. 98)
> **Exercise 6:** Lesson 7-7 (p. 99)

CRM Find Extra Practice for these concepts in the Practice Worksheets, pages A161–A181.

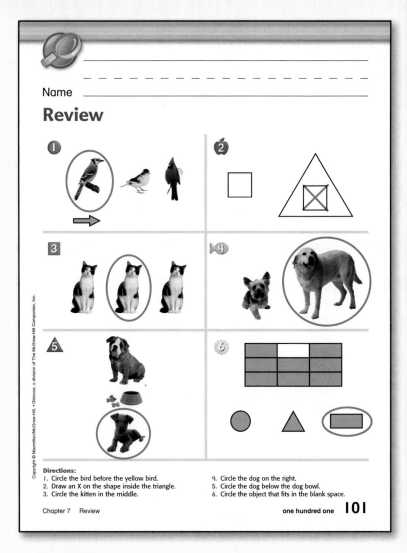

Name _____

Review

Directions:
1. Circle the bird before the yellow bird.
2. Draw an X on the shape inside the triangle.
3. Circle the kitten in the middle.
4. Circle the dog on the right.
5. Circle the dog below the dog bowl.
6. Circle the object that fits in the blank space.

Chapter 7   Review   **one hundred one 101**

 **Dinah Zike's Foldables**

Have students use the Foldable they created at the beginning of the chapter to review and reinforce the concepts and skills they learned during the chapter. (See Chapter Resource Master p. A157 for instructions.)

Intervention Strategy   Visual Learners

Drawings Draw a tree on the board. Remind students of the words they learned in this chapter: *before, after, top, middle, bottom, left, right, above, below, inside, outside.* Ask each student to add a bird to the tree and explain its location using one of the words, for example, "My bird is to the left of the tree." If sentences are too advanced, coach them for the word alone, for example, "left." Continue until all words are used. Coach students to use different words each time.

Name

Test

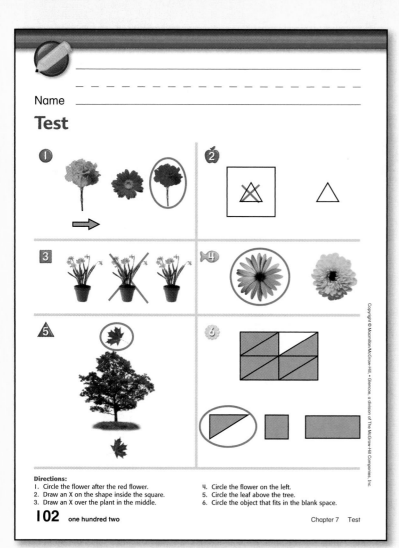

Directions:
1. Circle the flower after the red flower.
2. Draw an X on the shape inside the square.
3. Draw an X over the plant in the middle.
4. Circle the flower on the left.
5. Circle the leaf above the tree.
6. Circle the object that fits in the blank space.

102 one hundred two

Chapter 7 Test

Test

Chapter Resource Masters

Additional forms of the Chapter 7 Tests are available.

Test Format	Where to Find it
Chapter 7 Test	Math Online macmillanmh.com
Blackline Masters	Assessment Masters, pp. 84–85

Alternative Assessment

Portfolios You can also assess students' proficiency with position and location by monitoring portfolios of their work or by watching them solve position problems on the board. Additionally, you may assess students' understanding by using models, manipulatives, or drawings.

ExamView®
Assessment Suite

Customize and create multiple versions of the chapter tests and their answer keys. All of these questions from the chapter tests are available on ExamView® Assessment Suite.

Advance TRACKER

This online assessment tool allows teachers to track student progress with easily accessible, comprehensive reports available for every student. Assess students using any internet-ready computer.

Data-Driven Decision Making

Students missing Exercises . . .	Have trouble with . . .	Should review and practice . . .
1	before and after.	**TE** Lesson 7-1, p. 91 **CRM** Skills Practice, p. A162
2	inside and outside.	**TE** Lesson 7-6, p. 98 **CRM** Skills Practice, p. A177
3	top, middle, and bottom.	**TE** Lesson 7-3, p. 93 **CRM** Skills Practice, p. A168
4	left and right.	**TE** Lesson 7-4, p. 94 **CRM** Skills Practice, p. A171
5	above and below.	**TE** Lesson 7-2, p. 92 **CRM** Skills Practice, p. A165
6	fitting shapes to a given space.	**TE** Lesson 7-7, p. 99 **CRM** Skills Practice, p. A180

Chapter-at-a-Glance

Lesson	Math Objective	State/Local Standards
8-1 Same or Different (pp. 105A–105)	Identify items that are the same or different.	
8-2 Equal or Unequal (pp. 106A–106)	Identify items that are equal or unequal.	
8-3 More or Less (pp. 107A–107)	Identify which holds more or less.	
8-4 Long or Short (pp. 108A–108)	Identify items that are long or short.	
Progress Check 1 (p. 109)		
8-5 Tall or Short (pp. 111A–111)	Identify items that are tall or short.	
8-6 Heavy or Light (pp. 112A–112)	Compare items that are heavy or light.	
8-7 Full or Empty (pp. 113A–113)	Identify items that are full or empty.	
Progress Check 2 (p. 114)		

Content-at-a-Glance

The diagram below summarizes and unpacks Chapter 8 content.

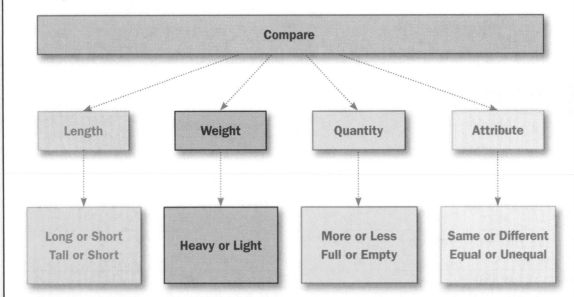

Online Assessment and Reporting
macmillanmh.com

Chapter Assessment Manager

Diagnostic Diagnose students' readiness.

	Student Study Guide/ Teacher Edition	Assessment Masters	Technology
Intensive Intervention Placement Test		1–4	💿 ExamView® Assessment Suite
Section Pretest (Chapters 8–10)		78–79	💿 ExamView® Assessment Suite
Chapter 8 Pretest		91–92	💿 ExamView® Assessment Suite
Get Ready	SSG 104		Math Online ▷ macmillanmh.com StudentWorks™ Plus

Formative Identify students' misconceptions of content knowledge.

	Student Study Guide/ Teacher Edition	Assessment Masters	Technology
Progress Checks	SSG 109, 114		Math Online ▷ macmillanmh.com StudentWorks™ Plus
Vocabulary Review	TE 115		Math Online ▷ macmillanmh.com
Lesson Assessments			💿 ExamView® Assessment Suite

Summative Determine student success in learning the concepts in the lesson, chapter, or section.

	Student Study Guide/ Teacher Edition	Assessment Masters	Technology
Chapter 8 Test	SSG 116	94–95	💿 ExamView® Assessment Suite
Alternative Assessment	TE 116	99–100	💿 ExamView® Assessment Suite
See It, Say It, Do It, Write It	TE 105, 106, 107, 108, 111, 112, 113		
Section Test (Chapters 8–10)		121–122	💿 ExamView® Assessment Suite

Backmapping and Vertical Alignment McGraw-Hill's *Math Triumphs* intervention program was conceived and developed with the final result in mind: student success in grade-level mathematics, including Algebra 1 and beyond. The authors, using the **NCTM Focal Points and Focal Connections** as their guide, developed this brand-new series by backmapping from grade-level and Algebra 1 concepts, and vertically aligning the topics so that they build upon prior skills and concepts and serve as a foundation for future topics.

	Lesson 8-1	**Lesson 8-2**	**Lesson 8-3**	**Lesson 8-4**
Concept	Same or Different	Equal or Unequal	More or Less	Long or Short
Objective	Identify items that are the same or different.	Identify items that are equal or unequal.	Identify which holds more or less.	Identify items that are long or short.
Math Vocabulary	different same	equal unequal	less more	long short
Lesson Resources	**Materials** • blocks, different colors • erasers • matching cards • paper bags • pencils • sheet of paper with "same" and "different" **Manipulatives** • attribute blocks • connecting cubes **Other Resources** [CRM] Vocabulary and English Language Development [CRM] Skills Practice [CRM] Practice at Home	**Materials** • crayons • index cards • pencils • small objects, such as paper clips **Manipulatives** • attribute blocks • connecting cubes • two-color counters **Other Resources** [CRM] Vocabulary and English Language Development [CRM] Skills Practice [CRM] Practice at Home	**Materials** • beans • blocks • containers of different capacities • marbles • rice **Manipulatives** • connecting cubes **Other Resources** [CRM] Vocabulary and English Language Development [CRM] Skills Practice [CRM] Practice at Home	**Materials** • 1-foot ruler • index cards • paper clips • yardstick **Manipulatives** • connecting cubes **Other Resources** [CRM] Vocabulary and English Language Development [CRM] Skills Practice [CRM] Practice at Home
Technology	**Math Online** ▸ macmillanmh.com StudentWorks™ Plus 💿 ExamView® Assessment Suite	**Math Online** ▸ macmillanmh.com StudentWorks™ Plus 💿 ExamView® Assessment Suite	**Math Online** ▸ macmillanmh.com StudentWorks™ Plus 💿 ExamView® Assessment Suite	**Math Online** ▸ macmillanmh.com StudentWorks™ Plus 💿 ExamView® Assessment Suite

Lesson 8-5	Lesson 8-6	Lesson 8-7	
Tall or Short	Heavy or Light	Full or Empty	**Concept**
Identify items that are tall or short.	Compare items that are heavy or light.	Identify items that are full or empty.	**Objective**
short tall	heavy light	empty full	**Math Vocabulary**
Materials • 1-foot ruler • blocks • index cards • yardstick	**Materials** • index cards • pennies or other small objects • tape • yardstick and book	**Materials** • blocks • open baskets • small objects such as marbles, beads, rice, cotton balls • various sized clear or transparent containers	**Lesson Resources**
Manipulatives • connecting cubes	**Manipulatives** • balance scale • blocks	**Manipulatives** • connecting cubes	
Other Resources **CRM** Vocabulary and English Language Development **CRM** Skills Practice **CRM** Practice at Home	**Other Resources** **CRM** Vocabulary and English Language Development **CRM** Skills Practice **CRM** Practice at Home	**Other Resources** **CRM** Vocabulary and English Language Development **CRM** Skills Practice **CRM** Practice at Home	
Math Online macmillanmh.com StudentWorks™ Plus 🔘 ExamView® Assessment Suite	**Math Online** macmillanmh.com StudentWorks™ Plus 🔘 ExamView® Assessment Suite	**Math Online** macmillanmh.com StudentWorks™ Plus 🔘 ExamView® Assessment Suite	**Technology**

Chapter Notes

 Home Connection

- Read the Home Connection letter with students and have them write their names in the space provided.
- Read and explain the activity under Help at Home. If time allows, complete a portion of the activity so students can introduce the activity to a parent or other caregiver.

 Real-World Applications

- Have four students come to the front of the room.
- Using a chair as a divider, have students sort themselves by girls on one side of the chair, boys on the other side of the chair.
- Have four new students take their place.
- Using the chair as divider, have students sort themselves by sneakers and non-sneaker shoes.
- Repeat with colors of clothing.

Math Online

Visit macmillanmh.com for ongoing support of chapter content and instruction, including:
- Online Games
- Concepts in Motion

CHAPTER 8 Sort Objects by Attributes

Home Connection

English

Dear Family,
Today I started in **Chapter 8, Sort Objects by Attributes**. I will learn to sort objects by their characteristics. I will describe objects using words such as "tall" and "short" or "full" and "empty."

Love, _____

Spanish

Querida Familia:
Hoy empecé el **Capítulo 8, Agrupar objetos por atributos**. Aprenderé a agrupar objetos por sus características. Describiré objetos usando palabras como "alto" y "corto" o "lleno" y "vacío".

Con cariño, _____

Help at Home

Work with your child to sort objects by their characteristics. Fill two cups with different amounts of cereal and have your child describe each cup. Is it full or empty?

Ayuda en casa

Ayude a su hijo a agrupar objetos de acuerdo a sus características. Llene dos tazas de diversas cantidades de cereal y haga que su niño describa cada taza. ¿Es llena o vacía?

Math Online Take the chapter Quick Check quiz at macmillanmh.com.

Chapter 8   Home Connection   one hundred three **103**

Key Vocabulary

Find interactive definitions in 13 languages in the **eGlossary** at macmillanmh.com.

English   Español *Introduce the most important vocabulary terms from Chapter 8.*

equal   igual
having the same value as or is the same as (p. 106A)

heavy   pesado
weighs more (p. 112A)

light   liviano
weighs less (p. 112A)

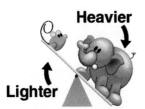

long   largo
a way to compare the lengths of two objects (p. 108A)

short   corto
to compare length or height of two (or more) objects (p. 108A)

unequal   desigual
having different values or is different than (p. 106A)

Get Ready

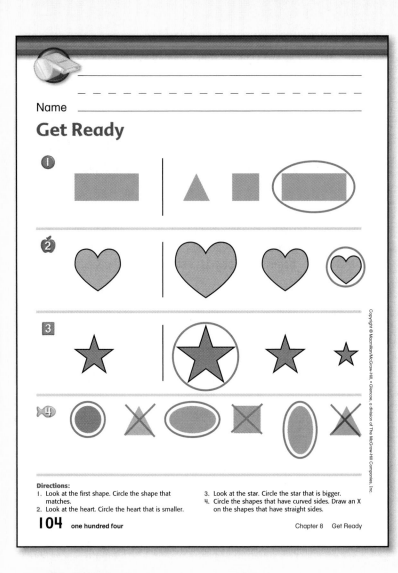

①

②

③

④

Directions:
1. Look at the first shape. Circle the shape that matches.
2. Look at the heart. Circle the heart that is smaller.
3. Look at the star. Circle the star that is bigger.
4. Circle the shapes that have curved sides. Draw an X on the shapes that have straight sides.

104 one hundred four

Chapter 8 Get Ready

Copyright © Macmillan/McGraw-Hill • Glencoe, a division of The McGraw-Hill Companies, Inc.

 **Dinah Zike's Foldables**

Guide students through the directions on p. A182 in the Chapter Resource Masters to create their own Foldable graphic organizer for use with this chapter.

Vocabulary Preview

• Consult the vocabulary list found on page 115. Identify the key words and create a word wall to reference throughout the chapter.
• As the students progress through the chapter, have them draw a picture to help them to understand and remember the meaning.

Get Ready

Diagnostic Assessment

Have students complete the exercises in Get Ready to assess readiness for the chapter concepts and skills. Refer to the lessons below for additional support for prerequisite skills.

> **Exercises 1–3:** Grade K, Chapter 7, Lesson 7 (p. 99)
> **Exercise 4:** Grade K, Chapter 5, Lesson 2 (p. 64)

You may also assess student readiness with the following resources:

> Assessment Masters: Chapter Pretest (pp. 91–92)
> **Math Online** ⟩ macmillanmh.com
> Online Readiness Quiz

Intervention Strategy

Step 1 Provide students with a paper showing various objects for them to sort. For each concept, present pictures of two objects to compare.

Step 2 After the chapter is complete, or as you complete each lesson, have students compare the objects by coloring, by circling, or another appropriate method.

McGraw Hill Professional Development

Targeted professional development has been articulated throughout **McGraw-Hill's Math Triumphs** intervention program. The **McGraw-Hill Professional Development Video Library** provides short videos that support the **NCTM Focal Points and Focal Connections.** For more information, visit macmillanmh.com.

Model Lessons   Instructional Strategies

Chapter 8 Get Ready **104**

Same or Different

Lesson Planner

Objective
Identify objects that are the same or different.

Vocabulary
different

same

Other Resources

Materials
matching cards

sheet of paper with "same" on one half and "different" on the other half

small paper bags, each filled with:
- 10 pencils (5 identical; 5 different from the other set and from each other)
- 10 erasers (5 identical; 5 different from the other set and from each other)
- 10 various items (5 identical; 5 different from the other set and from each other)

Manipulatives
attribute blocks

connecting cubes

On-Hand Manipulatives
20 blocks, different colors

CRM Chapter Resource Masters
Vocabulary and English Language Development (p. A185)
Skills Practice (p. A186)
Practice at Home (p. A187)

Teacher Tech Tools
TeacherWorks™ Plus
Math Online > macmillanmh.com
Advance Tracker

Student Tech Tools
StudentWorks™ Plus
Math Online > macmillanmh.com
eGlossary

1 Introduce

Prepare index cards with "same" and a picture of two squares on one side. On another card, write "different" and a picture of one triangle and one circle.

Give a student one of the five identical pencils, and the cards with "same" and "different." Have the other nine pencils in a bag. Use short and long pencils.

Have students practice showing the teacher "same" and "different" as pencils are pulled out of the bag.

2 Teach

Key Concept

Foundational Skills and Concepts   Reuse the "same" and "different" cards. Show students attribute blocks and ask them to show you their answers. Ask students to explain their thinking.
- Show a red circle and a red triangle. Some students will say "same" because of color; some will say "different" because of shape.
- Explain that all the objects are attribute blocks, but that some of them are the *same* and some are *different*.
- Model sorting red blocks.

Using Manipulatives

Attribute Blocks   Have students sort attribute blocks into groups according to shape. Discuss the characteristics of the sort. Have students repeat the sort according to size.

Intervention Strategy

Kinesthetic Learners

Matching Pictures   Have students play a matching game with a set of paired cards with matching pictures. Have students take turns choosing two cards. If the cards match, students should say, "These two cards are the same," and keep them. If the cards do not match, students should say, "These two cards are different," and turn them back over.

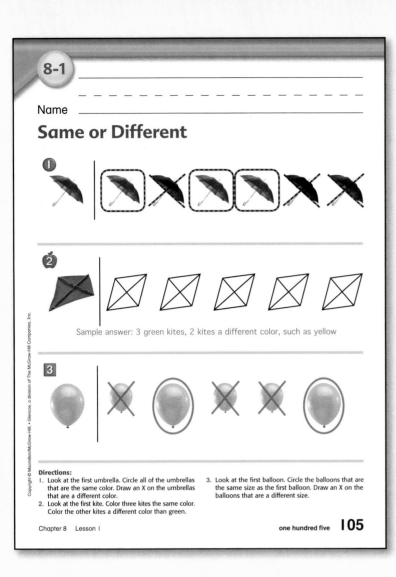

8-1

Name _____

Same or Different

①

② Sample answer: 3 green kites, 2 kites a different color, such as yellow

③

Directions:
1. Look at the first umbrella. Circle all of the umbrellas that are the same color. Draw an X on the umbrellas that are a different color.
2. Look at the first kite. Color three kites the same color. Color the other kites a different color than green.
3. Look at the first balloon. Circle the balloons that are the same size as the first balloon. Draw an X on the balloons that are a different size.

Chapter 8 Lesson 1

one hundred five **105**

---

③ Practice

Direct students to page 105 of their student workbook. Read the instructions at the bottom of the student page as they complete the exercises.

Remind students how they compared the items in the bags when they were the same or when they were different.

④ Assess

See It Show students two groups of attribute blocks: one with red items and the other triangles. Have students identify how they are the same or different.

Say It Give students five attribute blocks, all blue, but different shapes. Have students explain how they would sort the blocks.

Do It Have students use attribute blocks to make a group of four blocks that are the same shape and another group of four blocks that are different shapes.

Write It Have students choose a shape from the attribute blocks. Have students draw three shapes that are the same size and color.

> ⚠ **Common Error Alert**
>
> Some students become confused when sorting. Have students sort each color separately. Have students sort all red items into a pile. Then, from what is left, have students sort blue items into a pile, then purple items. Repeat sorting with another item, such as connecting cubes.

English Learner Strategy

Sorting Cubes Provide students with a sheet of paper divided into two columns labeled "same" and "different." Have students place colored connecting cubes in each column and repeat the words "same" or "different" as they place their cubes.

Equal or Unequal

Lesson Planner

Objective
Identify items that are equal or unequal.

Vocabulary

equal

unequal

Other Resources

Materials
crayons
index cards
pencils

Manipulatives
attribute blocks
connecting cubes
two-color counters

 **On-Hand
Manipulatives**
crayons
different sizes and colors of
  small objects, such as
  paper clips
pencils

CRM Chapter Resource Masters
Vocabulary and English Language
  Development (p. A188)
Skills Practice (p. A189)
Practice at Home (p. A190)

Teacher Tech Tools
TeacherWorks™ Plus
Math Online > macmillanmh.com
Advance Tracker

Student Tech Tools
StudentWorks™ Plus
Math Online > macmillanmh.com
eGlossary

① Introduce

Show students seven straws and 10 cups. Explain that you want to place one straw in each cup, and you need to know if you have an equal number of straws and cups. Ask students to think of ways to find out if there are an equal number of straws and cups.

② Teach

Key Concept

Foundational Skills and Concepts Place a straw in each cup. As all seven straws are placed, explain that there are more cups than straws.
- Tell students that the numbers of straws and cups are called "unequal," because there are different amounts of each.
- Remove the straws, and then remove three of the cups.
- Place the seven straws, one in each cup, and explain that now there are equal numbers of straws and cups. Emphasize that equal means having the same number or amount.

Using Manipulatives

Connecting Cubes Give each student a pile of connecting cubes (or counters). Have students make a train of cubes (or line of counters) and then create a train (or line) equal to the original, and one unequal to the original.

Intervention Strategy   Visual Learners

Using Counters Some students benefit from seeing how sets are equal or unequal. While completing page 106, have students place a red counter on each cow in Exercise 1 and a yellow counter on each deer.

Students can also create a group of four counters and trace them on two different index cards. Have students trace four cubes on one card and label it "equal." On the other card, have students trace more than four cubes (repeat with less than four cubes) and label it "unequal."

Name _____

Equal or Unequal

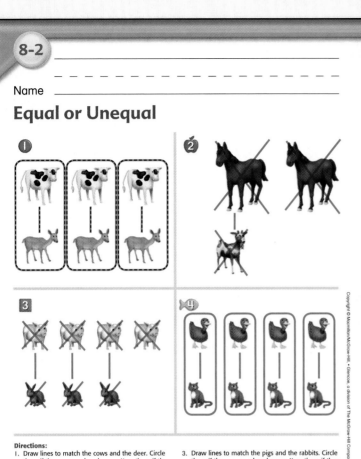

Directions:
1. Draw lines to match the cows and the deer. Circle them if they are equal or draw an X on them if they are unequal.
2. Draw lines to match the horses and the goat. Circle them if they are equal or draw an X on them if they are unequal.
3. Draw lines to match the pigs and the rabbits. Circle them if they are equal or draw an X on them if they are unequal.
4. Draw lines to match the ducks and the cats. Circle them if they are equal or draw an X on them if they are unequal.

106 one hundred six

Chapter 8   Lesson 2

③ Practice

Direct students to page 106 of their student workbook. Read the instructions at the bottom of the student page as they complete the exercises.

Remind students that equal means the same and unequal means different.

④ Assess

See It   Show students a set of five red counters, a set of two red counters, and another set of five red counters. Have students identify which sets are equal.

Say It   Have students count aloud the number of counters in each of the three sets. Have students say the word equal or unequal to describe each set.

Do It   Give each student a set of six yellow counters. Have students make an equal and an unequal set of red counters.

Write It   Have students make a row of four red counters on their papers. Have them draw a set of an equal number of circles above the counters, then draw a set of an unequal number of circles below the counters.

⚠ Common Error Alert

Equal or Unequal   Some students confuse equal and unequal. Have students compare equal and unequal sets of objects in the classroom, such as pieces of chalk to erasers, or caps to markers. As they compare groups, have them verbalize if they think the groups are equal or unequal and why. Encourage them to use "same" or "different," when describing the groups.

English Learner Strategy

Equal and Unequal Groups   Show students a set of five yellow connecting cubes. Have students connect five connecting cubes and say the word "equal." Have students connect an unequal number of cubes and say the word "unequal."

More or Less

Lesson Planner

Objective
Identify which holds more or less.

Vocabulary

less

more

Other Resources

Materials
containers and measuring cups of different capacities (1 cup, 1 quart, $\frac{1}{2}$ gallon, 1 gallon)
marbles

Manipulatives
connecting cubes

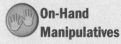 **On-Hand Manipulatives**
beans
blocks
rice

CRM Chapter Resource Masters
Vocabulary and English Language Development (p. A191)
Skills Practice (p. A192)
Practice at Home (p. A193)

Teacher Tech Tools
TeacherWorks™ Plus
Math Online > macmillanmh.com
Advance Tracker

Student Tech Tools
StudentWorks™ Plus
Math Online > macmillanmh.com
eGlossary

1 Introduce

Show students a set of three marbles and a set of 30 marbles. Ask students which set has more marbles.

Ask students to imagine a line at the water fountain. Tell students that one line is five students and one line is two students. Have students identify which line has more students and which line has less.

2 Teach

Key Concept

Foundational Skills and Concepts Show students two containers of different capacities and a box of marbles. Have students say which container they think would hold more marbles and which container would hold less.
- Have a student place marbles in each container, one at a time until one container is full. Define the full, smaller container as less.
- Have students continue filling the larger container until it is full. Define this container as more.
- Count the marbles in each container. Compare the number of marbles in each container.

Using Manipulatives

Rice or Beans Provide students with cups and 1 quart and 1 gallon containers. Have students pour rice or beans, 1 cup at a time, into each container. Have students compare which holds more and which holds less.

Intervention Strategy   Visual Learners

Filling Containers Some students need to "see" how containers relate. Give them three different-sized containers and rice or beans. Have students fill their own set of containers and see if they need more or less rice or beans to fill the containers.

8-3

Name _____

More or Less

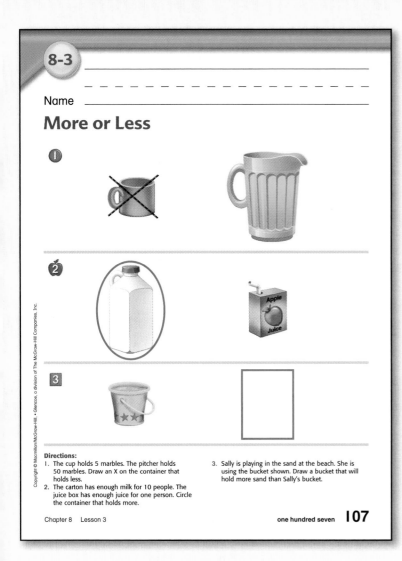

① ✕

② (circled)

③

Directions:
1. The cup holds 5 marbles. The pitcher holds 50 marbles. Draw an X on the container that holds less.
2. The carton has enough milk for 10 people. The juice box has enough juice for one person. Circle the container that holds more.

3. Sally is playing in the sand at the beach. She is using the bucket shown. Draw a bucket that will hold more sand than Sally's bucket.

Chapter 8   Lesson 3

one hundred seven **107**

3 **Practice**

Direct students to page 107 of their student workbook. Read the instructions at the bottom of the student page as they complete the exercises.

4 **Assess**

See It   Show students two containers, such as a 4-ounce cup and a 16-ounce jar. Have students identify which would hold more marbles.

Say It   Have students tell how they know which container would hold more and which would hold less.

Do It   Have students fill two different containers with marbles. When one is filled, have students decide which container holds "more" and which holds "less."

Write It   Have students draw pictures of containers that would hold "more" and "less." Have students explain their pictures.

Math Coach Notes

Have students use other containers and other fillers to practice more and less. Encourage students to use the words *more* and *less*.

English Learner Strategy

Counting Marbles   Provide each student with three marbles and a container. Ask students what they should do if they want more marbles in their container. Ask students what they should do if they want less marbles in their container.

Lesson 8-3 More or Less   **107**

Long or Short

Lesson Planner

Objective
Identify items that are long or short.

Vocabulary
long

short

Other Resources

Materials
1-foot ruler
index cards
yardstick

Manipulatives
connecting cubes

 **On-Hand Manipulatives**
paper clips

CRM Chapter Resource Masters
Vocabulary and English Language
  Development (p. A194)
Skills Practice (p. A195)
Practice at Home (p. A196)

Teacher Tech Tools
TeacherWorks™ Plus
Math Online ⟩ macmillanmh.com
Advance Tracker

Student Tech Tools
StudentWorks™ Plus
Math Online ⟩ macmillanmh.com
eGlossary

Intervention Strategy   Visual Learners

Index Card Examples   To help students remember the meaning of the words, make index cards with the words "long" and "short" on them. For "short," write the word very small and compact. For "long," write it very big and spread out. Students can use these to help to "see" what the words mean.

① Introduce

Show students a yardstick and a 1-foot ruler. Explain that you are going to call the yardstick "long" and the ruler "short."

Ask students to think about the distance from their seat to the door of the classroom and the distance from their seat to the front door of their home. Have students identify which is long and which is short.

② Teach

Key Concept

Foundational Skills and Concepts   Display two "trains" of connecting cubes of different lengths, one above the other, left ends even. Point out to students that the beginning of both trains are at the same place.
- Explain that the long train keeps going farther and the short train ends first.
- Have students use distances in the room to determine long or short. Students can use their desks as a starting line and count steps to the door, the chalkboard, or the teacher's desk.
- Model using the edge of a desk to align a crayon and a paper clip, then a crayon and a yardstick. Explain how a crayon can be long compared to one and short compared to the other.

Using Manipulatives

Connecting Cubes   Give each student 10 cubes. Have students make two trains: 6 cubes and 4 cubes. Have students put their trains side by side, aligned at the left. Have them tell which one is long and which one is short. Have students repeat using other addends of 10, such as 7 and 3.

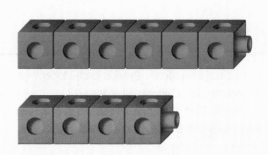

Name

Long or Short

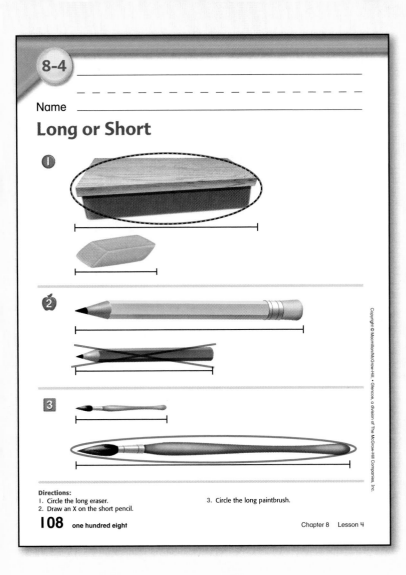

Directions:
1. Circle the long eraser.
2. Draw an X on the short pencil.
3. Circle the long paintbrush.

108 one hundred eight

Chapter 8   Lesson 4

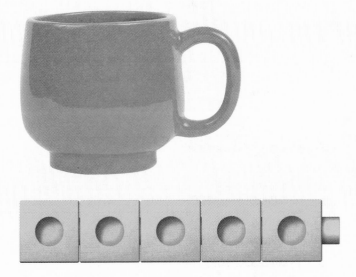

③ Practice

Direct students to page 108 of their student workbook. Read the instructions at the bottom of the student page as they complete the exercises.

Remind students that short objects end first. Allow students to make and compare connecting cube trains and place them over the objects in the exercises, if necessary.

④ Assess

See It   Show students two connecting cube trains: five cubes and seven cubes. Ask students to point to the long item and to the short item.

Say It   Show students two connecting cube trains: four cubes and eight cubes. Have students explain how the trains should be aligned, then say which is long and which is short. Assist students with aligning the trains as necessary.

Do It   Provide students with 15 cubes each. Have students construct a train of five cubes and a train of 10 cubes and identify them long or short.

Write It   Have students place the five cube train on a piece of paper. Have students use the left end of the train as a starting line to draw a row of squares that is long compared to the train.

 Common Error Alert

Students may not correctly compare objects by starting at a common endpoint. Use a "starting line" on the left when aligning two objects to compare length. Place masking tape on a table or tell students to align the end of the object with the edge of their desk.

Progress Check 1

Formative Assessment

Use the Progress Check to assess students' mastery of the previous lessons. Have students review the lesson indicated for the problems they answered incorrectly.

⚠️ Common Error Alert

Comparison Terms If students have difficulty remembering the comparison terms, provide them with the index cards that give more visual clues of the meaning behind the words.

Exercise 4 Students need to compare the lengths. Help them remember to look at cues such as the length markers.

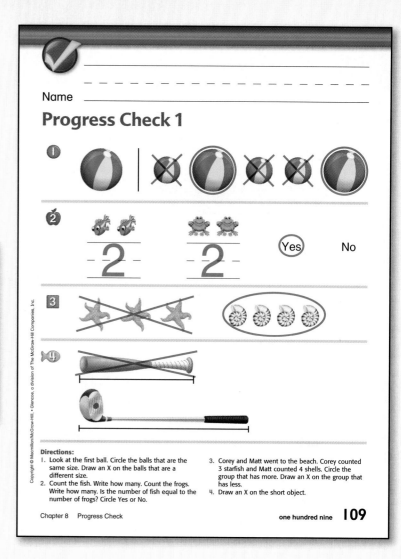

Directions:
1. Look at the first ball. Circle the balls that are the same size. Draw an X on the balls that are a different size.
2. Count the fish. Write how many. Count the frogs. Write how many. Is the number of fish equal to the number of frogs? Circle Yes or No.
3. Corey and Matt went to the beach. Corey counted 3 starfish and Matt counted 4 shells. Circle the group that has more. Draw an X on the group that has less.
4. Draw an X on the short object.

Chapter 8 Progress Check — one hundred nine **109**

Data-Driven Decision Making

Students missing Exercises . . .	Have trouble with . . .	Should review and practice . . .
1	identifying same or different.	TE Lesson 8-1, p. 105 CRM Skills Practice, p. A186
2	comparing equal and unequal.	TE Lesson 8-2, p. 106 CRM Skills Practice, p. A189
3	identifying more or less.	TE Lesson 8-3, p. 107 CRM Skills Practice, p. A192
4	identifying long or short.	TE Lesson 8-4, p. 108 CRM Skills Practice, p. A195

Name _____

Replay

Sample answer: Tamika has brown hair; Tamika's hair is shoulder-length; the shirts are blue; there is 1 apple on Evan's plate; there are 3 carrots on Evan's plate; Evan's container is orange.

Directions:
Tamika and Evan are having lunch. Follow the steps to complete the picture.

Step 1: Color Tamika's hair a different color from Evan's hair.

Step 2: Color both of their shirts the same color.

Step 3: Evan and Tamika have an equal number of apples. Draw Evan's apples.

Step 4: Evan has more carrots than Tamika. Draw Evan's carrots.

Step 5: Color the cup orange that holds more juice.

Chapter 8 Replay

Replay

Use the Replay activity to review and reinforce concepts and skills presented in Lessons 8-1 through 8-4.

Instructions

Explain to students that you are going to be reading instructions to help them complete the picture of two children eating lunch. It may be helpful to read the instructions more than one time, and to read each step separately.

Student Technology

Students can use the following technology resources to reinforce chapter content.

StudentWorks™ Plus

Math Online > macmillanmh.com
- eGames
- eGlossary

Tall or Short

Lesson Planner

Objective
Identify items that are tall or short.

Vocabulary
short

tall

Other Resources

Materials
1-foot ruler
index cards
yardstick

Manipulatives
connecting cubes

 **On-Hand Manipulatives**
blocks

CRM Chapter Resource Masters
Vocabulary and English Language
  Development (p. A197)
Skills Practice (p. A198)
Practice at Home (p. A199)

Teacher Tech Tools
TeacherWorks™ Plus
Math Online > macmillanmh.com
Advance Tracker

Student Tech Tools
StudentWorks™ Plus
Math Online > macmillanmh.com
eGlossary

1 Introduce

Have students compare the height of a book and a bookshelf. Tell students that the bookcase is tall compared to the books on its shelves. Have students compare the height of the teacher to the height of the door. Tell students that the height of the teacher is short compared to the height of the door.

2 Teach

Key Concept

Foundational Skills and Concepts Provide each student a 1-foot ruler. Show students a yardstick and hold up a ruler next to it, ends aligned.
- Explain that the yardstick is tall compared to the ruler and that the ruler is short compared to the yardstick.
- Have students identify objects in the room that are tall or short compared to the ruler, such as toys, books, chairs, desks, trash cans, windows, and doors.
- Have them work with a partner to explore the classroom for comparisons. Have each pair share their findings.

Using Manipulatives

Connecting cubes Provide each student with 12 cubes. Have each student build a tall tower and a short tower. Compare and discuss each student's pair of towers. Emphasize why some towers are tall and some towers are short.

Intervention Strategy   Visual Learners

More Index Card Examples To help students remember the meaning of the words *tall* and *short*, make index cards with the words on them. For the word *short*, write the word vertically very small and compact. For the word *tall*, write it very tall and spread out vertically. Students can use these to help to "see" what the words mean.

8-5

Name

Tall or Short

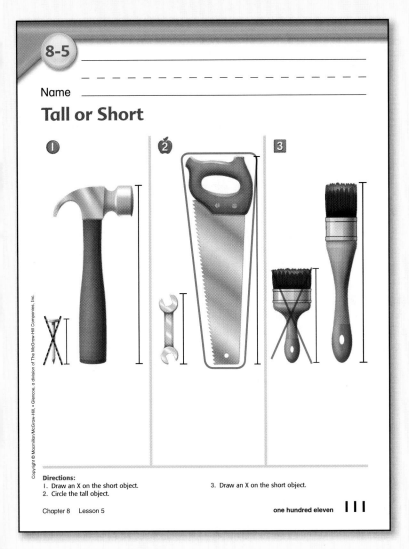

Directions:
1. Draw an X on the short object.
2. Circle the tall object.

3. Draw an X on the short object.

Chapter 8   Lesson 5

one hundred eleven   **I I I**

③ Practice

Direct students to page 111 of their student workbook. Read the instructions at the bottom of the student page as they complete the exercises.

Remind students that tall is higher and short is lower.

④ Assess

See It   Show students a 10-cube train and say that it is tall. Have students then choose an object in the classroom that would be short compared to the train.

Say It   Give students a seven-cube train and a three-cube train. Ask students to explain which is tall and which is short. Help students place the trains vertically on a flat surface before they give their explanations.

Do It   Give students a four-cube train. Have them create a train that is tall.

Write It   On an easel or on the board, draw a vertical line and say that it is tall. Ask students to draw a line that is short.

⚠ **Common Error Alert**

Students may not compare objects starting from the bottom. Remind students to always have both items they are comparing side by side with both bottoms flat. They cannot compare if the items are not started equally. Model how a short item could be called tall if it doesn't start at the same place as the other item.

TALL   SHORT

Heavy or Light

Lesson Planner

Objective
Compare items that are heavy or light.

Vocabulary

heavy

light

Other Resources

Materials
index cards
tape

Manipulatives
balance scale, as included
in the classroom
manipulatives kits
blocks

 **On-Hand
Manipulatives**
pennies
substitute balance created
from a yardstick and a
thick book as fulcrum

CRM Chapter Resource Masters
Vocabulary and English Language
Development (p. A200)
Skills Practice (p. A201)
Practice at Home (p. A202)

Teacher Tech Tools
TeacherWorks™ Plus
Math Online macmillanmh.com
Advance Tracker

Student Tech Tools
StudentWorks™ Plus
Math Online macmillanmh.com
eGlossary

1 Introduce

Give one student a stack of four books and a stack of four sheets of paper. Define each stack as heavy or light. Repeat with other classroom objects.

2 Teach

Key Concept

Foundational Skills and Concepts   Have students go on a virtual treasure hunt in the classroom. Point to different objects in the classroom and ask students if they think that the objects are lighter or heavier than their math book. Have students share and compare answers with the class.

Using Manipulatives

Heavy and Light Objects   Provide heavy and light objects for students to lift, such as paper clips, cotton balls, crayons, books, boxes of chalk, a sweater, and a coat. As students lift the objects, explain that heavy objects are harder to lift and light objects are easier to lift.

Intervention Strategy   Visual Learners

Using a Scale   Some students may need to "see" how an object is heavy compared to another object. Have students place each item on each side of a balance scale. Help them to see that the item that is heavy makes its side of the scale lower.

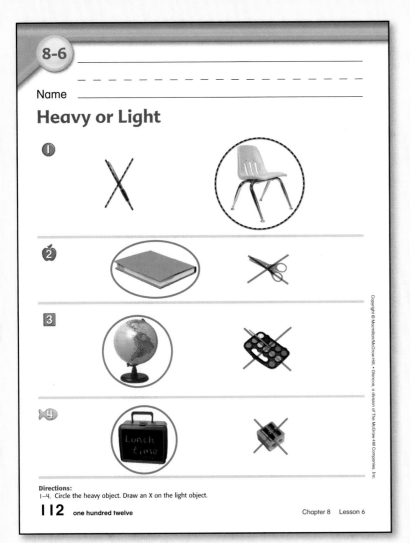

Name

Heavy or Light

Directions:
1–4. Circle the heavy object. Draw an X on the light object.

112 one hundred twelve

Chapter 8   Lesson 6

Copyright © Macmillan/McGraw-Hill • Glencoe, a division of The McGraw-Hill Companies, Inc.

③ Practice

Direct students to page 112 of their student workbook. Read the instructions at the bottom of the student page as they complete the exercises.

Remind students that heavy objects are harder to lift and light objects are easier to lift.

④ Assess

See It   Point out two objects from the classroom, such as a stapler and a bookshelf. Ask students to say which object is heavy and which is light, and to explain their answer.

Say It   Give students two objects, one heavy and one light. Ask students to label each object as heavy or light, and to explain their reasoning.

Do It   Allow students to find one heavy and one light object in the room.

Write It   Show students two pictures of two items. Have students write an X on the heavy item and circle the light item.

English Learner Strategy

Understanding Weight   To help students understand a simpler meaning behind heavy and light, give students separate cards with the words *heavy* and *light* on them. For the heavy card, write the word *heavy* in large and thick handwriting. Tape something to the card to give it weight. For the light card, write the word light in very tiny handwriting. Do not tape an object to the card. Encourage students to use the cards if they forget the meaning of the words.

Math Coach Notes

- Caution students to be careful when lifting heavier objects.
- Remind students to compare the objects one at a time, such as one book to one box of chalk or one sweater to one coat.
- Encourage students to "become the balance scale" when deciding heavy or light. Tell students to hold one object in each hand and move their hands up and down to feel the weight.

Full or Empty

Lesson Planner

Objective
Identify items that are full or empty.

Vocabulary

empty

full

Other Resources

Materials
open baskets students can
  see inside
small objects, such as
  marbles, beads, beans,
  cotton balls
various sized clear or
  transparent containers,
  jars, cups

Manipulatives
connecting cubes

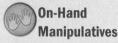 **On-Hand
Manipulatives**
blocks

CRM Chapter Resource Masters
Vocabulary and English Language
  Development (p. A203)
Skills Practice (p. A204)
Practice at Home (p. A205)

Teacher Tech Tools
TeacherWorks™ Plus
Math Online > macmillanmh.com
Advance Tracker

Student Tech Tools
StudentWorks™ Plus
Math Online > macmillanmh.com
eGlossary

1 Introduce

Have two clear containers at the table. Have one full of
marbles or beads and one empty. Have students tell
which one they think is full.

2 Teach

Key Concept

Foundational Skills and Concepts   Show
students two baskets, show one full of small objects,
such as cotton balls, and show another that is empty.

- Have students identify the full container. Explain
  that the other container is empty. Ask why the other
  is empty.
- Students should understand that a full container has
  no room for more and that an empty container has
  nothing in it.
- Model with two clear plastic cups, one full of water
  and the other with no water. Explain that the cup
  with the water is full and the cup with no water
  is empty.

Using Manipulatives

Connecting Cubes   Give each student the same
sized empty container. Provide different numbers of
cubes to each student.

- Have students tell whether the container without
  cubes is full or empty.
- Have students put their cubes into the container.
  Then have students tell whether the container is
  now full or empty.
- Encourage students to lift and shake full and empty
  containers to compare them.

Intervention Strategy
**Kinesthetic
Learners**

Using Containers   Students may need to feel the meaning
of the words. Give students two empty containers, along with
marbles, beads, or other small objects. Have students make the
empty container full by adding items until nothing else can fit in it.

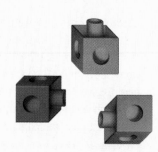

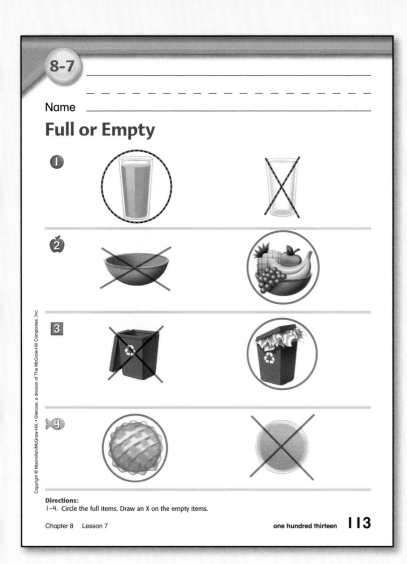

Name

Full or Empty

①

②

③

④

Copyright © Macmillan/McGraw-Hill • Glencoe, a division of The McGraw-Hill Companies, Inc.

Directions:
1–4. Circle the full items. Draw an X on the empty items.

Chapter 8   Lesson 7

one hundred thirteen   **113**

③ Practice

Direct students to page 113 of their student workbook. Read the instructions at the bottom of the student page as they complete the exercises.

Remind students that full means there is no room in the container and empty means there is nothing in the container.

④ Assess

See It   Give students five containers, three full and two empty. Have students sort the containers into groups of full and empty.

Say It   Show students two containers, one full and one empty. Have students say which is full and which is empty. Ask students to explain their answers.

Do It   Give students two empty containers and beads. Have students make one of the containers full and the other empty.

Write It   Give students pictures of empty containers. Have them color several pictures to show "full."

 Common Error Alert

Students may not understand the concept of full. Remind students that full means the item has no room for anything else, but is not overflowing. Allow students time to practice filling a small container with beads or buttons.

English Learner Strategy

Using Beans   Students may need more help to remember what each word means. Show clear plastic cups that are full of beans and cups that have no beans in them. Have students use the words "full" and "empty" as they identify which is full and which is empty.

Progress Check 2

Formative Assessment

Use the Progress Check to assess students' mastery of the previous lessons. Have students review the lesson indicated for the problems they answered incorrectly.

> ### ⚠ Common Error Alert
>
> **Comparison Terms** If students have difficulty remembering the comparison terms, provide them with the index cards that give more visual clues of the meaning behind the words.
>
> **Exercises 1–3** Students need to compare items to classify their properties. To help them with this page, have students think of the animals in real life. Students should use their knowledge to help them compare.

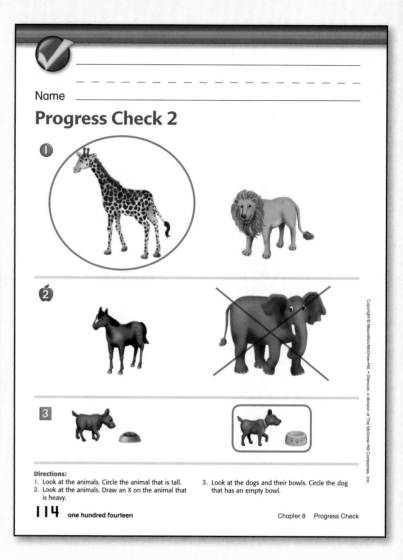

Name _____

Progress Check 2

Directions:
1. Look at the animals. Circle the animal that is tall.
2. Look at the animals. Draw an X on the animal that is heavy.
3. Look at the dogs and their bowls. Circle the dog that has an empty bowl.

114 one hundred fourteen   Chapter 8   Progress Check

Data-Driven Decision Making

Students missing Exercises . . .	Have trouble with . . .	Should review and practice . . .
1	identifying tall or short.	**TE** Lesson 8-5, p. 111 **CRM** Skills Practice, p. A198
2	comparing heavy or light.	**TE** Lesson 8-6, p. 112 **CRM** Skills Practice, p. A201
3	identifying full or empty.	**TE** Lesson 8-7, p. 113 **CRM** Skills Practice, p. A204

Intervention Strategies

Small Red Cube

Materials:

- one red cube per student
- two-dimensional shapes in various sizes
- three-dimensional shapes in different sizes such as two or three sizes of squares. It is not important that different students have the same set of blocks.

Step 1 Give students two-dimensional and three-dimensional blocks.

Step 2 Hold up a small red cube. Ask students to look at their blocks and to sort them into two piles: one pile of items of the color of the object you are holding (red items, any shape, any size); the other pile of items not of the color of the object you are holding (not red).

Step 3 Check to make sure all students have a red pile and a pile with all other colors.

Step 4 Hold up the red cube again. Ask students to sort their blocks into a pile of shapes like that of the block you are holding and a pile of shapes that are different.

Step 5 Check to make sure all students have a pile of cubes and a pile of all other shapes.

Step 6 Repeat Steps 2 and 3 with the red cube and use size as the criterion.

Step 7 Hold up a different block. Repeat Steps 1–6.

Time Management

Use this activity with Lesson 1 to give students some concrete practice with same and different. Can also adapt to other lessons by giving students; for example for Lesson 4, some longer things and some shorter things and sort by both long and short and color.

Review

Vocabulary

Before beginning the exercises, review vocabulary introduced in the chapter. Refer to the page numbers to revisit vocabulary activities in the lessons.

different (p. 105A)	**long** (p. 108A)
empty (p. 113A)	**more** (p. 107A)
equal (p. 106A)	**same** (p. 105A)
full (p. 113A)	**short** (p. 108A)
heavy (p. 112A)	**tall** (p. 111A)
less (p. 107A)	**unequal** (p. 106A)
light (p. 112A)	

Vocabulary Review Strategies

Vocabulary Cards   Have students review the vocabulary cards for the chapter. They should review the word pairs: same/different, equal/unequal, more/less, long/short, tall/short, heavy/light, and full/empty. Have pairs of students check each other by having one student hold up a pair of cards and the other student name items that the terms describe. Have students switch roles.

Concepts

The exercises in this section are grouped to cover content from each lesson in the chapter. The first exercise of each set is partially completed for the student in order to show the method for solving the other exercise(s) in the set.

> **Exercise 1:** Lesson 8-5 (p. 111)
> **Exercise 2:** Lesson 8-6 (p. 112)
> **Exercise 3:** Lesson 8-4 (p. 108)
> **Exercise 4:** Lesson 8-1 (p. 105)

CRM Find Extra Practice for these concepts in the Practice Worksheets, pages A185–A205.

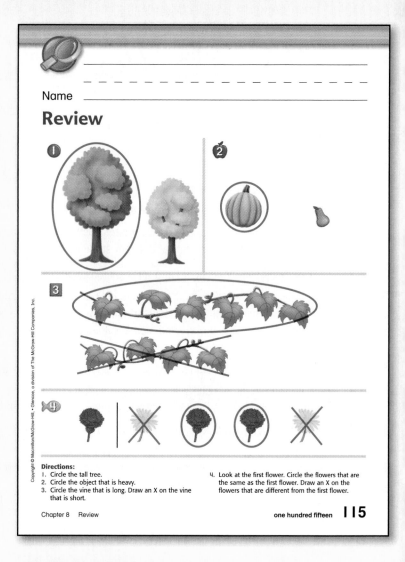

Name _____

Review

Directions:
1. Circle the tall tree.
2. Circle the object that is heavy.
3. Circle the vine that is long. Draw an X on the vine that is short.
4. Look at the first flower. Circle the flowers that are the same as the first flower. Draw an X on the flowers that are different from the first flower.

Chapter 8   Review

one hundred fifteen   **115**

Copyright © Macmillan/McGraw-Hill, • Glencoe, a division of The McGraw-Hill Companies, Inc.

FOLDABLES®
Study Organizer

Dinah Zike's Foldables

Have students use the Foldable they created at the beginning of the chapter to review and reinforce the concepts and skills they learned during the chapter. (See Chapter Resource Masters p. A182 for instructions.)

Intervention Strategy   **Visual Learners**

Picture Clues   Provide students with real-life objects or picture clues for the various vocabulary terms. The more they can see what each means, the better they can master the definition.

Name

Test

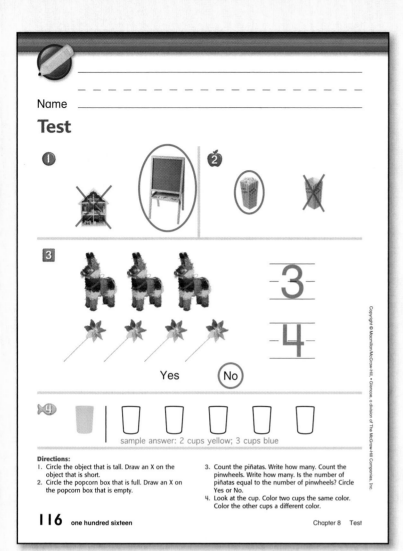

①

②

③

$-3-$

$-4-$

Yes   (No)

④   sample answer: 2 cups yellow; 3 cups blue

Directions:
1. Circle the object that is tall. Draw an X on the object that is short.
2. Circle the popcorn box that is full. Draw an X on the popcorn box that is empty.
3. Count the piñatas. Write how many. Count the pinwheels. Write how many. Is the number of piñatas equal to the number of pinwheels? Circle Yes or No.
4. Look at the cup. Color two cups the same color. Color the other cups a different color.

Test

Chapter Resource Masters

Additional forms of the Chapter 8 Tests are available.

Test Format	Where to Find it
Chapter 8 Test	Math Online > macmillanmh.com
Blackline Masters	Assessment Masters, pp. 94–95

Alternative Assessment

Use Portfolios   Have students cut out examples of the various attributes and glue them on a poster board and label them. Be sure the comparisons are grouped by appropriate measurements.

ExamView®
Assessment Suite

Customize and create multiple versions of the chapter tests and their answer keys. All of these questions from the chapter tests are available on ExamView® Assessment Suite.

Advance TRACKER

This online assessment tool allows teachers to track student progress with easily accessible, comprehensive reports available for every student. Assess students using any internet-ready computer.

Data-Driven Decision Making

Students missing Exercises . . .	Have trouble with . . .	Should review and practice . . .
1	identifying tall or short.	TE Lesson 8-5, p. 111 CRM Skills Practice, p. A198
2	identifying full or empty.	TE Lesson 8-7, p. 113 CRM Skills Practice, p. A204
3	identifying equal or unequal.	TE Lesson 8-2, p. 106 CRM Skills Practice, p. A189
4	identifying same or different.	TE Lesson 8-1, p. 105 CRM Skills Practice, p. A186

Chapter-at-a-Glance

Lesson	Math Objective	State/Local Standards
9-1 Long, Longer, Longest (pp. 119A–119)	Compare objects using the terms *long, longer, longest*.	
9-2 Tall, Taller, Tallest (pp. 120A–120)	Compare objects using the terms *tall, taller, tallest*.	
9-3 Short, Shorter, Shortest (pp. 121A–121)	Compare objects using the terms *short, shorter, shortest*.	
9-4 Heavy and Heavier (pp. 122A–122)	Compare objects using the terms *heavy* and *heavier*.	
Progress Check 1 (p. 123)		
9-5 Light and Lighter (pp. 125A–125)	Compare objects using the terms *light* and *lighter*.	
9-6 More and Most (pp. 126A–126)	Compare objects using the terms *more* and *most*.	
9-7 Less and Least (pp. 127A–127)	Compare objects using the terms *less* and *least*.	
Progress Check 2 (p. 128)		

Content-at-a-Glance

The diagram below summarizes and unpacks Chapter 9 content.

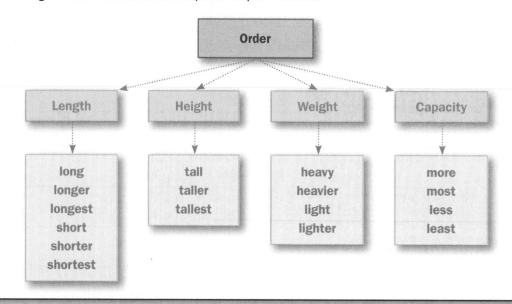

Order

Length: long, longer, longest, short, shorter, shortest

Height: tall, taller, tallest

Weight: heavy, heavier, light, lighter

Capacity: more, most, less, least

Chapter Assessment Manager

Online Assessment and Reporting
macmillanmh.com

Diagnostic Diagnose students' readiness.

	Student Study Guide/ Teacher Edition	Assessment Masters	Technology
Intensive Intervention Placement Test		1–4	💿 ExamView® Assessment Suite
Section Pretest (Chapters 8–10)		78–79	💿 ExamView® Assessment Suite
Chapter 9 Pretest		101–102	💿 ExamView® Assessment Suite
Get Ready	SSG 118		Math Online macmillanmh.com StudentWorks™ Plus

Formative Identify students' misconceptions of content knowledge.

	Student Study Guide/ Teacher Edition	Assessment Masters	Technology
Progress Checks	SSG 123, 128		Math Online macmillanmh.com StudentWorks™ Plus
Vocabulary Review	TE 129		Math Online macmillanmh.com
Lesson Assessments			💿 ExamView® Assessment Suite

Summative Determine student success in learning the concepts in the lesson, chapter, or section.

	Student Study Guide/ Teacher Edition	Assessment Masters	Technology
Chapter 9 Test	SSG 130	104–105	💿 ExamView® Assessment Suite
Alternative Assessment	TE 130	109–110	💿 ExamView® Assessment Suite
See It, Say It, Do It, Write It	TE 119, 120, 121, 122, 125, 126, 127		
Section Test (Chapters 8–10)		121–122	💿 ExamView® Assessment Suite

Backmapping and Vertical Alignment McGraw-Hill's *Math Triumphs* intervention program was conceived and developed with the final result in mind: student success in grade-level mathematics, including Algebra 1 and beyond. The authors, using the **NCTM Focal Points and Focal Connections** as their guide, developed this brand-new series by backmapping from grade-level and Algebra 1 concepts, and vertically aligning the topics so that they build upon prior skills and concepts and serve as a foundation for future topics.

	Lesson 9-1	Lesson 9-2	Lesson 9-3	Lesson 9-4
Concept	Long, Longer, Longest	Tall, Taller, Tallest	Short, Shorter, Shortest	Heavy and Heavier
Objective	Compare objects using the terms *long, longer, longest.*	Compare objects using the terms *tall, taller, tallest.*	Compare objects using the terms *short, shorter, shortest.*	Compare objects using the terms *heavy* and *heavier.*
Math Vocabulary	long longer longest	tall taller tallest	short shorter shortest	heavier heavy
Lesson Resources	**Materials** • drinking straw • pencils • string	**Materials** • building blocks • pencils • tracing paper	**Materials** • crayons • pencils • string	**Materials** • classroom objects • small paper bags
	Manipulatives • connecting cubes	**Manipulatives** • connecting cubes	**Manipulatives** • connecting cubes	**Manipulatives** • bucket balance
	Other Resources [CRM] Vocabulary and English Language Development [CRM] Skills Practice [CRM] Practice at Home	**Other Resources** [CRM] Vocabulary and English Language Development [CRM] Skills Practice [CRM] Practice at Home	**Other Resources** [CRM] Vocabulary and English Language Development [CRM] Skills Practice [CRM] Practice at Home	**Other Resources** [CRM] Vocabulary and English Language Development [CRM] Skills Practice [CRM] Practice at Home
Technology	**Math Online** macmillanmh.com StudentWorks™ Plus ⊙ ExamView® Assessment Suite	**Math Online** macmillanmh.com StudentWorks™ Plus ⊙ ExamView® Assessment Suite	**Math Online** macmillanmh.com StudentWorks™ Plus ⊙ ExamView® Assessment Suite	**Math Online** macmillanmh.com StudentWorks™ Plus ⊙ ExamView® Assessment Suite

Lesson 9-5	Lesson 9-6	Lesson 9-7	
Light and Lighter	More and Most	Less and Least	**Concept**
Compare objects using the terms *light* and *lighter*.	Compare objects using the terms *more* and *most*.	Compare objects using the terms *less* and *least*.	**Objective**
light lighter	more most	least less	**Math Vocabulary**
Materials • classroom objects • small paper bags	**Materials** • containers (small cup, bucket, pitcher)	**Materials** • buttons • containers • masking tape • measuring cup • plastic bags • water, sand, rice, dried beans, pasta, or pebbles	**Lesson Resources**
Manipulatives • bucket balance • connecting cubes	**Manipulatives** • connecting cubes	**Manipulatives** • connecting cubes	
Other Resources **CRM** Vocabulary and English Language Development **CRM** Skills Practice **CRM** Practice at Home	**Other Resources** **CRM** Vocabulary and English Language Development **CRM** Skills Practice **CRM** Practice at Home	**Other Resources** **CRM** Vocabulary and English Language Development **CRM** Skills Practice **CRM** Practice at Home	
Math Online macmillanmh.com StudentWorks™ Plus 💿 ExamView® Assessment Suite	**Math Online** macmillanmh.com StudentWorks™ Plus 💿 ExamView® Assessment Suite	**Math Online** macmillanmh.com StudentWorks™ Plus 💿 ExamView® Assessment Suite	**Technology**

Chapter Notes

Home Connection

- Read the Home Connection letter with students and have them write their name in the space below.
- Read and explain the activity under Help at Home. If time allows, complete a portion of the activity so students can introduce the activity to a parent or other caregiver.

Real-World Applications

- Display a variety of everyday objects whose length, height, weight, or capacity are different.
- Have students identify items in the group based on given attributes.
- **Who can name something that is tall? short? heavy?**
- Encourage students to explain why they chose the object they did.

Math Online

Visit macmillanmh.com for ongoing support of chapter content and instruction, including:
- Online Games
- Concepts in Motion

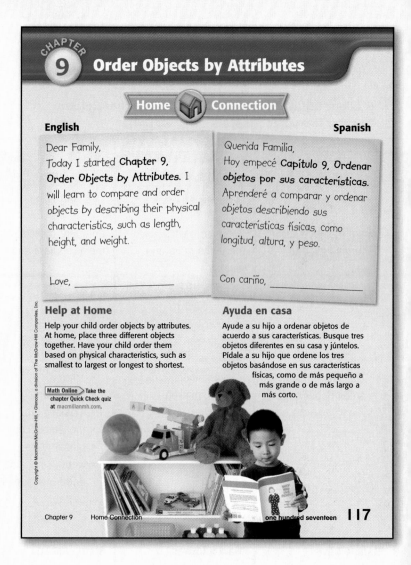

CHAPTER 9 Order Objects by Attributes

Home Connection

English

Dear Family,
Today I started **Chapter 9, Order Objects by Attributes.** I will learn to compare and order objects by describing their physical characteristics, such as length, height, and weight.

Love, _____

Spanish

Querida Familia,
Hoy empecé **Capítulo 9, Ordenar objetos por sus características.** Aprenderé a comparar y ordenar objetos describiendo sus características físicas, como longitud, altura, y peso.

Con cariño, _____

Help at Home

Help your child order objects by attributes. At home, place three different objects together. Have your child order them based on physical characteristics, such as smallest to largest or longest to shortest.

Math Online Take the chapter Quick Check quiz at macmillanmh.com.

Ayuda en casa

Ayude a su hijo a ordenar objetos de acuerdo a sus características. Busque tres objetos diferentes en su casa y júntelos. Pídale a su hijo que ordene los tres objetos basándose en sus características físicas, como de más pequeño a más grande o de más largo a más corto.

Chapter 9   Home Connection   one hundred seventeen **117**

Key Vocabulary

Find interactive definitions in 13 languages in the **eGlossary** at macmillanmh.com.

English   Español *Introduce the most important vocabulary terms from Chapter 9.*

heavy (heavier)   pesado (más pesado)
weighs more (p. 122A)

light (lighter)   liviano (más liviano)
weighs less (p. 125A)

long (longer, longest)
largo (más largo, el más largo) a way to compare the lengths of two objects (p. 119A)

short (shorter, shortest)
carto (más carto, el más carto) to compare length or height of two (or more) objects (p. 121A)

short

shorter

shortest

Name _____

Get Ready

①

②

③

④

Directions:
1. Circle the bigger plant.
2. Circle the smaller watering can.
3. Circle the bigger flower pot.
4. Circle the smaller flower.

118 one hundred eighteen

![FOLDABLES Study Organizer] **Dinah Zike's Foldables**

Guide students through the directions on p. A206 in the Chapter Resource Masters to create their own Foldable graphic organizer for use with this chapter.

Vocabulary Preview

- Assess students' knowledge of the basic vocabulary words in this chapter.
- Say a vocabulary word and have students name something that the word describes. For example, if you say "tall," students may name a giraffe.
- This will give you an idea of which vocabulary terms students need more help to understand.

Get Ready

Diagnostic Assessment

Have students complete the Get Ready exercises to assess readiness. Refer to the lessons below for additional support for prerequisite skills.

Exercises 1–4: Grade K, Chapter 8, Lesson 3 (p. 107)
Exercises 1–4: Grade K, Chapter 8, Lesson 4 (p. 108)
Exercises 1–4: Grade K, Chapter 8, Lesson 5 (p. 111)
Exercises 1–4: Grade K, Chapter 8, Lesson 6 (p. 112)

You may also assess student readiness with:
Assessment Masters: Chapter Pretest (pp. 101–102)
Math Online macmillanmh.com
Online Readiness Quiz

Intervention Strategy

Step 1 Show pictures that illustrate the basic concepts from the chapter, such as *long, tall, short, heavy,* and *light.*

Step 2 Have students cut out pictures in magazines that illustrate the concept in each picture.

Step 3 Have students glue their pictures onto sheets of paper and make a book titled "My Book of Comparing."

Mc Graw Hill Professional Development

Targeted professional development has been articulated throughout **McGraw-Hill's Math Triumphs** intervention program. The **McGraw-Hill Professional Development Video Library** provides short videos that support the **NCTM Focal Points and Focal Connections.** For more information, visit macmillanmh.com.

Model Lessons   Instructional Strategies

Long, Longer, Longest

Lesson Planner

Objective
Compare objects using the terms *long, longer,* and *longest.*

Vocabulary
long

longer

longest

Other Resources

Materials
drinking straw
string

Manipulatives
connecting cubes

 **On-Hand Manipulatives**
pencils of different lengths

CRM Chapter Resource Masters
Vocabulary and English Language
  Development (p. A210)
Skills Practice (p. A211)
Practice at Home (p. A212)

Teacher Tech Tools
⊙ TeacherWorks™ Plus
Math Online > macmillanmh.com
Advance Tracker

Student Tech Tools
⊙ StudentWorks™ Plus
Math Online > macmillanmh.com
eGlossary

① Introduce

- Cut a straw into two different lengths, and identify the pieces as long or longer.
- Holding both pieces in your fist, ask two students to draw straws and compare their lengths.
- Have the holder of the long straw lead the class in jumping jacks.
- Repeat with different students and different exercises.

② Teach

Key Concept
Foundational Skills and Concepts
- Tape a 6-inch-long string to the chalkboard.
- **This is a long string.**
- Tape an 8-inch-long string beneath the first string.
- Point to the second string. **This string is longer.**
- Repeat with a third string that is 10 inches in length. **This string is the longest of all.**
- Have students use the terms *long, longer,* and *longest* to describe the strings.

Using Manipulatives

Connecting Cubes   Arrange students in groups of three and provide each student in a group with a different number of connecting cubes.

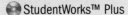

- Tell students to connect the cubes to make trains. Then have students line up their trains at one end.
- Students should compare their trains and identify and order them as long, longer, longest.
- As you circulate, ask questions about the trains. **How did lining up the trains help you compare them? How did you figure out which train is the longest?** Sample answer: We lined up the ends to see which is longest.

Intervention Strategy   Naturalist Learners

Objects from Nature   Students can find objects in nature, such as twigs or leaves, and compare their lengths. Have students share their collections with the rest of the class. Encourage students to identify the items using the terms *long, longer,* and *longest.* Remind students not to disturb living things. You may wish to keep the collected items to use during Lesson 9-5.

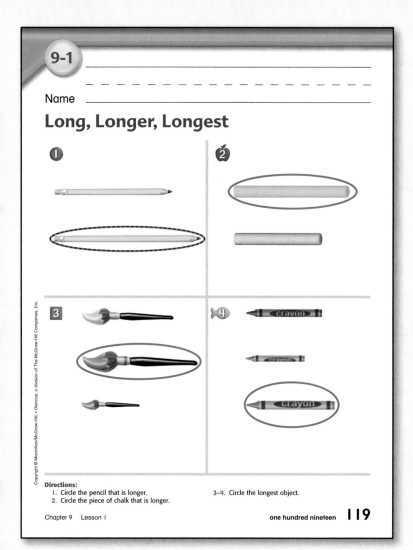

9-1

Name _____

Long, Longer, Longest

①

②

③

④

Directions:
1. Circle the pencil that is longer.
2. Circle the piece of chalk that is longer.

3–4. Circle the longest object.

Chapter 9   Lesson 1

one hundred nineteen   **119**

③ Practice

Direct students to page 119 of their student workbook. Read the directions at the bottom of the student page as they complete the exercises.

④ Assess

See It   Display three pencils of different lengths and have students point to the longest one.

Say It   Have students compare three objects of different lengths using the words *long, longer,* and *longest.*

Do It   Have students arrange three objects of different lengths in the order long, longer, longest.

Write It   Have students draw one line. Then have them draw a line that is longer than the first.

English Learner Strategy

Cube Trains   Make a train using four connecting cubes and ask students to make a longer train. Compare their trains to yours.

• **Is your train longer than mine? Whose train is the longest?** Have students arrange their trains by length and describe the trains using the words *long, longer,* and *longest.* Point to a train.

• **Which train is longer than this train? Which train is the longest?** Help students form complete sentences as they respond to your questions. Emphasize the root word *long* each time you say the words *longer* and *longest.*

Tall, Taller, Tallest

Lesson Planner

Objective
Compare objects using the terms *tall, taller,* and *tallest.*

Vocabulary
tall

taller

tallest

Other Resources

Materials
building blocks
tracing paper

Manipulatives
connecting cubes

 **On-Hand Manipulatives**
pencils of different lengths

CRM Chapter Resource Masters
Vocabulary and English Language
  Development (p. A213)
Skills Practice (p. A214)
Practice at Home (p. A215)

Teacher Tech Tools
TeacherWorks™ Plus
Math Online > macmillanmh.com
Advance Tracker

Student Tech Tools
StudentWorks™ Plus
Math Online > macmillanmh.com
eGlossary

① Introduce

- Begin by having two students hold a yardstick and a ruler vertically side by side. Identify the yardstick as taller than the ruler.
- **What are some things that are tall?** Sample answers: giraffe, skyscraper, tree
- Tell students that you will first name two things and they should repeat the name of the thing that is taller. Make sure students are familiar with the items you name. You might use these pairs: baby/mother; house/skyscraper; tree/grass; giraffe/chicken.

② Teach

Key Concept

Foundational Skills and Concepts
- Use three or four building blocks or connecting cubes to make a vertical tower.
- **This is a tall tower.**
- Next to the first tower, make a taller tower.
- Point to the second tower. **This tower is taller.**
- Build the tallest tower. **This tower is the tallest of all.**
- Have students describe the towers using the terms *tall, taller,* and *tallest.*

Using Manipulatives

Building Blocks or Connecting Cubes Arrange students into three groups at each table. Provide each group with a collection of building blocks or connecting cubes. Each group should have a different number of blocks or cubes. Have each group build a tower.
- Guide students to identify the towers as tall, taller, and tallest.
- **Which of these two towers is taller? Which tower is the tallest of all? How do you know?**
- Have groups put their towers in order, using the words *tall, taller,* and *tallest.*

Intervention Strategy   Visual Learners

Cube Towers Arrange students in groups of three and have each student make a connecting-cube tower of any height. Ask students to put their towers next to each other and arrange them in order by height. Rather than focusing on vocabulary, students should visually see the difference in height and arrange the towers accordingly.

Name _____

Tall, Taller, Tallest

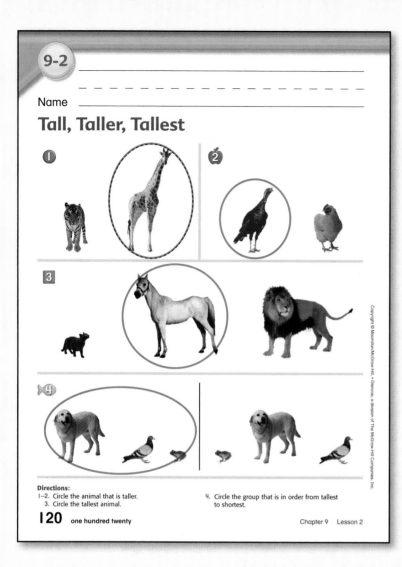

Directions:
1–2. Circle the animal that is taller.
3. Circle the tallest animal.

4. Circle the group that is in order from tallest to shortest.

120 one hundred twenty

---

(3) Practice

Direct students to page 120 of their student workbook. Read the directions at the bottom of the student page as they complete the exercises.

Exercises 1 and 2 Have students draw a circle around the animal that is taller than the other animal.
Exercises 3 and 4 Have students draw a circle around the animal that is tallest of the three.

(4) Assess

See It Display a book and have students find a book that is taller than your book. Then have them find another book that is the tallest of all three.

Say It Show students three block towers of different heights. Have students order them as they use the words tall, taller, and tallest.

Do It Have three students build connecting-cube towers in three heights and identify them as tall, taller, and tallest.

Write It Have students draw pictures of rectangular buildings to illustrate *tall, taller,* and *tallest*.

⚠ Common Error Alert

Exercises 1–4 If students have difficulty comparing the heights of the pictures, give them a piece of tracing paper. Have them trace the general outline of the first animal and use it to compare the height of the remaining animal(s).

Short, Shorter, Shortest

Lesson Planner

Objective
Compare objects using the terms *short, shorter,* and *shortest.*

Vocabulary
short

shorter

shortest

Other Resources

Materials
string

Manipulatives
connecting cubes

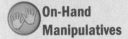 **On-Hand Manipulatives**
crayons of different lengths
pencils of different lengths

CRM Chapter Resource Masters
Vocabulary and English Language
  Development (p. A216)
Skills Practice (p. A217)
Practice at Home (p. A218)

Teacher Tech Tools
 TeacherWorks™ Plus
Math Online > macmillanmh.com
Advance Tracker

Student Tech Tools
 StudentWorks™ Plus
Math Online > macmillanmh.com
eGlossary

Intervention Strategy   Logical Learners

Common Objects   One alternative method to teach
comparing length is to have students use numbers to order
objects by length. Have students find three classroom objects of
different lengths, such as three pencils, three blocks, or three
shoes. Instruct them to write the numbers "1," "2," and "3" on
separate pieces of paper and place their objects in order by
length above the corresponding numbers.

1 Introduce

- Show students a collection of crayons. Some should
  be short, others should be shorter. Sort the crayons
  into two groups—short crayons and shorter crayons.
  Tell students to let you know when they figure out how
  you are sorting the crayons. Guide students to identify
  the groups as short crayons and shorter crayons.
- Then have students sort their own crayons into
  groups of short and shorter crayons.

2 Teach

Key Concept

Foundational Skills and Concepts   Tape a
4-inch-long string to the chalkboard.
- **This is a short string.**
- Tape a 2-inch-long string beneath the first string.
- Point to the second string. **This string is shorter.**
- Repeat with a third string that is about an inch in
  length. **This string is the shortest of all.**
- Have students use the terms *short, shorter,* and
  shortest to describe the strings.

Using Manipulatives

Connecting Cubes   Arrange students in groups of
three. Provide each student in the group with a different
number and color of connecting cubes.

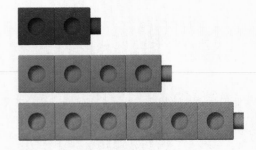

- Have each student make a cube train.
- Students should line up the trains at one end and
  then order them by length.
- To help students order trains, ask questions. **Which
  is the shortest train? Is the red train shorter than
  the green train? How do you know?**
- Have students answer with complete sentences using
  the words *short, shorter,* and *shortest.*

9-3

Name _____

Short, Shorter, Shortest

Copyright © Macmillan/McGraw-Hill • Glencoe, a division of The McGraw-Hill Companies, Inc.

Directions:
1–2. Circle the shorter animal.
3. Circle the shortest animal.
4. Circle the group that is in order from shortest to tallest.

Chapter 9   Lesson 3

one hundred twenty-one **121**

③ Practice

Direct students to page 121 of their student workbook. Read the directions at the bottom of the student page as they complete the exercises.

Exercises 1 and 2 Have students circle the animal that is shorter than the other animal.
Exercises 3 and 4 Have students circle the animal that is the shortest of all three animals.

④ Assess

See It   Show students three pieces of string of different lengths. Have them point to the shortest string.

Say It   Have students describe three pencils of different lengths using the words *short, shorter,* and *shortest.*

Do It   Have students make three different connecting-cube trains: *short, shorter,* and *shortest.*

Write It   Ask students to draw a short line, then a shorter line, then a shortest line.

English Learner Strategy

Suffixes   Provide several examples of how the suffixes *-er* and *-est* are used in other words students are familiar with, such as *bigger, biggest, smaller, smallest, taller, tallest, longer, longest.* Use objects and point to each as you say the adjective describing the object. Emphasize the suffix each time you say the word. Have students repeat each word.

Heavy and Heavier

Lesson Planner

Objective
Compare objects using the terms *heavy* and *heavier*.

Vocabulary
heavier

heavy

Other Resources

Materials
small paper bags

Manipulatives
bucket balance

 On-Hand Manipulatives
classroom objects

CRM Chapter Resource Masters
Vocabulary and English Language
Development (p. A219)
Skills Practice (p. A220)
Practice at Home (p. A221)

Teacher Tech Tools
● TeacherWorks™ Plus
Math Online > macmillanmh.com
Advance Tracker

Student Tech Tools
● StudentWorks™ Plus
Math Online > macmillanmh.com
eGlossary

Intervention Strategy   Tactile Learners

Weigh by Hand   It may be beneficial for some students if they
can pick up different items and feel the weight of each object in
their hands. Collect several rather heavy classroom items and
some relatively light items. Hand one light and one heavy item to
students. **Which is heavier, the book or the eraser?** After
students have compared several items, encourage them to use
the words *heavy* and *heavier*.

 **1 Introduce**

- Begin by comparing the weights of two classroom
objects. Hold up one object in each hand to model
objects in a bucket balance. Hold the heavier object
lower as you describe one object as heavy and the
other as heavier.
- Tell students that you are going to think of a heavy
object in the classroom such as a bookcase. Have
them guess what it is.
- Give clues about the object, beginning with **It is
heavy.** Continue giving clues until a student guesses
the object.
- Continue to play, allowing students to lead the game.

2 Teach

Key Concept

Foundational Skills and Concepts
- Gather various classroom objects that will fit in a
bucket balance, such as crayons, scissors, and glue.
- Have students hold two objects at a time, one in
each hand.
- **Which object do you think is heavier?**
- To check, place one object in each bucket of the
balance. Have students observe what happens. Point
out that the object on the lower side of the balance
is heavier.
- Repeat with other objects.
- Compare two objects, such as a desk and a
paper clip, with scissors. **Which is heavier than
the scissors?**

Using Manipulatives

Bucket Balance   Organize students in groups of
three. Give each student a small bag. Tell students to
put three objects in it.
- Help each group compare the weight of two bags
and predict which bag is heavier.
- Help groups use the bucket balance to compare the
bags' weights.
- Continue until all groups have weighed their bags.

Name _____

Heavy and Heavier

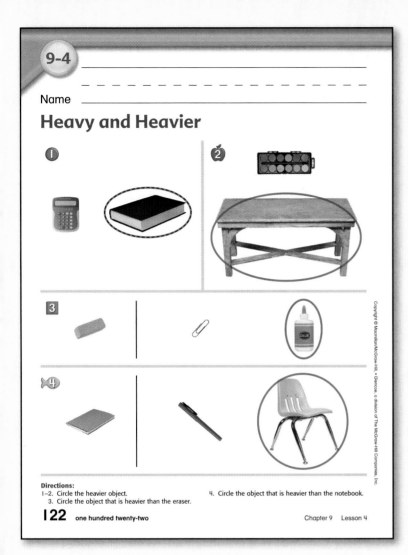

Directions:
1–2. Circle the heavier object.
3. Circle the object that is heavier than the eraser.
4. Circle the object that is heavier than the notebook.

122 one hundred twenty-two

Chapter 9   Lesson 4

---

③ Practice

Direct students to page 122 of their student workbook. Read the directions at the bottom of the student page as they complete the exercises.

Exercises 1 and 2 Tell students to circle the object that is heavier than the other object.
Exercise 3 Tell students to circle the object that is heavier than the eraser.
Exercise 4 Tell students to circle the object that is heavier than the book.

④ Assess

See It   Hold up a book and a pencil and have students point to the one that is heavier. book

Say It   Give students a book and a pencil. Have students complete the sentence: A _____ is heavier than a _____. book, pencil

Do It   Ask students to find two objects and arrange them by their weight. Students should name them *heavy* and *heavier*.

Write It   Hold up an object and have students draw something that is heavier.

⚠ Common Error Alert

If students are confusing the words for different attributes, review the words *long, tall, short,* and *heavy.* Then ask students to act out each word for you. For example, they can stand on tiptoes to act out *tall* or crouch down to act out *short.* Focus on the meaning of *heavy* by having them pretend to lift heavy classroom items, such as a crate or a desk.

Progress Check 1

Formative Assessment

Use the Progress Check to assess students' mastery of the previous lessons. Have students review the lesson indicated for the problems they answered incorrectly.

⚠ Common Error Alert

Ordering Objects Remind students of the connection between the terms *longest* and *tallest* and the familiar word *bigger*, as well as the connection between the terms *shortest* and *smallest*.

Exercises 1–4 You may find it necessary to repeat the directions, emphasizing the key word (longest, taller, shortest, heaviest).

Exercise 4 Remind students that when comparing the weight of two objects, the heavier one is usually the one that is more difficult to lift.

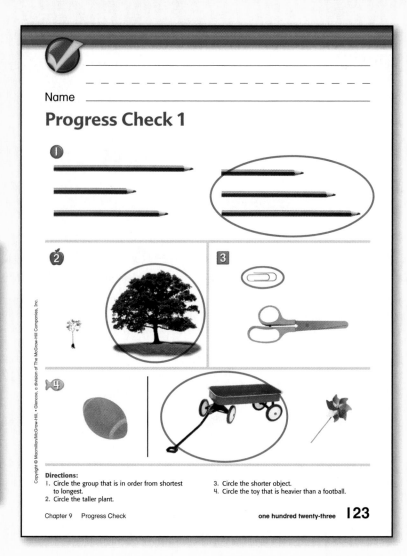

Data-Driven Decision Making

Students missing Exercises . . .	Have trouble with . . .	Should review and practice . . .
1	identifying *long, longer,* and *longest.*	TE Lesson 9-1, p. 119 CRM Skills Practice, p. A211
2	identifying *tall, taller,* and *tallest.*	TE Lesson 9-2, p. 120 CRM Skills Practice, p. A214
3	identifying *short, shorter,* and *shortest.*	TE Lesson 9-3, p. 121 CRM Skills Practice, p. A217
4	identifying *heavy* and *heavier.*	TE Lesson 9-4, p. 122 CRM Skills Practice, p. A220

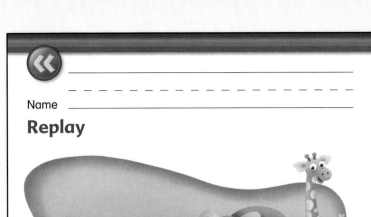

Name _____

Replay

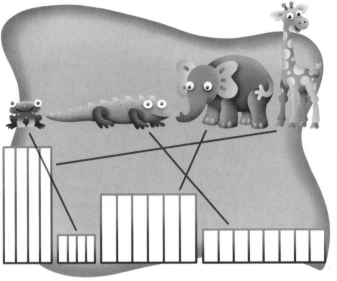

Directions:
Oh, no! There is a problem at the zoo! Last night, the zookeeper forgot to lock some of the cages and now the animals are free. Help the zookeeper get the animals back in their cages.
Step 1: Draw a line from the shortest animal to the shortest cage.

Step 2: Draw a line from the tallest animal to the tallest cage.
Step 3: Draw a line from the longest animal to the longest cage.
Step 4: Draw a line from the heaviest animal to the last cage.

Replay

Use the Replay activity to review and reinforce concepts and skills presented in Lessons 9-1, 9-2, 9-3, and 9-4.

Instructions

Explain to students that they will draw a line from an animal in the first row to its cage in the second row. You will provide directions to follow so students will know which animal belongs in which cage.

Student Technology

Students can use the following technology resources to reinforce chapter content.

💿 StudentWorks™ Plus

Math Online ⟩ macmillanmh.com

- eGames
- eGlossary

Light and Lighter

Lesson Planner

Objective
Compare objects using the terms *light* and *lighter*.

Vocabulary
light

lighter

Other Resources

Materials
small paper bags

Manipulatives
bucket balance
connecting cubes

 **On-Hand Manipulatives**
classroom objects

CRM Chapter Resource Masters
Vocabulary and English Language
  Development (p. A222)
Skills Practice (p. A223)
Practice at Home (p. A224)

Teacher Tech Tools
TeacherWorks™ Plus
Math Online > macmillanmh.com
Advance Tracker

Student Tech Tools
StudentWorks™ Plus
Math Online > macmillanmh.com
eGlossary

Intervention Strategy
Naturalist Learners

Objects from Nature Have students collect items found in nature, such as rocks, pine cones, acorns, and twigs. Have students use the bucket balance to compare weights and then record their findings with drawings that show the items in the bucket balance.

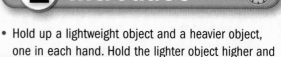

1 Introduce

- Hold up a lightweight object and a heavier object, one in each hand. Hold the lighter object higher and describe it as lighter.
- Ask students whether they have ever heard the saying "light as a feather." Explain that when something is light, people often describe it as being as "light as a feather."
- Name objects of varying weight. If you name a lightweight object, students say, "light as a feather." If you name a heavy object, students say, "heavy as a horse."
- You may want to name the following items: heavy—elephant, tree, bed, table, computer; light—balloon, pencil, flower, key, paper clip.

2 Teach

Key Concept

Have several students come to the front of the room and close their eyes. Hand each student two classroom objects, one for each hand.
- Ask each student to identify which object is lighter.
- Repeat the activity with different students until each student has had a turn.

Using Manipulatives

Bucket Balance Gather classroom objects that will fit in the bucket balance.
- Have students hold two objects at a time, one in each hand, to compare weights.
- **Which object do you think is lighter?**
- To check, place one object in each bucket of the balance. Have students observe what happens to each side of the balance.
- **Which is lighter? How do you know?**
- Compare two items to a third. **Which item is lighter than a stack of cards? The cotton ball or the book?**

9-5

Name _____

Light and Lighter

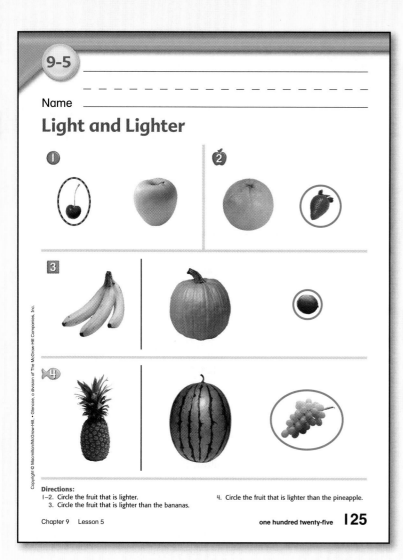

Directions:
1–2. Circle the fruit that is lighter.
3. Circle the fruit that is lighter than the bananas.
4. Circle the fruit that is lighter than the pineapple.

Practice

Direct students to page 125 of their student workbook. Read the directions at the bottom of the student page as they complete the exercises.

For Exercises 1 and 2, have students circle the fruit that is lighter than the other. For Exercises 3 and 4, have students circle the fruit that is lighter than the first fruit. Make sure students do not confuse light with small. Talk about large objects that might be light, such as a helium balloon.

Assess

See It   Show students three different classroom objects of different weights and have them use the term *lighter* to compare two of the items.

Say It   Display two objects and have students use the words *light* or *lighter*.

Do It   Hold up an object and have students find something that is lighter.

Write It   Hold up an object and have students draw something that is lighter.

Math Coach Notes

Strategies

- To extend the lesson, fill three small bags with connecting cubes to three obviously different weights. Label the bags *A*, *B*, and *C*. Fill the bags so that *A* is lightest and *B* is heaviest.
- Compare the weights of *A* and *C*, then compare *B* and *C*. Ask students to make predictions about the relative weights of *A* and *B*. Help them see that if *A* is lighter than *C*, and *C* is lighter than *B*, then *A* must be lighter than *B*.
- Allow students to explore with the three bags and then make and test their own predictions.

More and Most

Lesson Planner

Objective
Compare objects using the terms *more* and *most*.

Vocabulary
more

most

Other Resources

Materials
small cup, pitcher, bucket
(or similar containers)

Manipulatives
connecting cubes

 **On-Hand Manipulatives**
collection of containers of
varying capacities

CRM Chapter Resource Masters
Vocabulary and English Language
Development (p. A225)
Skills Practice (p. A226)
Practice at Home (p. A227)

Teacher Tech Tools
TeacherWorks™ Plus
Math Online > macmillanmh.com
Advance Tracker

Student Tech Tools
StudentWorks™ Plus
Math Online > macmillanmh.com
eGlossary

1 Introduce

- Show students a small cup, a pitcher, and a bucket (or three similar containers).
- **Pretend that you're going to the beach, and you want to collect seashells. Which container should you take to hold the most shells?**
- Allow students to examine the containers before answering. Have them explain their reasoning.

2 Teach

Key Concept

Foundational Skills and Concepts

- Show students two of the containers from the previous activity.
- Ask two students to fill each container with connecting cubes. Then have the students make trains with the connecting cubes so they can compare the capacity of each container.
- **Which holds more? Why do you think so?**
- Introduce the third container. Have a student fill it with connecting cubes and then make a train with the cubes.
- **Which container holds the most? How do you know?**

Using Manipulatives

Connecting Cubes   Arrange students in small groups. Have them repeat the above activity using three different containers.

- Each group should arrange its containers in order by how much the containers can hold.
- Groups should share their results with the class, identifying a container that holds more than the first container and the container that holds the most of all three.

Intervention Strategy   Auditory Learners

Which Holds More?   One alternative method to teach the concepts of *more* and *most* is to name familiar containers (such as a cereal bowl, a bathtub, and a bucket) and have students tell you which one holds the most. Be sure students are able to explain their answers.

Name

More and Most

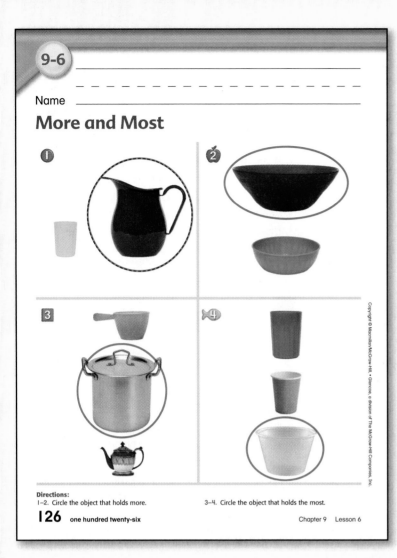

①

② 🍎

③ ▣

④ 🐟

Directions:
1–2. Circle the object that holds more.

3–4. Circle the object that holds the most.

126 one hundred twenty-six

Chapter 9   Lesson 6

---

③

③ **Practice**

Direct students to page 126 of their student workbook. Read the directions at the bottom of the student page as they complete the exercises.

Exercises 1 and 2 Have students circle the item that holds more than the other item.
Exercises 3 and 4 Have students circle the item that holds the most of all three.

④ **Assess**

See It Display a group of containers and have students point to the one that holds the most.

Say It Show students two different-size containers and have them predict which would hold more. Students should use connecting cubes to check their predictions.

Do It Have students arrange three containers in order of capacity from least to most.

Write It Display a container and have students draw something that holds more.

⚠ **Common Error Alert**

Exercises 1–4 If students have difficulty determining which container holds more, help them understand that if one container is bigger than another it will likely hold *more*. The biggest container will hold the *most*.

Less and Least

Lesson Planner

Objective
Compare objects using the terms *less* and *least*.

Vocabulary

least

less

Other Resources

Materials
3 sizes of plastic bags
containers of various sizes
masking tape
measuring cup
sand, rice, dried beans,
  pasta, or pebbles

Manipulatives
connecting cubes

 **On-Hand
Manipulatives**
buttons
water

CRM Chapter Resource Masters
Vocabulary and English Language
  Development (p. A228)
Skills Practice (p. A229)
Practice at Home (p. A230)

Teacher Tech Tools
TeacherWorks™ Plus
Math Online > macmillanmh.com
Advance Tracker

Student Tech Tools
StudentWorks™ Plus
Math Online > macmillanmh.com
eGlossary

1 Introduce

- Using masking tape, make three different-sized squares on the floor.
- Fill each square with as many students as possible.
- Count the students in each square.
- Discuss the relative capacity of the squares using the terms *more* and *less*.

2 Teach

Key Concept

Foundational Skills and Concepts   Use three different-sized plastic bags. Fill two bags with connecting cubes.
- **Which bag holds less? How do you know?**
- Fill the third bag with connecting cubes.
- **Which bags holds the least? How do you know?**
- **Which would you rather have filled with pennies— a bag that holds the most or one that holds the least?**
- Repeat with other examples.

Using Manipulatives

Connecting Cubes   Give each student connecting cubes. Display three empty containers of different sizes.
- Have students take turns dropping one cube at a time into each container.
- Once the smallest container is filled, point out that that container holds *less* than the other containers.
- When the second smallest container is filled, have students describe the relative capacities of the containers using the term *less*.
- Once the largest container is filled, use the terms *less* and *least* to compare the capacities of the three containers.

Intervention Strategy
Intrapersonal
Learners

Working Alone   Allow students who learn best when working independently to work alone. Have them fill containers with connecting cubes, and then count the cubes to determine which container holds the least. If possible, allow students to explore capacity by filling different-sized plastic cups with water, sand, rice, or pebbles and identifying the container that holds the least. Ask students to draw pictures to record their work.

Name

Less and Least

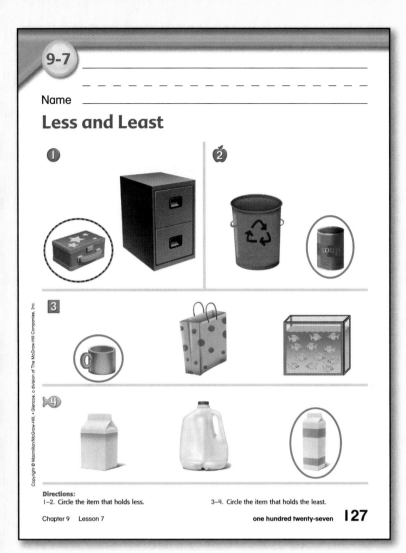

Directions:
1–2. Circle the item that holds less.

3–4. Circle the item that holds the least.

Chapter 9   Lesson 7   one hundred twenty-seven   **127**

Practice

Direct students to page 127 of their student workbook. Read the directions at the bottom of the student page as they complete the exercises.

Assess

See It   Show students three containers and have them point to the one that holds the least. Students can use connecting cubes to check their answer.

Say It   Have students tell how they know that a drinking glass holds less than a bucket.

Do It   Have students use water and a measuring cup to determine which of three containers holds the least.

Write It   Have students draw two containers and circle the one that holds less.

English Learner Strategy

Use Containers   Provide students with a 1-cup measuring cup and three different-sized containers. Have children fill the containers with rice, dried beans, or small pieces of pasta, counting each cup as they pour it. Ask them to draw pictures of the containers, labeled with the number of cups they used to fill it. Then have students tell about the containers using the terms *less* and *least*.

Progress Check 2

Formative Assessment

Use the Progress Check to assess students' mastery of the previous lessons. Have students review the lesson indicated for the problems they answered incorrectly.

> ### ⚠ Common Error Alert
>
> **Ordering Objects** Remind students that the largest items will usually hold the most and the smallest items will usually hold the least.
>
> **Exercise 1** Make sure students do not confuse the term *light* with the term *heavy*. Remind them that light items weigh very little and heavy items weigh a lot.
>
> **Exercises 2–5** You may want to review the terms *less*, *least*, *more*, and *most*.

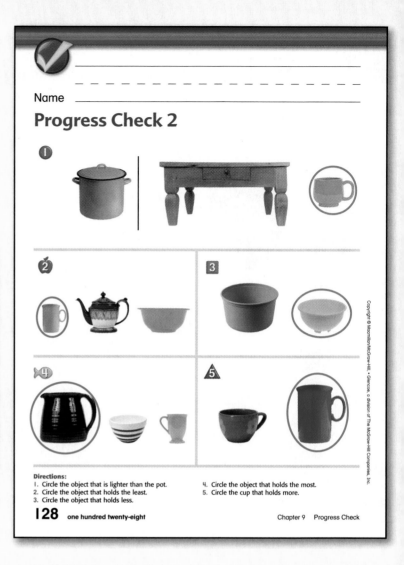

Name

Progress Check 2

Directions:
1. Circle the object that is lighter than the pot.
2. Circle the object that holds the least.
3. Circle the object that holds less.
4. Circle the object that holds the most.
5. Circle the cup that holds more.

128 one hundred twenty-eight

Chapter 9   Progress Check

Data-Driven Decision Making

Students missing Exercises . . .	Have trouble with . . .	Should review and practice . . .
1	identifying *light* and *lighter*.	**TE** Lesson 9-5, p. 125 **CRM** Skills Practice, p. A223
2 and 3	identifying *less* and *least*.	**TE** Lesson 9-7, p. 126 **CRM** Skills Practice, p. A229
4 and 5	identifying *more* and *most*.	**TE** Lesson 9-6, p. 127 **CRM** Skills Practice, p. A226

Intervention Strategies

English Language Learners

Materials: yarn, classroom objects, containers, materials to weigh, and so on

Step 1   **Whole Class** Show students two lengths of yarn, one long and one short. Ask students to say or point to the piece of yarn that is longer. Then ask them to say or point to which piece is shorter.

Step 2   Ask students whose first language is not English to say the word for "longer" in their native language. Then have them repeat the word *longer* in English. Assist them with pronunciation if necessary.

Step 3   Direct each student to use the word "longer" in a sentence. Encourage them to look around the classroom for examples.

Step 4   Follow the same steps for other words students will encounter in this chapter: *taller, shorter, heavier, lighter, more, less,* and so on.

> **Teaching Strategies**
>
> Devote additional time to saying and pronouncing the words with students who may need help with English. Show clear examples, whenever possible, while pronouncing the word.

Vocabulary Presentations

Materials: classroom objects

Step 1   **Small Groups** Organize students into groups if necessary. Write the following vocabulary list on the board.

heavier	**long**	**shorter**
heavy	**longer**	**shortest**
least	**longest**	**tall**
less	**more**	**taller**
light	**most**	**tallest**
lighter	**short**	

Step 2   Assign each group two or three terms from the list.

Step 3   Tell the groups that they will need to think of some examples that can be described by their terms. Encourage students to do whatever they like to show the words. They can use objects in the room to show-and-tell, draw examples on the board or on paper, or act out a (pretend) play.

Step 4   Have groups share their examples with the class and explain how they can be described by their vocabulary terms.

> **Time Management**
>
> Use this activity before or after the chapter. Modify it by assigning terms to individual students and having them present the words as definitions or examples.

Review

Vocabulary

Before beginning the exercises, review vocabulary introduced in the chapter. Refer to the page numbers to revisit vocabulary activities in the lessons.

heavier (p. 122A)	**more** (p. 126A)
heavy (p. 122A)	**most** (p. 126A)
least (p. 127A)	**short** (p. 121A)
less (p. 127A)	**shorter** (p. 121A)
light (p. 125A)	**shortest** (p. 121A)
lighter (p. 125A)	**tall** (p. 120A)
long (p. 119A)	**taller** (p. 120A)
longer (p. 119A)	**tallest** (p. 120A)
longest (p. 119A)	

Vocabulary Review Strategies

Use Objects   Give students many opportunities to use the new vocabulary words. For example, if students are working with manipulatives, have them order them from shortest to longest. Students can line up according to height. They can also compare the weight of their backpacks.

Concepts

The exercises in this section are grouped to cover content from each lesson in the chapter.

> **Exercises 1–3:** Lessons 9-1, 9-2, 9-3 (pp. 119–121)
> **Exercise 4:** Lessons 9-4, 9-5 (pp. 122 and 125)
> **Exercise 5:** Lessons 9-6, 9-7 (pp. 126 and 127)

CRM Find Extra Practice for these concepts in the Practice Worksheets, pages A210–A230.

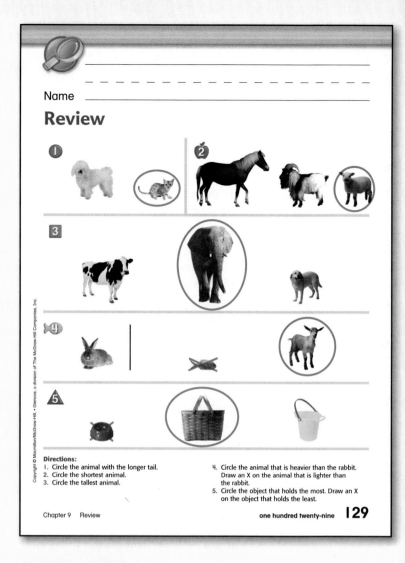

Name

Review

Directions:
1. Circle the animal with the longer tail.
2. Circle the shortest animal.
3. Circle the tallest animal.
4. Circle the animal that is heavier than the rabbit. Draw an X on the animal that is lighter than the rabbit.
5. Circle the object that holds the most. Draw an X on the object that holds the least.

Chapter 9   Review

one hundred twenty-nine **129**

 **Dinah Zike's Foldables**

FOLDABLES® **Study Organizer**

Have students use the Foldable they created at the beginning of the chapter to review and reinforce the concepts and skills they learned during the chapter. (See Chapter Resource Masters p. A206 for instructions.)

Intervention Strategy   Linguistic Learners

Use Pictures   Encourage students to use the terms from the chapter to describe and compare the pictures. It may help to prompt students by pointing to one of the pictures in the row and asking students to compare it to the other pictures. Ask students to explain the difference between words such as *longer* and *longest, shorter* and *shortest,* or *taller* and *tallest.*

Name

Test

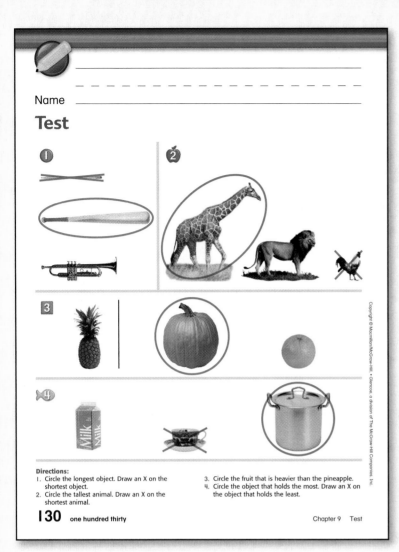

Directions:
1. Circle the longest object. Draw an X on the shortest object.
2. Circle the tallest animal. Draw an X on the shortest animal.
3. Circle the fruit that is heavier than the pineapple.
4. Circle the object that holds the most. Draw an X on the object that holds the least.

130 one hundred thirty

Chapter 9 Test

Test

Chapter Resource Masters

Additional forms of the Chapter 9 Tests are available.

Test Format	Where to Find it
Chapter 9 Test	Math Online macmillanmh.com
Blackline Masters	Assessment Masters, pp. 104–105

Alternative Assessment

Order Objects Make groups of objects that can be ordered by length, height, weight, and capacity. Display one group at a time, and ask students to order the objects by an appropriate attribute. Then have students use the comparative terms for the attribute to compare the objects and explain why they arranged them in the order they did.

ExamView®
Assessment Suite

Customize and create multiple versions of your chapter tests and their answer keys. All of these questions from the chapter tests are available on ExamView® Assessment Suite.

Advance TRACKER

This online assessment tool allows teachers to track student progress with easily accessible, comprehensive reports available for every student. Assess students using any internet-ready computer.

Data-Driven Decision Making

Students missing Exercises ...	Have trouble with ...	Should review and practice ...
1–2	comparing lengths and heights.	**TE** Lessons 9-1, 9-2, 9-3, pp. 119, 120, and 121 **CRM** Skills Practice, pp. A211, A214, and A217
3	comparing weights.	**TE** Lessons 9-4 and 9-5, pp. 122 and 125 **CRM** Skills Practice, pp. A220 and A223
4	comparing capacities.	**TE** Lessons 9-6 and 9-7, pp. 126 and 127 **CRM** Skills Practice, pp. A226 and A229

Chapter Overview

Chapter-at-a-Glance

Lesson	Math Objective	State/Local Standards
10-1 More than One Attribute (pp. 133A-133)	Sort shapes by more than one attribute.	
10-2 AB Patterns (pp. 134A-134)	Identify and create AB patterns.	
10-3 AAB Patterns (pp. 135A-135)	Identify and create AAB patterns.	
10-4 ABB Patterns (pp. 136A-136)	Identify and create ABB patterns.	
Progress Check 1 (p. 137)		
10-5 ABC Patterns (pp. 139A-139)	Identify and create ABC patterns.	
10-6 Identify and Extend Patterns (pp. 140A-140)	Identify and extend a variety of patterns.	
10-7 Create Patterns (pp. 141A-141)	Create a variety of patterns independently.	
Progress Check 2 (p. 142)		

Content-at-a-Glance

The diagram below summarizes and unpacks Chapter 10 content.

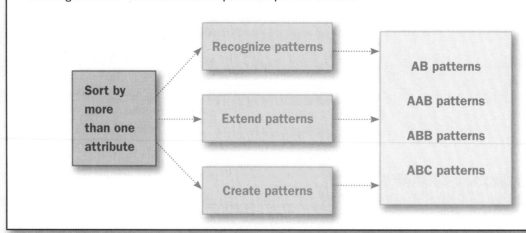

Online Assessment and Reporting
macmillanmh.com

Chapter Assessment Manager

Diagnostic   Diagnose students' readiness.

	Student Study Guide/ Teacher Edition	Assessment Masters	Technology
Intensive Intervention Placement Test		1–4	💿 ExamView® Assessment Suite
Section Pretest (Chapters 8–10)		78–79	💿 ExamView® Assessment Suite
Chapter 10 Pretest		111–112	💿 ExamView® Assessment Suite
Get Ready	SSG 132		Math Online ▷ macmillanmh.com StudentWorks™ Plus

Formative   Identify students' misconceptions of content knowledge.

	Student Study Guide/ Teacher Edition	Assessment Masters	Technology
Progress Checks	SSG 137, 142		Math Online ▷ macmillanmh.com StudentWorks™ Plus
Vocabulary Review	TE 143		Math Online ▷ macmillanmh.com
Lesson Assessments			💿 ExamView® Assessment Suite

Summative   Determine student success in learning the concepts in the lesson, chapter, or section.

	Student Study Guide/ Teacher Edition	Assessment Masters	Technology
Chapter 10 Test	SSG 144	114–115	💿 ExamView® Assessment Suite
Alternative Assessment	TE 144	119–120	💿 ExamView® Assessment Suite
See It, Say It, Do It, Write It	TE 133, 134, 135, 136, 139, 140, 141		
Section Test (Chapters 8–10)		121–122	💿 ExamView® Assessment Suite

Backmapping and Vertical Alignment McGraw-Hill's *Math Triumphs* intervention program was conceived and developed with the final result in mind: student success in grade-level mathematics, including Algebra 1 and beyond. The authors, using the **NCTM Focal Points and Focal Connections** as their guide, developed this brand-new series by backmapping from grade-level and Algebra 1 concepts, and vertically aligning the topics so that they build upon prior skills and concepts and serve as a foundation for future topics.

	Lesson 10-1	Lesson 10-2	Lesson 10-3	Lesson 10-4
Concept	More than One Attribute	AB Patterns	AAB Patterns	ABB Patterns
Objective	Sort shapes by more than one attribute.	Identify and create AB patterns.	Identify and create AAB patterns.	Identify and create ABB patterns.
Math Vocabulary	alike different sort	AB pattern pattern	AAB pattern order repeat	ABB pattern
Lesson Resources	**Materials** • common objects to sort (pencils, erasers, markers, rulers, and so on) • construction paper shapes **Manipulatives** • attribute blocks • pattern blocks **Other Resources** [CRM] Vocabulary and English Language Development [CRM] Skills Practice [CRM] Practice at Home	**Materials** • crayons • drawing paper • index cards • pencils **Manipulatives** • pattern blocks **Other Resources** [CRM] Vocabulary and English Language Development [CRM] Skills Practice [CRM] Practice at Home	**Materials** • chart paper • index cards • paper • pencils **Manipulatives** • connecting cubes **Other Resources** [CRM] Vocabulary and English Language Development [CRM] Skills Practice [CRM] Practice at Home	**Materials** • chart paper • crayons • markers • pencils **Manipulatives** • color tiles • connecting cubes **Other Resources** [CRM] Vocabulary and English Language Development [CRM] Skills Practice [CRM] Practice at Home
Technology	Math Online ▷ macmillanmh.com StudentWorks™ Plus ◉ ExamView® Assessment Suite	Math Online ▷ macmillanmh.com StudentWorks™ Plus ◉ ExamView® Assessment Suite	Math Online ▷ macmillanmh.com StudentWorks™ Plus ◉ ExamView® Assessment Suite	Math Online ▷ macmillanmh.com StudentWorks™ Plus ◉ ExamView® Assessment Suite

Lesson 10-5	Lesson 10-6	Lesson 10-7	
ABC Patterns	Identify and Extend Patterns	Create Patterns	**Concept**
Identify and create ABC patterns.	Identify and extend a variety of patterns.	Create a variety of patterns independently.	**Objective**
ABC pattern	down next up	growing pattern sequential pattern	**Math Vocabulary**
Materials • beads • construction paper • markers	**Materials** • cardboard cut-out shapes • craft sticks	**Materials** • chart paper • crayons • drawing paper • erasers • markers • paper clips • pencils	**Lesson Resources**
Manipulatives • attribute buttons • color tiles • string	**Manipulatives** • attribute blocks	**Manipulatives** • color tiles • connecting cubes • pattern blocks	
Other Resources **CRM** Vocabulary and English Language Development **CRM** Skills Practice **CRM** Practice at Home	**Other Resources** **CRM** Vocabulary and English Language Development **CRM** Skills Practice **CRM** Practice at Home	**Other Resources** **CRM** Vocabulary and English Language Development **CRM** Skills Practice **CRM** Practice at Home	
Math Online ▷ macmillanmh.com StudentWorks™ Plus ● ExamView® Assessment Suite	**Math Online** ▷ macmillanmh.com StudentWorks™ Plus ● ExamView® Assessment Suite	**Math Online** ▷ macmillanmh.com StudentWorks™ Plus ● ExamView® Assessment Suite	**Technology**

Chapter Notes

Home Connection

- Read the Home Connection letter with students and have them write their names in the space below.
- Read and explain the activity under Help at Home. If time allows, complete a portion of the activity so students can introduce the activity to a parent or other caregiver.

Real-World Applications

- Ask students to stand and join you in an exercise routine.
- Tell students to follow along as you touch your toes, touch your shoulders, then reach for the stars. Repeat the routine several times. Then, stop after touching your shoulders and have students tell you what move comes next.
- Repeat with a different set of exercises such as hopping on one foot, turning around, and a jumping jack.

Math Online

Visit macmillanmh.com for ongoing support of chapter content and instruction, including:
- Online Games
- Concepts in Motion

Patterns

Home Connection

English

Dear Family,
Today I started **Chapter 10, Patterns.** I will learn how to identify and extend simple patterns related to sight, sound, and texture.

Love, _____

Spanish

Querida Familia:
Hoy empecé el **Capítulo 10, Patrones.** Aprenderé cómo identificar y ampliar patrones simples relacionados con la vista, el sonido y el tacto.

Con cariño, _____

Help at Home
Help your child identify and extend simple patterns. Clap, slap your knees, and hop on one foot in a pattern for your child to copy. Have your child make up a different pattern.

Math Online ▶ Take the chapter Quick Check quiz at macmillanmh.com.

Ayuda en casa
Ayude a su hijo a identificar y ampliar patrones simples. Aplauda, golpee sus rodillas y golpee con sus pies siguiendo un patrón ABCABC para que su hijo lo copie. Pídale a su hijo que él cree su patrón diferente.

Chapter 10　Home Connection

one hundred thirty-one **131**

Key Vocabulary

Find interactive definitions in 13 languages in the **eGlossary** at macmillanmh.com.

English　Español *Introduce the most important vocabulary terms from Chapter 10.*

next　después
immediately following (p. 140A)

pattern　patrón
An order that a set of objects or numbers follows over and over. A, A, B, A, A, B, A, A, B (p. 134A)

repeat　repetición
to say or do again; to duplicate (p. 135A)

sort　ordenar ○○○ ☐☐☐☐
to group together like items (p. 133A)

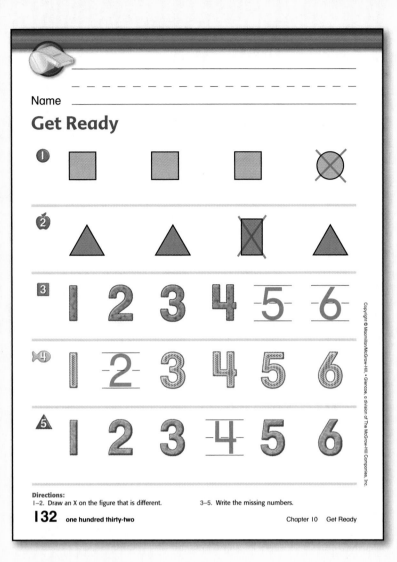

Name _____

Get Ready

① ▢ ▢ ▢ ⊗

② ▲ ▲ ⊠ ▲

③ 1 2 3 4 5 6

④ 1 2 3 4 5 6

⑤ 1 2 3 4 5 6

Directions:
1–2. Draw an X on the figure that is different.   3–5. Write the missing numbers.

132 one hundred thirty-two   Chapter 10 Get Ready

Get Ready

Diagnostic Assessment

Have students complete the Get Ready exercises to assess readiness. Refer to the lessons below for support for prerequisite skills.

Exercises 1–5: Grade K, Chapter 2, Lesson 7 (p. 27)
Exercises 1–5: Grade K, Chapter 2, Lesson 8 (p. 28)

You may also assess student readiness with:
Assessment Masters: Chapter Pretest (pp. 78–79)

Math Online ⟩ macmillanmh.com
Online Readiness Quiz

Intervention Strategy

Step 1 Have students look for patterns found in everyday objects such as beaded jewelry, fabric, quilts, picture frames, and so on.

Step 2 Provide students with poster board divided into six sections. Challenge students to either copy the patterns they find or draw their own patterns in each section on the poster.

Step 3 Display posters in the classroom.

FOLDABLES
Study Organizer
Dinah Zike's Foldables

Guide students through the directions on p. A231 in the Chapter Resource Masters to create their own Foldable graphic organizer for use with this chapter.

Vocabulary Preview

- Before students begin the chapter, make a word wall of important terms. Refer to Review on page 143.

- Make a set of index cards with vocabulary words written on one side and a corresponding picture on the other side. Leave the set of cards in an accessible area for students to view.

- As the students progress through the chapter, have them draw their own pictures to help them to understand and remember the meaning.

Mc Graw Hill
Professional Development

Targeted professional development has been articulated throughout **McGraw-Hill's Math Triumphs** intervention program. The **McGraw-Hill Professional Development Video Library** provides short videos that support the **NCTM Focal Points and Focal Connections.** For more information, visit macmillanmh.com.

Model Lessons   Instructional Strategies

More than One Attribute

Lesson Planner

Objective
Sort shapes by more than one attribute.

Vocabulary
alike

different

sort

Other Resources

Materials
construction-paper shapes in the same shapes, sizes, and colors as pattern blocks

Manipulatives
attribute blocks
pattern blocks

On-Hand Manipulatives
common objects to sort (pencils, erasers, markers, rulers, and so on)

CRM Chapter Resource Masters
Vocabulary and English Language Development (p. A234)
Skills Practice (p. A235)
Practice at Home (p. A236)

Teacher Tech Tools
TeacherWorks™ Plus
Advance Tracker

Student Tech Tools
StudentWorks™ Plus
Math Online macmillanmh.com
eGlossary

---

1 Introduce

Use pattern blocks (or construction-paper shapes). Group students into pairs. Give each pair of students 3 large blue rectangles and 3 small yellow circles.
- Ask students to group the shapes that are alike.
- Have students tell what the color, size, and shape of the pattern blocks are in each of their groups.

2 Teach

Key Concept

Foundational Skills and Concepts Give each student one of these pattern blocks: large red square, small green square, large red triangle, small green triangle.
- Point to a block and ask the class to say together the name of the shape (square or triangle), its size (large or small), and its color (red or green).
- Show that the pattern blocks can be grouped by shape: two squares and two triangles. Show that the pattern blocks can be grouped by size: two large blocks and two small blocks.
- Show that the pattern blocks can be grouped by color: two red blocks and two green blocks.
- Explain that groups of objects can sometimes be sorted in more than one way, in this case objects can be sorted by shape, size, or color.

Using Manipulatives

Pattern Blocks Distribute 2 large red squares, 2 small green squares, 2 large red triangles, and 2 small green triangles from a set of pattern blocks to each pair of students. Ask partners to sort the pattern blocks by shape, color, and size. Let pairs share their sorted pattern blocks and tell why the pattern blocks in each group go together. If pattern blocks are not available, construction paper shapes may also be used.

Intervention Strategy
Kinesthetic Learners

Using Attribute Blocks Display a group of three attribute blocks that represent the beginning of one sorting, such as three small squares of different colors.

Ask students to identify the attributes (size, shape) of the blocks by allowing them to trace the outline of the shapes with their fingers. Then ask students to choose another block that could be added to the sort and to place it beside the existing blocks. In this case, students would choose a small square of any color.

10-1

Name _____

More than One Attribute

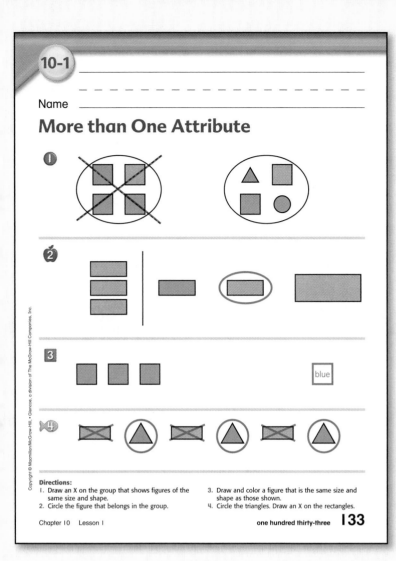

Directions:
1. Draw an X on the group that shows figures of the same size and shape.
2. Circle the figure that belongs in the group.
3. Draw and color a figure that is the same size and shape as those shown.
4. Circle the triangles. Draw an X on the rectangles.

Chapter 10   Lesson 1

one hundred thirty-three **133**

Copyright © Macmillan/McGraw-Hill • Glencoe, a division of The McGraw-Hill Companies, Inc.

③ Practice

Direct students to page 133 of their student workbook. Read the instructions at the bottom of the student page as they complete the exercises.

If students struggle with Exercises 1 and 2, they may not be able to recognize shapes. Be certain to review shapes with struggling students.

④ Assess

See It   Display three large red squares in a group and three red circles in another group. Ask students to explain how the two groups are sorted.

Say It   Say "red circle." Ask students to name the shape that is the same.

Do It   Give each student three small red squares and three large green triangles. Have students sort the objects by size, shape, and color.

Write It   Have students draw their groupings of shapes sorted by size and color.

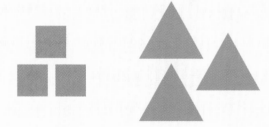

English Learner Strategy

Pattern Block Sort   Review the names of the shapes (circle, square, triangle, rectangle), the color names (red, blue, green, yellow), and the words for sizes (large, small). Have available pattern blocks of the shapes in different colors and sizes. Write the words for shapes, colors, and sizes on large cards or paper. Ask students to sort the pattern blocks under selected cards. Start with two descriptive words, and then gradually add terms according to the student's reading level.

Lesson 10-1 More than One Attribute   **133**

AB Patterns

Lesson Planner

Objective
Identify and create AB patterns.

Vocabulary

AB pattern

pattern

Other Resources

Materials
drawing paper
index cards

Manipulatives
pattern blocks

 **On-Hand Manipulatives**
crayons
pencils

CRM Chapter Resource Masters
Vocabulary and English Language
Development (p. A237)
Skills Practice (p. A238)
Practice at Home (p. A239)

Teacher Tech Tools
⊙ TeacherWorks™ Plus
Advance Tracker

Student Tech Tools
⊙ StudentWorks™ Plus
Math Online ‣ macmillanmh.com
eGlossary

1 Introduce

- Ask students to join you in a rhythmic pattern of clapping hands and patting thighs.
- When students have the rhythm and pattern, have them say, "Clap, pat, clap, pat" as they perform the actions.
- Invite students to suggest other actions, such as hands up, hands down.

2 Teach

Key Concept

Foundational Skills and Concepts
- Draw an AB pattern on the board, using circles and squares.

- Ask students to identify the pattern by reciting the names of the shapes.

Using Manipulatives

Pattern Blocks   Divide the class into small groups. Give each group six pattern blocks, three each of two different shapes (or use crayons and pencils).

Tell groups to make the same kind of pattern as that on the board, using their pattern blocks. Let groups share their patterns and explain them by describing or naming the pattern blocks.

Intervention Strategy   Auditory Learners

Making Sound Patterns   Ask students to close their eyes and to listen. Create a sound pattern (such as clap, stomp, clap, stomp, clap, stomp). Ask students to open their eyes and recreate the pattern. Repeat, using a word pattern (such as cat, mat, cat, mat, cat, mat). Then use a letter pattern (such as ABABAB). Finally ask students to create sound, word, or letter patterns for other students to listen to and identify.

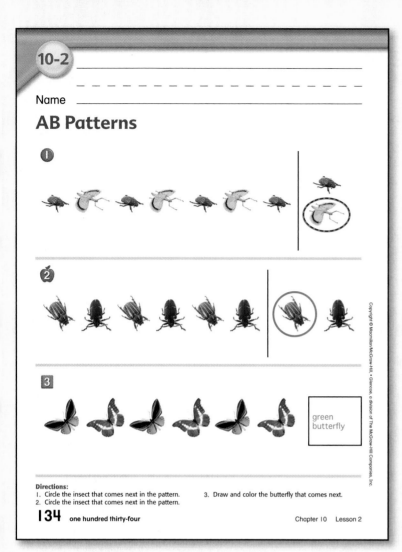

Name _____

AB Patterns

1

2

3

green butterfly

Directions:
1. Circle the insect that comes next in the pattern.
2. Circle the insect that comes next in the pattern.
3. Draw and color the butterfly that comes next.

134 one hundred thirty-four

Chapter 10   Lesson 2

③ Practice

Direct students to page 134 of their student workbook. Read the instructions at the bottom of the student page as they complete the exercises.

If students struggle to identify the patterns of insects in Exercises 1–3, duplicate the pattern with shapes of one color. This will help students focus on one attribute.

④ Assess

See It   Draw an AB pattern with stars and moons on the board. Ask students to explain the pattern you have written.

Say It   Draw a circle and star pattern on the board. Ask students to identify the pattern by naming the objects.

Do It   Create a pattern by holding your arms out and then by crossing your arms. Ask students to repeat the pattern. Have students create and perform a different pattern.

Write It   Distribute drawing paper and crayons. Ask students to create an AB pattern using two shapes of their choosing.

English Learner Strategy

Follow a Pattern   Draw an AB pattern of rectangles and triangles on an index card. Give students pattern blocks of rectangles and triangles and ask them to make the pattern they see on the card. Allow students to use their native language to identify and explain the pattern. Then ask students to say the pattern together in English by naming the figures: rectangle, triangle, rectangle, triangle, rectangle, triangle.

Lesson 10-2 AB Patterns   **134**

AAB Patterns

Lesson Planner

Objective
Identify and create AAB patterns.

Vocabulary

AAB pattern

order

repeat

Other Resources

Materials
chart paper
index cards

Manipulatives
connecting cubes

 On-Hand Manipulatives
paper
pencils

CRM Chapter Resource Masters
Vocabulary and English Language
  Development (p. A240)
Skills Practice (p. A241)
Practice at Home (p. A242)

Teacher Tech Tools
TeacherWorks™ Plus
Advance Tracker

Student Tech Tools
StudentWorks™ Plus
Math Online > macmillanmh.com
eGlossary

Intervention Strategy
Interpersonal Learners

Making AAB Shape Patterns Ask pairs of students to work together to solve a problem. Give each pair an index card on which is drawn the pattern square, square, circle, square, square, circle, square, square, circle. Tell partners to create the same pattern using different shapes. Have partners draw their solution under the shapes already on the card. Partners can share and compare their patterns with other pairs of students.

1 Introduce

Invite six boys and three girls to come to the front of the room.
- Arrange them in a boy, boy, girl pattern.
- Ask students to tell how the boys and girls are arranged.
- Have students take turns saying the pattern: boy, boy, girl.

2 Teach

Key Concept

Foundational Skills and Concepts Tell students they can use letters to make patterns.
- Write AABAABAAB on the board.
- Have students read the letters in the pattern together.
- **How do the letters repeat in the pattern?** AAB
- Let students circle the letter groups in the pattern.
- **What do you notice about the pattern?** Possible answer: A is used twice and then B is used once.
- Pass out index cards or have students use paper.
- Tell students to choose two letters other than A and B and to make a letter pattern like the one on the board.
- Let students share their letter patterns by holding up their cards and reading their letter patterns.

Using Manipulatives

Connecting Cubes Distribute 12 connecting cubes, six in each color, to pairs of students. Ask students to create their own AAB pattern with the cubes.

Let the pairs share their patterns and tell why they are AAB patterns. Discuss with the students why there are three cubes left over.

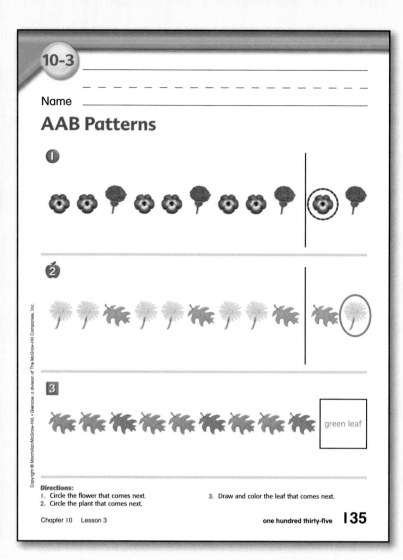

10-3

Name _____

AAB Patterns

1

2

3

green leaf

Directions:
1. Circle the flower that comes next.
2. Circle the plant that comes next.
3. Draw and color the leaf that comes next.

Chapter 10 Lesson 3

one hundred thirty-five **135**

 **Practice**

Direct students to page 135 of their student workbook. Read the directions at the bottom of the student page as they complete the exercises.

Have students circle the pattern unit for each exercise.

Exercise 3 If students have difficulty drawing a leaf, allow them to draw a circle and color it to indicate the pattern.

4 Assess

See It Draw the pattern triangle, triangle, circle, triangle, triangle, circle, triangle, triangle, circle, on the board. Ask students to tell in their own words what the pattern is.

Say It Use CCDCCDCCD. Choose a musical note for each letter. Help students sing the pattern.

Do It Write LL, f, LL, f, LL, and f on separate index cards. Scramble the cards. Invite students to take turns making the AAB pattern.

Write It On chart paper, write the pattern YYZYYZYY___. Ask students to write the next letter.

⚠ Common Error Alert

Exercise 1 Students may incorrectly identify the pattern. Have them study the entire sequence and then identify the pattern unit and circle it.

Exercise 2 Finding objects or images in patterns that do not belong can be confusing. Explain that the incorrect image normally appears only one time, whereas the normal images of the pattern appear over and over.

ABB Patterns

Lesson Planner

Objective
Identify and create ABB patterns.

Vocabulary
ABB pattern

Other Resources

Materials
chart paper

Manipulatives
color tiles
connecting cubes

 **On-Hand Manipulatives**
crayons
markers
pencils

CRM Chapter Resource Masters
Vocabulary and English Language
   Development (p. A243)
Skills Practice (p. A244)
Practice at Home (p. A245)

Teacher Tech Tools
TeacherWorks™ Plus
Advance Tracker

Student Tech Tools
StudentWorks™ Plus

Math Online > macmillanmh.com
eGlossary

① Introduce

Ask students to join you in a rhythmic pattern of clap, stomp, clap, stomp, clap, stomp.
- Tell students to watch and listen as you do a new pattern: clap, stomp, stomp, clap, stomp, stomp.
- Have students join in.
- **How are the two patterns different?**

② Teach

Key Concept

Foundational Skills and Concepts   Write ABBABBABB on the board.
- Have students read the letters in the pattern together.
- **How do the letters repeat?** ABB
- Let a student draw a box around the pattern.
- **What do you notice about the pattern?** Answers vary.
- **What should be written next to add to the pattern?** ABB
- Have another student write ABB and draw a box around it.

Using Manipulatives

Color Tiles   Give each student nine color tiles, three in one color and six in a different color. Ask students to make an ABB pattern like the one on the board, using the color tiles. Let students experiment with the color tiles. Then call on students to share their patterns with the class.

Intervention Strategy   Logical Learners

Using Connecting Cubes   Build a model of an ABBABBBABB pattern using red and green connecting cubes. Give students eight connecting cubes, four each of two different colors. Ask students to use the connecting cubes to create a pattern like yours. Then ask students to explain how they went about making their pattern.

Name _____

ABB Patterns

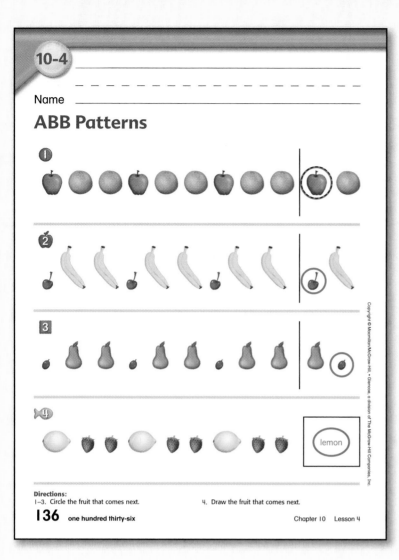

① 🍎 🍎 🍎 🍎 🍎 🍎 🍎 🍎 🍎 | Ⓐ 🍎

② 🍌 🍌 🍌 🍌 🍌 🍌 🍌 🍌 | Ⓐ 🍌

③ 🍐 🍐 🍐 🍐 🍐 🍐 🍐 🍐 | 🍐 Ⓐ

④  🍋 🍓 🍓 🍋 🍓 🍓 🍋 🍓 🍓 | ⬜ lemon

Directions:
1–3. Circle the fruit that comes next.   4. Draw the fruit that comes next.

136 one hundred thirty-six   Chapter 10   Lesson 4

Direct students to page 136 of their student workbook. Read the directions at the bottom of the student page as they complete the exercises.

Have students circle the pattern unit in each exercise.

Exercise 4   If students have difficulty drawing a lemon, allow them to draw a circle and color it to indicate the pattern.

④ Assess

See It   Create this pattern, using classroom objects: pencil, crayon, crayon, pencil, crayon, crayon, pencil, crayon, crayon. Ask students to identify the pattern unit.

Say It   Make funny sounds in a pattern, such as, "crunch, zoom, zoom." Let students recite and extend the pattern.

Do It   Let students suggest two actions that could be used to make an ABB pattern (clapping, jumping, etc.). Perform the pattern together.

Write It   Have students choose two letters other than A and B to use in an ABB pattern. Let students take turns writing their patterns on chart paper.

⚠ Common Error Alert

Finding the Repeating Part   Students may have difficulty understanding the word *pattern* and the concept of an ABB pattern. Use red and green connecting cubes. Connect two red and one green cube to make a pattern unit. Explain that this is the first part of a pattern, something that repeats over and over.

Give each student two red and one green cube and have them connect the cubes to make an ABB pattern unit. Let each student add his or her cubes to yours. Together recite the names of the colors. Then have students disconnect each group of three cubes to help students see the part that repeats.

Progress Check 1

Formative Assessment

Use the Progress Check to assess students' mastery of the previous lessons. Have students review the lesson indicated for the problems they answered incorrectly.

 Common Error Alert

Recognizing Patterns Remind students that there are many different types of patterns. When looking for a pattern, they should look for an arrangement of colors, shapes, or objects that repeat more than once.

Exercises 2–4 If students have difficulty identifying patterns, read the patterns aloud, placing emphasis on your words to create a rhythm that students can associate with the objects in the pattern.

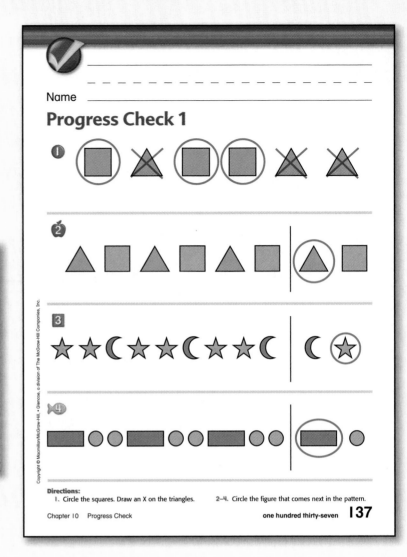

Data-Driven Decision Making

Students missing Exercises . . .	Have trouble with . . .	Should review and practice . . .
1	sorting objects.	**TE** Lesson 10-1, p. 133 **CRM** Skills Practice, p. A235
2	AB patterns.	**TE** Lesson 10-2, p. 134 **CRM** Skills Practice, p. A238
3	AAB patterns.	**TE** Lesson 10-3, p. 135 **CRM** Skills Practice, p. A241
4	ABB patterns.	**TE** Lesson 10-4, p. 136 **CRM** Skills Practice, p. A244

Name _____

Replay

Copyright © Macmillan/McGraw-Hill • Glencoe, a division of The McGraw-Hill Companies, Inc.

Directions:
The squirrel collects vegetables. Draw a line from each row to show which vegetable comes next.

Replay

Use the Replay activity to review and reinforce concepts and skills presented in Lessons 10-1 through 10-4.

Instructions

Read the directions one at a time. Encourage students to circle the pattern unit in each row of vegetables.

Student Technology

Students can use the following technology resources to reinforce chapter content.

💿 StudentWorks™ Plus

Math Online ▷ macmillanmh.com

- eGames
- eGlossary

ABC Patterns

Lesson Planner

Objective
Identify and create ABC patterns.

Vocabulary
ABC pattern

Materials
construction paper, four each of red, blue, and yellow
markers

Manipulatives
attribute buttons
color tiles
string

 On-Hand Manipulatives
beads

Other Resources

CRM Chapter Resource Masters
Vocabulary and English Language Development (p. A246)
Skills Practice (p. A247)
Practice at Home (p. A248)

Teacher Tech Tools
🖸 TeacherWorks™ Plus
Advance Tracker

Student Tech Tools
🖸 StudentWorks™ Plus
Math Online macmillanmh.com
eGlossary

English Learner Strategy

Using Color Tiles Set out three each of red, green, and yellow color tiles. Make an ABC pattern using the tiles. Then ask how students can figure out what comes next in the pattern. Discuss different ways of finding out, such as looking at the pattern, describing the pattern with words, or dividing the pattern into parts. Give students six more color tiles (two each of red, green, and yellow) and have them add to the pattern.

① Introduce

- Post a pattern with red, yellow, and blue sheets of construction paper on the chalk ledge. Use at least three pattern units.
- **What comes next in the pattern?** red
- When red is identified, have a student add a red sheet of construction paper to the pattern.
- Continue in the same way with remaining sheets of construction paper until the next two units of the pattern have been completed.

② Teach

Key Concept

Foundational Skills and Concepts Draw the following pattern on the board: square, circle, triangle, square, circle, triangle, square, circle, triangle.
- Have students read the shapes in the pattern together.
- Explain that the square, circle, and triangle repeat to make a pattern.
- Let a student draw a box around the pattern.
- **What do you notice about the pattern?** Sample answer: Three different figures repeat.
- **What should be drawn next to add to the pattern?** square
- Have another student draw a square, circle, and triangle and draw a box around them.

Using Manipulatives

Attribute Buttons Divide the class into groups. Give each group 12 attribute buttons of the same size—four red, four green, four blue—and a string. Ask students to string the buttons in an ABC pattern like the one on the chalk ledge and on the board. Then ask groups to share their pattern with the class. Have one student in each group show where their pattern begins again, or repeats.

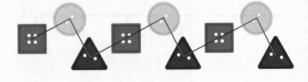

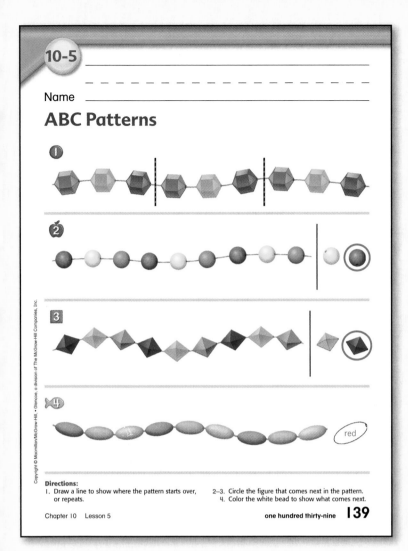

10-5

Name _____

ABC Patterns

①

②

③

④

Directions:

1. Draw a line to show where the pattern starts over, or repeats.

2–3. Circle the figure that comes next in the pattern.

4. Color the white bead to show what comes next.

Chapter 10   Lesson 5

one hundred thirty-nine **139**

③ Practice

Direct students to page 139 of their student workbook. Read the directions at the bottom of the student page as they complete the exercises.

Have students string beads to have real-world examples of the exercises.

④ Assess

See It   Draw the pattern circle-square-triangle four times to make an extended shape pattern. Have students draw vertical lines to separate the pattern units.

Say It   Use the long vowel sounds E, I, and O. Have students say an ABC pattern using these three letters. Allow students to use letter cards if needed.

Do It   Have students nod their head, pat their head, and blink their eyes as they say "Nod, pat, blink" in a repeating chant.

Write It   Ask students to draw an ABC pattern using markers of three different colors. Suggest that they draw simple figures such as circles, squares, or triangles. Have students draw twelve shapes in all.

⚠ **Common Error Alert**

Exercise 4   Students may have trouble continuing the pattern. Have students identify the colors used in the pattern shown in the exercise. Encourage students to say the pattern aloud, while pointing to each bead, to help them identify which color comes next in the pattern.

Identify and Extend Patterns

Lesson Planner

Objective
Identify and extend a variety of patterns.

Vocabulary

down

next

up

Other Resources

Materials
craft sticks

Manipulatives
attribute blocks

On-Hand Manipulatives
cardboard cut-out shapes

CRM Chapter Resource Masters
Vocabulary and English Language
  Development (p. A249)
Skills Practice (p. A250)
Practice at Home (p. A251)

Teacher Tech Tools
TeacherWorks™ Plus
Advance Tracker

Student Tech Tools
StudentWorks™ Plus
Math Online > macmillanmh.com
eGlossary

Intervention Strategy   Visual Learners

Using Craft Sticks   Give each pair of students 15–20 craft
sticks. Demonstrate an AB pattern alternating vertical and
horizontal craft sticks. Have pairs create a pattern of their own.
When each pair has created a pattern, have them share it with
the class and describe the pattern unit.

1 Introduce

- Point out that patterns are everywhere. Take students
  on a pattern hunt in the classroom.
- Students might notice stripes on the American flag,
  floor tiles, and patterns on books, or clothing.
- Ask students to describe the patterns they find.

2 Teach

Key Concept

Foundational Skills and Concepts   Draw an AB
pattern using at least three pattern units with triangles
pointing up and down.
- Explain how the triangles make an AB pattern by
  showing the position of the triangles—points up,
  points down, points up, points down.
- Then draw an AAB pattern using at least three
  pattern units with triangles pointing up and
  pointing down.
- **What comes next in the pattern?** 2 triangles
  pointing up
- Have a student draw a box around the pattern unit
  and another student add a pattern unit.
- Finally, draw an ABC pattern using at least three
  pattern units with triangles pointing up, down, and
  to the side. Have students describe the pattern.

Using Manipulatives

Attribute Blocks   Give each pair of students
12 triangle blocks of different sizes in the same color.
Have one student in each pair start a pattern with one
pattern unit. Tell the other student to copy the pattern.
Have students continue their patterns until the blocks
are used up. Then have the second student start a
different pattern and repeat the activity. Have students
describe their patterns to the class.

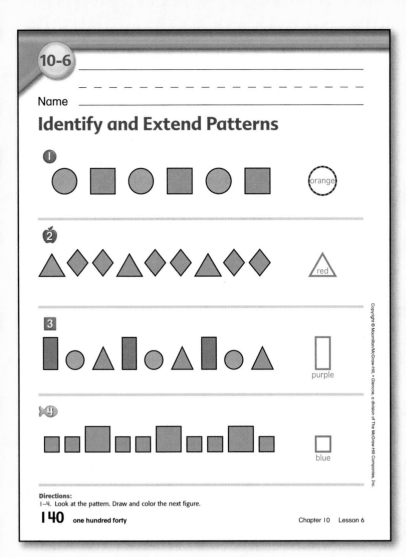

10-6

Name _____

Identify and Extend Patterns

① ⬤ ▢ ⬤ ▢ ⬤ ▢ ◯ orange

② △ ◇ ◇ △ △ ◇ △ ◇ △ red

③ ▮ ⬤ △ ▮ ⬤ △ ▮ ⬤ △ ▯ purple

④ ▪ ▪ ◼ ▪ ▪ ◼ ▪ ▪ ◼ ▪ ▫ blue

Directions:
1–4. Look at the pattern. Draw and color the next figure.

140 one hundred forty

Chapter 10 Lesson 6

Copyright © Macmillan/McGraw-Hill • Glencoe, a division of The McGraw-Hill Companies, Inc.

Direct students to page 140 of their student workbook.

③ Practice

Direct students to page 140 of their student workbook. Read the directions at the bottom of the student page as they complete the exercises.

Before students draw and color the next two shapes, ask them to circle the shapes that repeat.

④ Assess

See It   Use purple, green, and yellow connecting cubes. Make an ABC pattern using at least three pattern units. Ask students to describe the pattern and to add to it using additional cubes.

Say It   Ask students to listen to this pattern: stop, go, go, stop, go, go, stop, go, go. Have students say together what would come next.

Do It   Sing and act out "The Hokey Pokey." Ask which actions are repeated.

Write It   Write XYZ on three index cards. Tell students to extend the pattern by writing the pattern on a blank index card.

Math Coach Notes

- Remind students that many things have patterns. Have students check their clothing to see if anything they are wearing has a pattern.
- Tell students that patterns can be made in many ways, such as with shapes, with objects, with words, with sounds, and with actions. Invite students to suggest a word pattern (dog, dog, cat, dog, dog, cat) or an action pattern (hop, clap, stomp, hop, clap, stomp, hop, clap, stomp).
- Point out that patterns can be extended or added to. Invite students to add to the word pattern or the action pattern they suggested earlier.

Create Patterns

Lesson Planner

Objective
Create a variety of patterns independently.

Vocabulary
growing pattern

sequential pattern

Other Resources

Materials
chart paper
erasers
markers
paper clips

Manipulatives
color tiles
connecting cubes
pattern blocks

 **On-Hand Manipulatives**
crayons
drawing paper
pencils

CRM Chapter Resource Masters
Vocabulary and English Language Development (p. A252)
Skills Practice (p. A253)
Practice at Home (p. A254)

Teacher Tech Tools
TeacherWorks™ Plus
Advance Tracker

Student Tech Tools
StudentWorks™ Plus
Math Online macmillanmh.com
eGlossary

1 Introduce

- Have six students stand in front of the class.
- **What could we have these students do to create a pattern?**
- Students might suggest having two people face the class, two turn around, and two sit for an ABC pattern.
- Recite the pattern together: For example, face, turn, sit, face, turn, sit, face, turn, sit.

2 Teach

Key Concept

Foundational Skills and Concepts   On the board, draw the AB pattern using shapes.
- Circle the parts that repeat.
- Explain how the shapes make patterns.
- Give 12 connecting cubes, six in each of two colors, to each pair of students.
- Have the student pairs create their own pattern.
- Repeat using the AAB, ABB, and ABC patterns one at a time.

Using Manipulatives

Variety of Manipulatives   Form groups or pairs. Tell each group or pair to make a pattern. Give one group or pair pattern blocks, one group or pair connecting cubes, and one group or pair color tiles. Have them share their patterns with the class. Then give groups or pairs drawing paper and markers. Have groups or pairs create a pattern using letters, a number pattern, or an action pattern. Let each group or pair share their pattern.

Intervention Strategy
Intrapersonal Learners

Making Sound Patterns   Ask students to work in pairs. Have one partner clap and tap out a repeated pattern for the other partner to imitate. Then ask them to clap and tap the pattern together. Finally, have partners switch roles and repeat the activity.

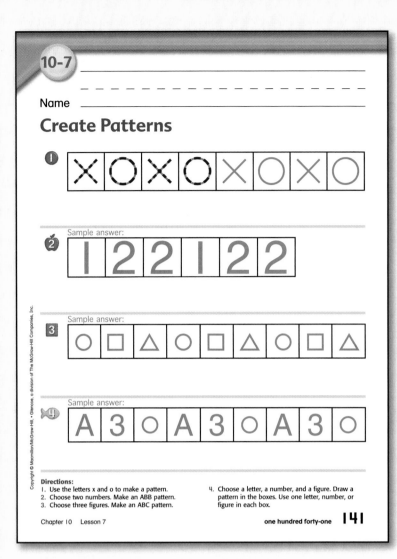

Create Patterns

1

| X | O | X | O | X | O | X | O |

2 Sample answer:

| 1 | 2 | 2 | 1 | 2 | 2 |

3 Sample answer:

| ○ | □ | △ | ○ | □ | △ | ○ | □ | △ |

4 Sample answer:

| A | 3 | ○ | A | 3 | ○ | A | 3 | ○ |

Directions:
1. Use the letters x and o to make a pattern.
2. Choose two numbers. Make an ABB pattern.
3. Choose three figures. Make an ABC pattern.
4. Choose a letter, a number, and a figure. Draw a pattern in the boxes. Use one letter, number, or figure in each box.

Chapter 10 Lesson 7

one hundred forty-one **141**

3 Practice

Direct students to page 141 of their student workbook. Read the directions at the bottom of the student page as they complete the exercises.

All answers on this page may vary. Sample answers are provided. You may allow students to use manipulatives, such as counters or connecting cubes, to complete this page.

Remind students that they can use an AB, AAB, or ABC pattern in exercise 4. If students struggle with a pattern, encourage them to try using figures or drawings of simple objects that they prefer.

4 Assess

See It Ask several students to create letter patterns on the board. Have other students circle the parts that repeat.

Say It Ask students to choose two words from the class word wall or use *repeat* and *pattern.* Have students create oral patterns using the two words.

Do It Have students use pencils, crayons, markers, paper clips, or erasers to create a pattern. Have students explain the pattern.

Write It Ask students to write a letter or number pattern on chart paper. Have students explain the pattern.

English Learner Strategy

Physical Patterns Help students create an action pattern such as sit, stand, jump, sit, stand, jump, sit, stand, jump. Have students say the actions in their native language as they model what the words mean. Then have students say the words in English as the entire class performs the actions.

Math Coach Notes

The patterns covered in this chapter have all been *sequential* patterns, that is, patterns that repeat the same unit. The patterns mostly have involved actions, shapes, and letters. Other common patterns involve numbers. *Growing* patterns involve units that continually increase in some way, such as ABAABBAAABBB. Students will encounter this type of pattern in future mathematics study.

Progress Check 2

Formative Assessment

Use the Progress Check to assess students' mastery of the previous lessons. Have students review the lesson indicated for the problems they answered incorrectly.

For Exercise 4, answers may vary. A sample answer is provided.

 Common Error Alert

Exercise 3 Once students have identified the repeating part of a pattern, have them circle it. They can look at only the circled part of the pattern when they extend the pattern.

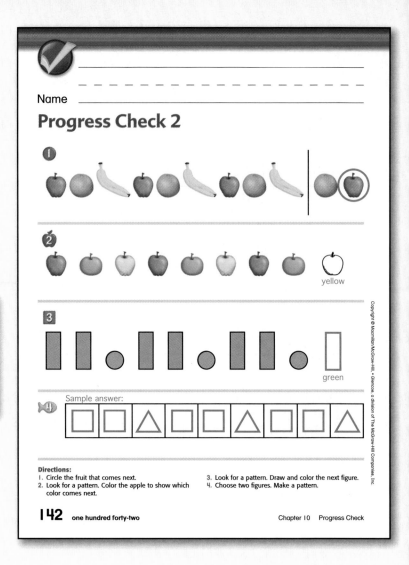

Directions:
1. Circle the fruit that comes next.
2. Look for a pattern. Color the apple to show which color comes next.
3. Look for a pattern. Draw and color the next figure.
4. Choose two figures. Make a pattern.

142 one hundred forty-two

Chapter 10 Progress Check

Data-Driven Decision Making

Students missing Exercises . . .	Have trouble with . . .	Should review and practice . . .
1–2	ABC patterns.	TE Lesson 10-5, p. 139 CRM Skills Practice, p. A247
3	identifying and extending patterns.	TE Lesson 10-6, p. 140 CRM Skills Practice, p. A250
4	creating patterns.	TE Lesson 10-7, p. 141 CRM Skills Practice, p. A253

Intervention Strategies

Visual/Tactile Explorations

Materials: pattern blocks

Step 1 **Small Groups** Give each group eight pattern blocks that include sets of three types of pattern blocks: square, circle, and triangle.

Step 2 Ask students to arrange the pattern blocks in an AB pattern. After they have finished, review the pattern to make sure students have correctly arranged the shapes.

Step 3 Ask students to arrange the pattern blocks in an AAB pattern. After they have finished, review the pattern to make sure students have correctly arranged the shapes.

Step 4 Ask students to arrange the pattern blocks in an ABB pattern. After they have finished, review the pattern to make sure students have correctly arranged the shapes.

Step 5 Ask students to arrange the pattern blocks in an ABC pattern. After they have finished, review the pattern to make sure students have correctly arranged the shapes.

Teaching Strategies

Depending upon the amount of difficulty students are having with the patterns, you may begin each of the proposed patterns and then have them extend them based upon your design. You may choose to complete one step of this strategy per day, or on one day to review for the Chapter Test.

Vocabulary Presentations

Materials: markers, paper, pencils

Step 1 **Small Groups** Organize students into groups if necessary. Write the following vocabulary list on the board.

AAB pattern	different	pattern
AB pattern	down	repeat
ABB pattern	growing pattern	sequential pattern
ABC pattern	next	sort
alike	order	up

Step 2 Assign each group two or three terms from the list.

Step 3 Instruct groups to prepare some examples that illustrate their terms. Encourage students to do whatever they like to show the words. Suggest that they can use objects in the room to "show-and-tell." Or they can draw examples on the board or on paper, or act out a little play (pretend).

Step 4 Have groups present their examples to the class and explain how their terms describe them.

Time Management

Use this activity either before or after the chapter. Modify it by assigning terms to individual students and having them present the words as definitions or examples.

Review

Vocabulary

Before beginning the exercises, review vocabulary introduced in the chapter. Refer to the page numbers to revisit vocabulary activities in the lessons.

AAB pattern (p. 135A)

AB pattern (p. 134A)

ABB pattern (p. 136A)

ABC pattern (p. 139A)

alike (p. 133A)

different (p. 133A)

down (p. 140A)

growing pattern (p. 141A)

next (p. 140A)

order (p. 135A)

pattern (p. 134A)

repeat (p. 135A)

sequential pattern (p. 141A)

sort (p. 133A)

up (p. 140A)

Vocabulary Review Strategies

Write *sort* and *pattern* on the board. Display some pattern blocks. Ask students to describe their size, shape, and color. Have students sort the pattern blocks. Next, write *ABC pattern, pattern,* and *repeat* on the board. Use connecting cubes to create a pattern. Ask students to use one or more of the words to describe the pattern. Let students form other patterns, extend them, and use other vocabulary words to describe them.

Concepts

The exercises in this section are grouped to cover content from each lesson in the chapter.

Exercise 1: Lesson 10-2 (p. 134)
Exercise 2: Lesson 10-3 (p. 135)
Exercise 3: Lesson 10-4 (p. 136)
Exercise 4: Lesson 10-5 (p. 139)

CRM Find Extra Practice for these concepts in the Practice Worksheets, pages A234–A254.

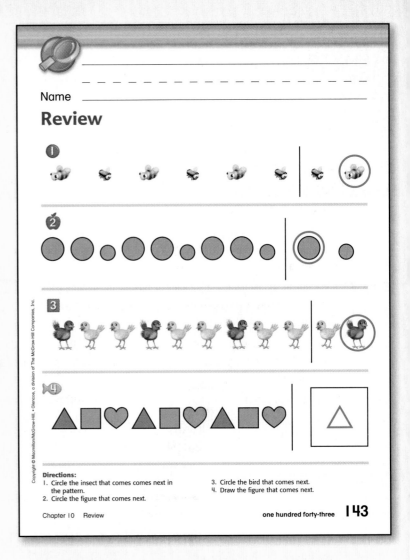

Name

Review

Directions:
1. Circle the insect that comes comes next in the pattern.
2. Circle the figure that comes next.
3. Circle the bird that comes next.
4. Draw the figure that comes next.

Chapter 10   Review

one hundred forty-three **143**

 **Dinah Zike's Foldables**

Have students use the Foldable they created at the beginning of the chapter to review and reinforce the concepts and skills they learned during the chapter. (See Chapter Resource Masters p. A231 for instructions.)

Intervention Strategy — Auditory Learners

Rhythm Patterns   One alternative method to help students is to ask them to quietly name the animals in the pattern to help them hear the pattern and the rhythm of the pattern. Students could also use a horizontal line to mark where they hear one pattern end and a new one begin.

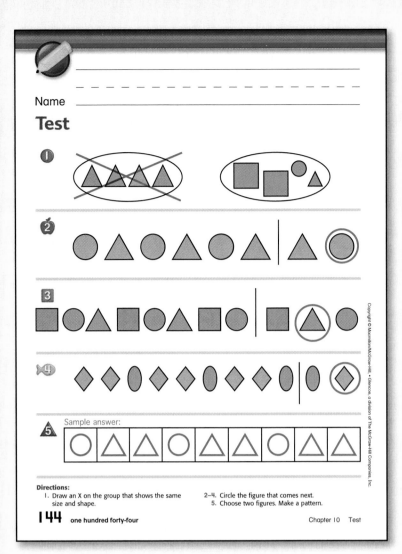

Name _____

Test

①

②

③

④

⑤ Sample answer:

Directions:
1. Draw an X on the group that shows the same size and shape.

2–4. Circle the figure that comes next.
5. Choose two figures. Make a pattern.

Test

Chapter Resource Masters

Additional forms of the Chapter 10 Tests are available.

Test Format	Where to Find it
Chapter 10 Test	**Math Online**  macmillanmh.com
Blackline Masters	Assessment Masters, pp. 114–115

Alternative Assessment

If students have difficulty identifying a pattern, use connecting cubes. Give students sets of connecting cubes of two or three colors. Create a pattern using some connecting cubes and have students create the same pattern. Together, separate the connecting cubes into pattern units so that students can see the parts that repeat.

ExamView®
Assessment Suite

Customize and create multiple versions of the chapter tests and their answer keys. All of these questions from the chapter tests are available on ExamView® Assessment Suite.

This online assessment tool allows teachers to track student progress with easily accessible, comprehensive reports available for every student. Assess students using any internet-ready computer.

Data-Driven Decision Making

Students missing Exercises . . .	Have trouble with . . .	Should review and practice . . .
1	sorting objects by more than one attribute.	**TE** Lesson 10-1, p. 133 **CRM** Skills Practice, p. A235
2	identifying the AB pattern.	**TE** Lesson 10-2, p. 134 **CRM** Skills Practice, p. A238
3	identifying the ABC pattern and extending patterns.	**TE** Lessons 10-5, 10-6, pp. 139, 140 **CRM** Skills Practice, pp. A247, A250
4	identifying the AAB pattern.	**TE** Lesson 10-3, p. 135 **CRM** Skills Practice, p. A241
5	creating patterns.	**TE** Lesson 10-7, p. 141 **CRM** Skills Practice, p. A253

Red type denotes items only in the Teacher's Wraparound Edition.

Image Credits

Chapter Resource Masters

Chapter Resource Masters

Foldables Study Organizer

Dinah Zike's Foldables

Create an Accordion Book Foldable to represent whole numbers 1-10.

① Fold eight pieces of paper into hamburgers. Fold one side $\frac{1}{2}$-inch shorter than the other side.

② Fold this tab forward over the shorter side, and then fold it back away from the shorter piece of paper.

③ Glue together to form an accordion by gluing a straight edge of one section into the valley of another section.

④ Write the numbers 1-10 on the top left side of each of the two sections.

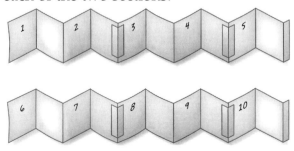

TAKING NOTES

As you read the chapter together, have students place pictures on the appropriate sections of their Foldable to illustrate each of the numbers. Students can use magazines, catalogs, or advertisements to find pictures.

USING THE FOLDABLE

As students review, have students use their Foldable to practice counting forward and backward.

USING THE FOLDABLE

In pairs, have students quiz each other by counting forward and backward. Students will take turns using their Foldable to count forward and backward. Have students check each other's answers and give the correct answer if needed.

Games and Puzzles
Set Stampede

GET READY

- Place students in pairs or small groups.
- Give each student a copy of the **Set Stampede** game board and the **Set Stampede** animal cards.
- Have students cut out their animal cards and place them in a pile or a zip-top bag.

DIRECTIONS:

- Students roll the number cube to determine the first player. The player with the lowest number has the first turn.
- The first player rolls the number cube. The player states the number and removes the corresponding number of animals from his or her pile and places them in the corral. The first player's turn is over.
- Play continues until the first player has all of the animals in the corral. The player must roll an exact number to put in the last animals. If the player has three animals and rolls a 4, the player does not put in any animals, and play passes to the next player.

VARIATION

Follow the same directions, but alter the number cube to include the number *zero*.

What You Need

- Set Stampede game board, per student
- Set Stampede animal cards, per student
- number cube
- scissors

Number of Players
2–4

Math Triumphs

Game Board
Set Stampede

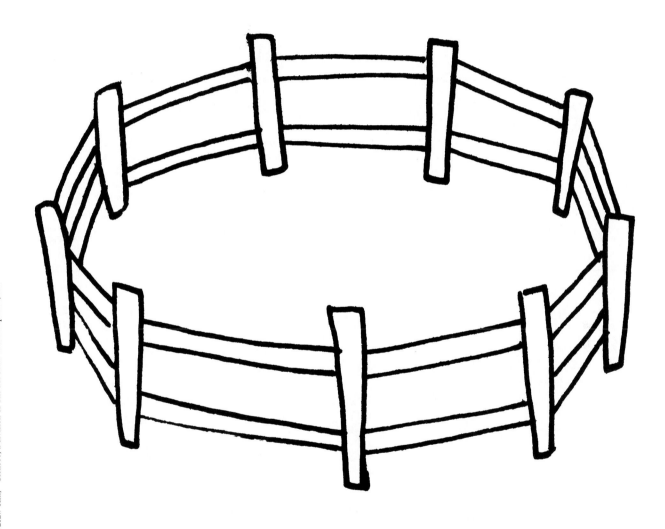

Animal Cards
Set Stampede

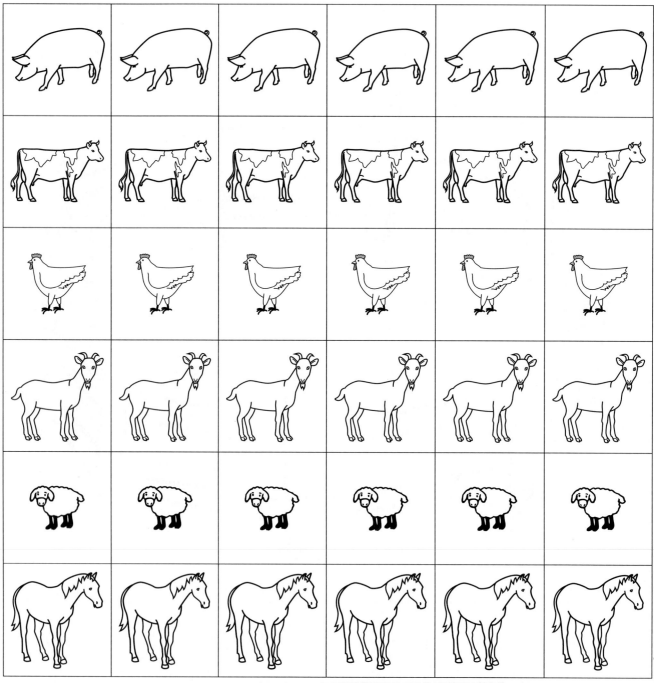

Name _____

Vocabulary and English Language Development

①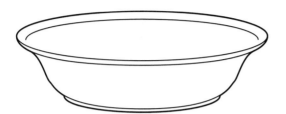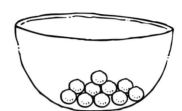

②

③

ACTIVITY Gather a plate, bowl, placemat, and five crackers. Show the plate without crackers on it, and ask students: "How many crackers are on the plate?" (zero) Help students in understand that *zero* means *none*. Then have students put a cracker on the plate. Now ask: "How many crackers are on the plate?" (one) Repeat with the bowl and the placemat, emphasizing the word, *zero*.

WORKSHEET DIRECTIONS Circle the picture that shows *zero*.

Name

Skills Practice

 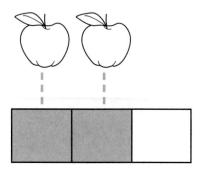

Directions:

1–2. Count the objects. Draw a line from each object to one box. Color the boxes to show how many.

3. Draw Xs on 2 pineapples.
4. Draw Xs on 5 pears.

Math Triumphs

Lesson 1-1

Name

Practice at Home

1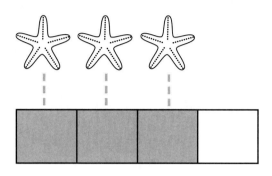

2
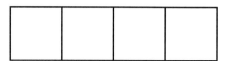

3

4

Directions:

1–2. Count the objects. Draw a line from each object to one box. Color the boxes to show how many.

3. Draw an X on 1 octopus.

4. Draw Xs on 4 fish.

Math Triumphs

Name _____

Vocabulary and English Language Development

7

10

6

9

8

ACTIVITY Write the numbers *6, 7, 8, 9,* and *10* on separate sheets of blank paper. Tape the paper to the floor. Give students directions such as: "Hop on the number eight; skip to the number six; sit on the number nine."

WORKSHEET DIRECTIONS
1. Circle the number 7.
2. Draw an X on the number 10.
3. Underline the number 6.

4. Draw a square around number 9.
5. Trace the number 8.

Math Triumphs

Name

Skills Practice

Directions:
1. Circle 10 hearts.
2. Draw Xs on 6 stars.
3. Draw Xs on 7 diamonds.

Math Triumphs

Name _____

Practice at Home

1
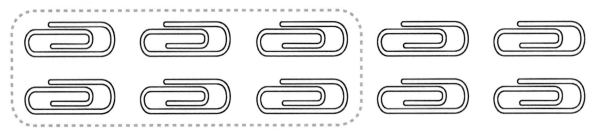

2
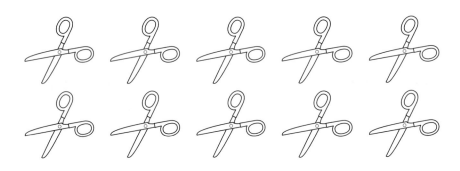

3
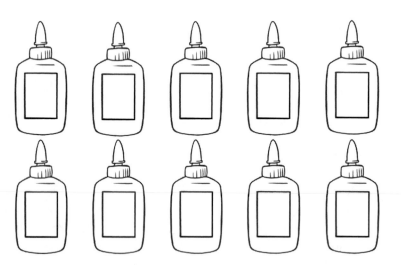

Directions:
1. Circle 6 paper clips.
2. Draw Xs on 10 pairs of scissors.
3. Draw Xs on 9 glue bottles.

Math Triumphs

Name _____

Vocabulary and English Language Development

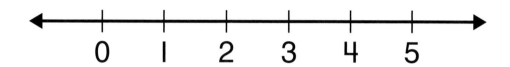

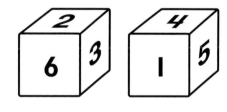

ACTIVITY Write the numbers *1–10* on index cards. Cut a length of yarn or string 40 inches long. Lay the string in a line. Have students arrange the numbers from 1–10 on the string to create a number line. Explain to students how a **number line** is used, and have them use it to count forward to 10.

WORKSHEET DIRECTIONS Circle the number line. Trace the line with your finger. Touch the number 1.

Name _____

Skills Practice

1

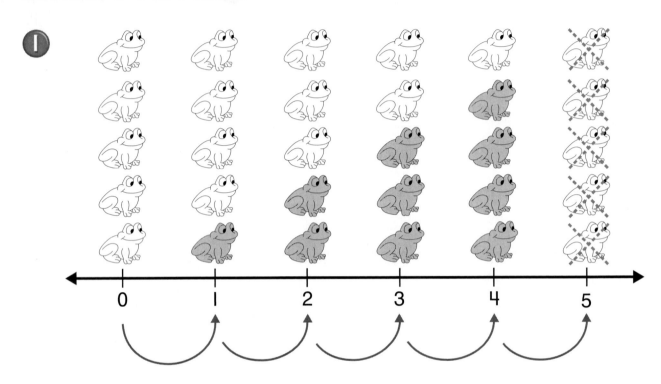

2

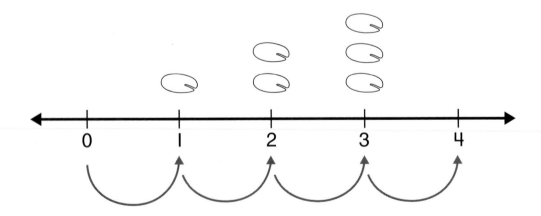

Directions:
1. Count forward to find the group of 5 shaded frogs. Draw Xs on the group of 5.
2. Draw the number of lily pads that comes next.

Name _____

Practice at Home

1

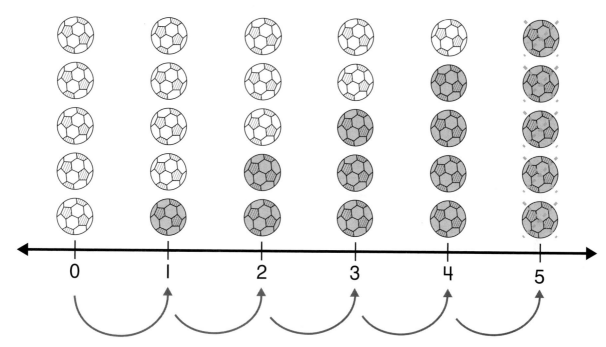

2

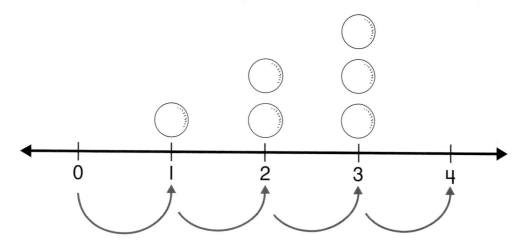

Directions:
1. Count forward to find the group of 5 soccer balls. Draw Xs on the group of 5.
2. Draw the number of balls that comes next.

Math Triumphs

Name _____

Vocabulary and English Language Development

1

2

3

ACTIVITY Have students follow oral directions, using the vocabulary words, **forward** and **backward.** For example, say: "Jump forward three hops," or "Walk backward two steps."

WORKSHEET DIRECTIONS
1. Help the frog hop forward 2 hops. Make lines to show where the frog hops.
2. Help the frog hop forward 3 hops. Make lines to show where the frog hops.
3. Help the frog hop backward 3 hops. Make lines to show where the frog hops.

Name

Skills Practice

1

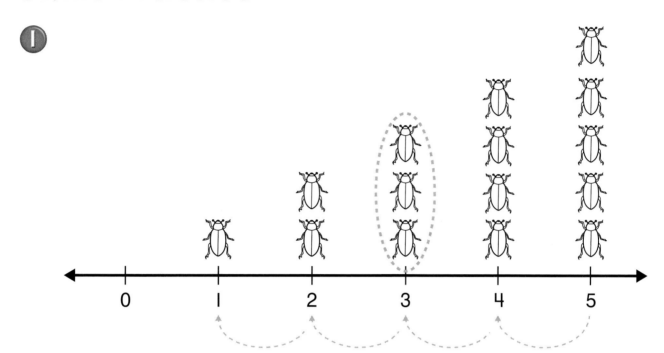

2

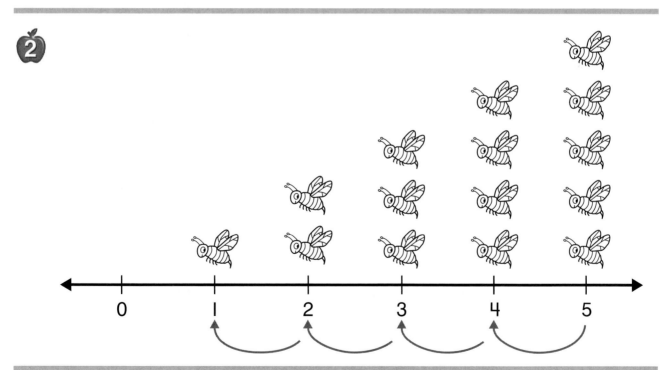

Directions:
1. Start at 5 and count backward. Circle the group of 3.
2. Start at 5 and count backward. Draw Xs on the group of 2.

Math Triumphs

Name

Practice at Home

1

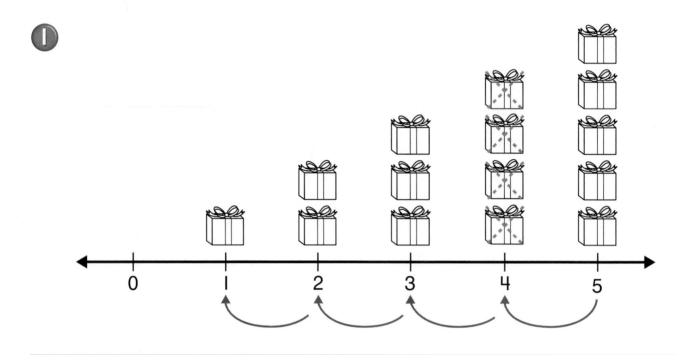

2

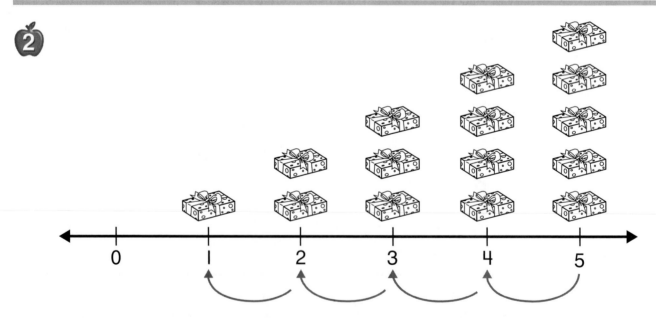

Directions:
1. Start at 5 and count backward. Draw Xs on the group of 4.
2. Start at 5 and count backward. Circle the group of 2.

Math Triumphs

Name _____

Vocabulary and English Language Development

ACTIVITY Write the numbers: *1* and *0* on index cards. Ask students questions such as: "How many elephants are in the kitchen?" (**zero**) and "How many noses do you have?" (**one**) Have the student hold up the answer card and say the number aloud.

WORKSHEET DIRECTIONS Look at the pictures of different containers. Circle the containers that hold *zero*. Draw an X on the containers that hold *one*.

Name _____

Skills Practice

1

2

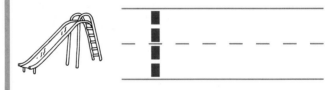

3

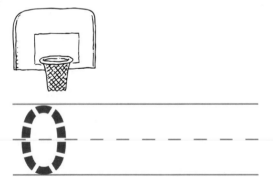

4

Directions:

Here are some things you might see at a park.

1. How many sandboxes are there? Trace the number. Then write the number two times.

2. How many slides are there? Trace the number. Then write the number two times.

3. How many basketball hoops are there? Trace the number. Then write the number three times.

4. How many swings are there? Trace the number. Then write the number three times.

Math Triumphs

Name

Practice at Home

  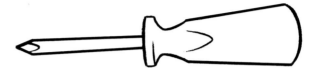

①

②

 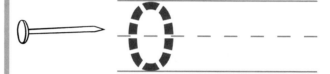

③

④

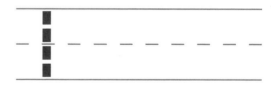

Directions:
Here are some things you might find in a garage.

1. How many screws are there? Trace the number. Then write the number two times.

2. How many nails are there? Trace the number. Then write the number two times.

3. How many hoes are there? Trace the number. Then write the number three times.

4. How many hammers are there? Trace the number. Then write the number three times.

Name _____

Vocabulary and English Language Development

2

3

ACTIVITY Make multiple sets of index cards with either *2* or *3* written on them. Have students go on a scavenger hunt looking for items in pairs (e.g., **two** shoes) and groups of **three** (e.g., three pillows on a couch). Have students match and then tape the cards to pairs or groups of three. Allow students to take turns showing their items to the class.

WORKSHEET DIRECTIONS Read the number. Look for a picture of something you find in your house that matches the number. Tape the picture in the box.

Name

Skills Practice

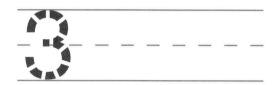

Directions:

1. Color three muffins. Trace the number 3. Write it three times.
2. Draw two rectangles. Trace the number 2. Write it three times.
3. Count the juice boxes. Trace the number 3. Write it three times.

Name _____

Practice at Home

   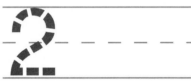

3

Directions:

1. Color three bananas. Trace the number 3. Write it three times.
2. Color two watermelon slices. Trace the number 2. Write it three times.
3. Draw two cherries. Trace the number 2. Write it three times.

Name _____

Vocabulary and English Language Development

ACTIVITY Ask students: "Have you played with a group of friends on the playground? Have you joined a group or club? Have you ever seen a group of birds?" Explain that a **group** is more than two things that are together. Have students identify groups of objects in the classroom (e.g., a group of pencils).

WORKSHEET DIRECTIONS Circle the objects that are in groups.

Name _____

Skills Practice

Directions:
1. Count the dogs. Trace the number 5. Write it three times.
2. Draw 4 dog balls. Trace the number 4. Write it three times.
3. Circle the group of 4. Trace the number 4. Write it three times.

Name

Practice at Home

1

2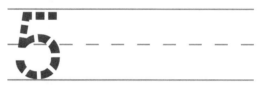

3

Directions:
1. Count the dinosaurs. Trace the number 5. Write it three more times.
2. Circle the group of 5. Trace the number 5. Write it three more times.
3. Circle the group of 4. Trace the number 4. Write it three more times.

Name _____

Vocabulary and English Language Development

①

②

③

④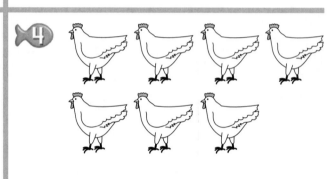

⑤

⑥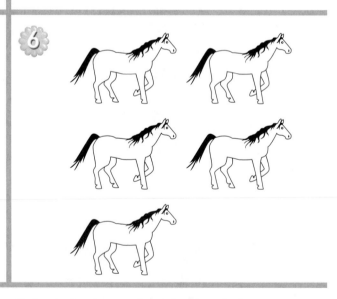

ACTIVITY Cut a piece of string or yarn to make a large circle. Gather some play animals. Ask: "Have you ever seen animals in a pen or corral?" Use the string to make a ring around some animals. Explain that the animals are a **set**. Ask: "How many pigs (for example) are in the set?" Repeat with other animals, emphasizing the term *set*.

WORKSHEET DIRECTIONS Draw a circle around each group of animals to make a set.

Lesson 1-8

Name _____

Skills Practice

1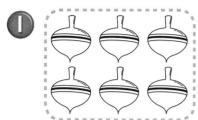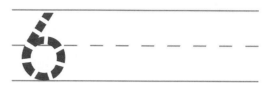

2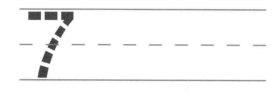

3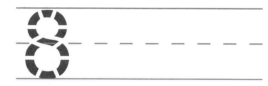

4

5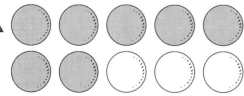

Directions:

1. Circle the group of 6. Trace the number 6. Write it three times.

2. Draw Xs on 7 balloons. Trace the number 7. Write it three times.

3. Color 8 marbles. Trace the number 8. Write it three times.

4. Color 9 teddy bears. Trace the number 9. Write it three times.

5. Color 3 more balls to make 10. Trace the number 10. Write it 3 times.

Math Triumphs

Lesson 1-8   A27

Name _____

Practice at Home

1

2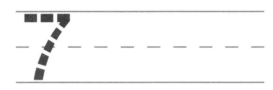

3

 4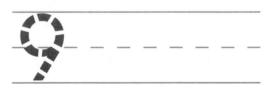

5

Directions:

1. Color 6 helmets. Trace the number 6. Write it three times.
2. Color 7 skateboards. Trace the number 7. Write it three times.
3. Circle the group of 8. Trace the number 8. Write it three times.
4. Draw 9 soccer balls. Trace the number 9. Write it three times.
5. Color 4 more basket balls to make 10. Trace the number 10. Write it 3 times.

Math Triumphs

Foldables Study Organizer

Study Organizer

Dinah Zike's Foldables

Create four Pocket Foldables for Representing Whole Numbers.

1 Fold an $8\frac{1}{2}'' \times 11''$ sheet of paper in half like a hamburger.

2 Open the folded paper and fold one of the long sides up two inches to form a pocket. Refold along the hamburger fold so that the newly formed pockets are on the inside.

3 Glue the outer edges of the two-inch fold with a small amount of glue.

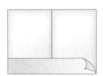

4 Make four sets of Pocket Foldables (enough for each lesson). Glue pockets together to form a Pocket Book.

 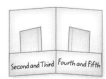

TAKING NOTES

As you read the chapter together, record the lesson titles on the pockets, and have students find pictures of objects that can be glued or taped onto their index cards in a group(s).

 USING THE FOLDABLE

As students review, have them check their understanding by using manipulatives to model the group(s) on each index card. Have students identify the number the model represents, then use the model to complete the exercise.

USING THE FOLDABLE

In pairs, have students take turns using their foldable to represent whole numbers by identifying the picture that corresponds with the title on the pocket.

Games and Puzzles
Under the Big Top

GET READY

- Arrange the students in pairs.
- Give each pair a copy of the **Under the Big Top** game board and a set of **Under the Big Top** animal cards (in a paper bag).

DIRECTIONS:

- Students take turns drawing an animal card out of the bag.
- The first animal should be placed on the 1. The student should say, "first."
- The second animal is placed on the 2. The student should say, "second."
- Students take turns drawing until they have drawn their fourth animal card.
- Play continues until three matching animal cards are placed in a row.
- The first player to get three matching animals cards in a row wins.

VARIATION

Instead of the four numbered game board spaces, have the students place their animal cards on three blank index cards. The students say "first, next, and last" as they place the animal cards on the index cards. The goal is to get two matching animal cards in a row.

What You Need
- Under the Big Top game board
- Under the Big Top animal cards
- small paper bag

Number of Players
2

Game Board
Under the Big Top

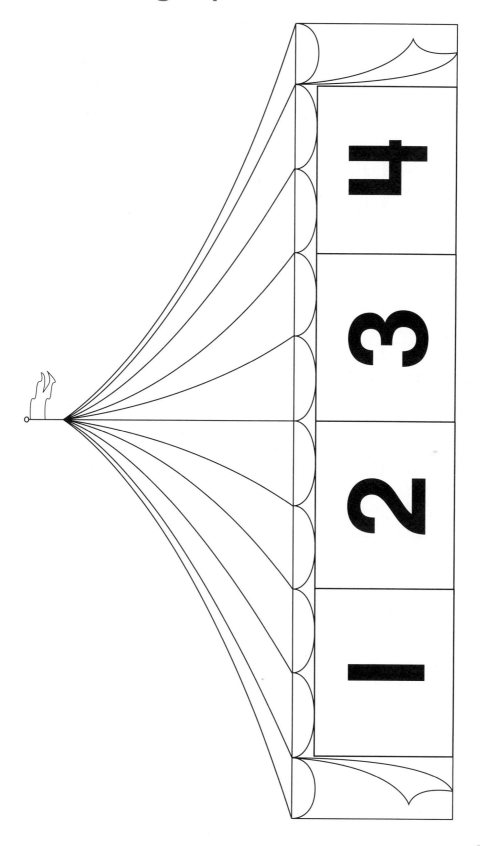

Chapter 2

Animal Cards

Under the Big Top

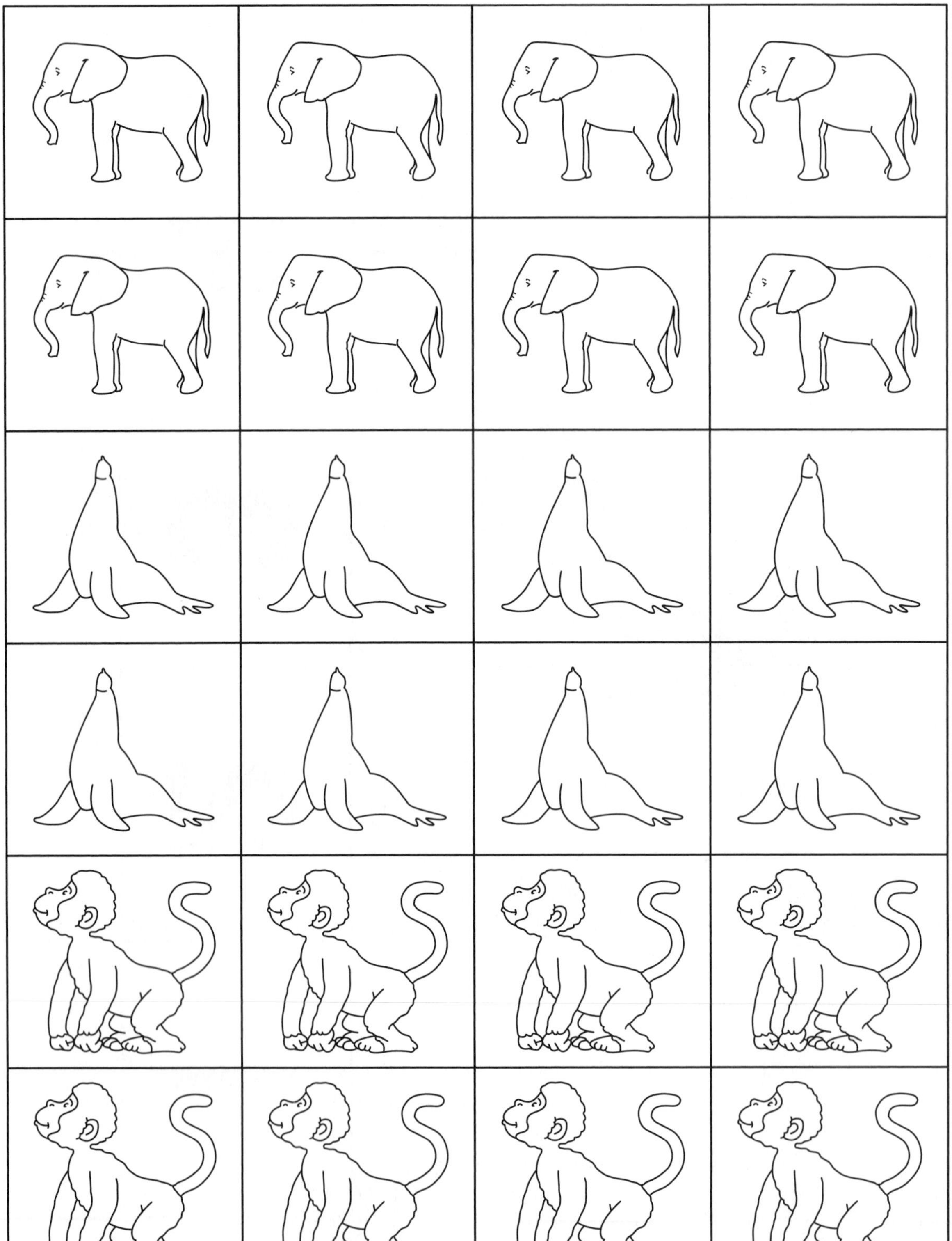

Name _____

Vocabulary and English Language Development

1

2

ACTIVITY Talk about a student's day, emphasizing the words *before* and *after*. For example, ask: "What do you do **after** you get up? What do you do **before** you go to bed?" Help students cut out a magazine picture of a child doing an activity (e.g., putting on shoes, picking up toys, sleeping). Have students share their pictures, and ask them: "What do you think happened before this? What do you think happened after this?"

WORKSHEET DIRECTIONS
1. Look at the boy sleeping. Circle the picture that shows what happened before he went to sleep.
2. Look at the girl washing her hands. Circle the picture that shows what will happen after she washes her hands.

Math Triumphs

Name _____

Skills Practice

①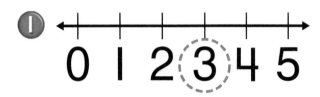

②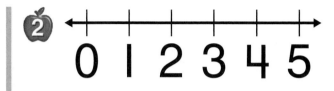

3

1 _____ 3

 4

2 3 _____

Directions:

1. Circle the number that comes just after 2.
2. Circle the number that comes just before 5.
3. Write the number that comes just before 3.
4. Write the number that comes just after 3.

Math Triumphs

Name _____

Practice at Home

①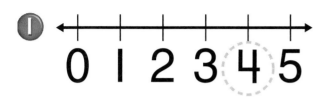

②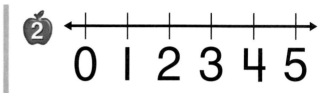

3

            1

   **2**

_ _ _ _ _

④

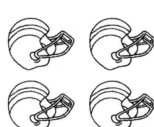

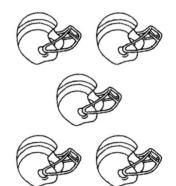

3   **4**

_ _ _ _ _

Directions:
1. Circle the number that comes just before 5.
2. Circle the number that comes just after 1.
3. Write the number that comes just before 1.
4. Write the number that comes just after 4.

Name

Vocabulary and English Language Development

①

②

ACTIVITY Place a shirt, a sweater, and a jacket in a row on a flat surface, such as a table or desk. Have students look at the three items. Ask: "Which will you wear **first**? Which will you wear **next**? Which will you wear **last**?" Discuss with students other activities that are done in order, such as waking up (first); brushing teeth (next); and eating breakfast (last).

WORKSHEET DIRECTIONS
1. Color the picture that shows what the boy does first. Circle the picture that shows what the boy does last.
2. Color the picture that shows what the girl does first. Circle the picture that shows what the girl does last.

Name

Skills Practice

   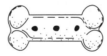 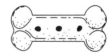

 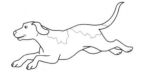  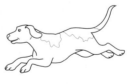 

1   2   3

Directions:
1. Circle the dog that is last in line.
2. Circle the dog that is first in line.

3. Find the first dog biscuit that will go into the jar. Then, circle the next dog biscuit that will go into the jar.
4. Write the number that comes next.

Math Triumphs   **Lesson 2-2   A37**

_____

– – – – – – – – – – – – – – – –

Name _____

Practice at Home

   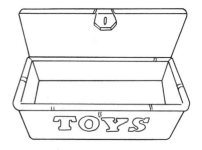

1   2   – – – –

Directions:
1. Circle the last train car that the engine is pulling.
2. Circle the first top that will go into the toy box.
3. Circle the last teddy bear that will go into the toy box.
4. Write the number that comes next.

Name _____

Vocabulary and English Language Development

ACTIVITY Place a container of pencils on a desk. Have three volunteers stand in line facing the container. Ask the first student in line to get a pencil from the container. Then ask the second student, followed by the third student. Have students form the line again. Ask: "Who was the **first** student to get the pencil?" (Students should say the name of the first student in line.) Repeat the question for the **second** student and **third** student. Reinforce *first, second,* and *third* throughout the day.

WORKSHEET DIRECTIONS
1. Circle the second bee that will go into the beehive.
2. Draw an X on the first bee that will go into the beehive.
3. Color the third bee that will go into the beehive.

Name _____

Skills Practice

1

 2

3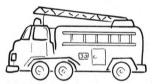

 4

Directions:
1. Circle the third car that will pass through the traffic light.
2. Circle the second bus that will pass through the traffic light.
3. Circle the third fire truck that will pass through the traffic light.
4. Circle the first car that will pass through the traffic light.

Math Triumphs

Name

Practice at Home

 1

 2

 3

 4

Directions:

1. Circle the second clown who will enter the circus tent.
2. Circle the first elephant that will enter the circus tent.

3. Circle the third seal that will enter the circus tent.
4. Circle the third monkey that will enter the circus tent.

Math Triumphs

Name _____

Vocabulary and English Language Development

ACTIVITY Review *first, second,* and *third* with students by having three students form a line facing one direction. Have them repeat after you, stating who is first, who is second, and who is third. Have another two students join the line. Explain that the student after the third is **fourth** and the student after the fourth is **fifth.** Help them say aloud the position of each student, using the words *first, second, third, fourth,* and *fifth.* Emphasize *fourth* and *fifth.*

WORKSHEET DIRECTIONS
1. Circle the third frog that will jump on the lily pad.
2. Draw an X on the fifth frog that will jump on the lily pad.
3. Color the fourth frog that will jump on the lily pad.

Name _____

Skills Practice

1

2

3

4

Directions:
1. Circle the fourth duck that will go into the pond.
2. Circle the fifth turtle that will go into the pond.
3. Circle the fourth frog that will go into the pond.
4. Circle the fifth snake that will go into the pond.

Name

Practice at Home

1

2

3

4

Directions:
1. Circle the fourth fish that will go into the fishbowl.
2. Circle the fourth fish that will go into the fishbowl.
3. Circle the fifth fish that will go into the fishbowl.
4. Circle the fifth fish that will go into the fishbowl.

Name _____

Vocabulary and English Language Development

ACTIVITY Gather two bowls and some O-shaped cereal. Tell students that **equal** means "the same." Place two pieces of cereal in a bowl. Place one piece of cereal in another bowl. Ask: "Are these equal?" (No.) Add another piece of cereal to the bowl with only one. Ask: "Are these equal?" (Yes.) Repeat with other numbers. Challenge students to make equal sets, using the bowls and cereal.

WORKSHEET DIRECTIONS Draw a line to connect the sets that are equal.

Name _____

Skills Practice

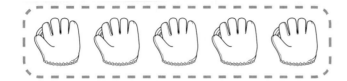 

Directions:
1. Circle the group with the same number of items as the group of baseballs.
2. Circle the group with the same number of items as the group of helmets.
3. Draw circles to make a group equal to the group of basketballs.

Math Triumphs

Name

Practice at Home

    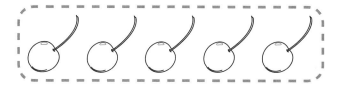

Directions:
1. Circle the group with the same number of items as the group of strawberries.
2. Circle the group with the same number of items as the group of broccoli stems.
3. Draw circles to make a group of circles equal to the group of oranges.

Name _____

Vocabulary and English Language Development

 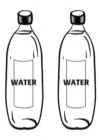 

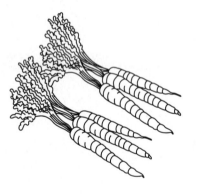 

ACTIVITY Gather small items, such as small blocks or cereal pieces. Place them in a pile. Take a handful of the items. Then, have a student take a handful of the same items. Make a row with each handful of items, and place one row above the other. Ask: "Are the rows equal?" (No.) "Which row has more items?" Explain to students that the row with the greater number of items is **greater than** the other. Ask: "Which has less?" Explain to students that the row with fewer items is **less than** the other.

WORKSHEET DIRECTIONS
1. Circle the group that is greater than the other.
2. Circle the group that is less than the other.
3. Circle the group that is greater than the other.

Name

Skills Practice

  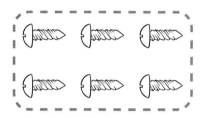

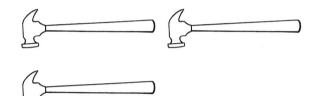 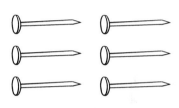

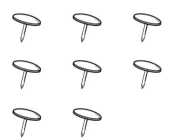    

Directions:

1. Circle the group that is greater than the other.
2. Circle the group that is less than the other.

3. Draw an X on the group that is greater than the other.
4. Draw an X on the group that is less than the other.

Name

Practice at Home

1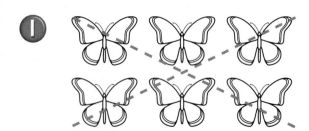

2

3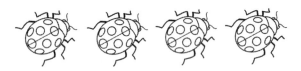

4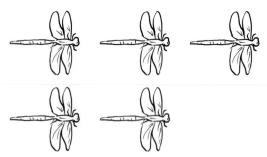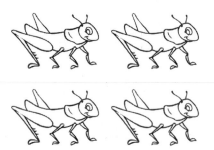

Directions:

1. Draw an X on the group that is greater than the other.

2. Draw an X on the group that is less than the other.

3. Circle the group that is greater than the other.

4. Circle the group that is less than the other.

Name

Vocabulary and English Language Development

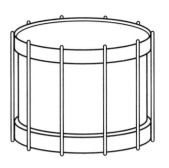

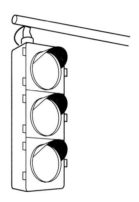

ACTIVITY Ask: "How tall were you were you when you were born?" Say: "You are **growing** each year." Remind students that when something **grows**, it gets larger. Have students think of things that grow (e.g., plants, pets).

WORKSHEET DIRECTIONS Circle the items that grow.

Name

Skills Practice

1   2   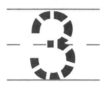   4   5

1   2   3   4   _____

3

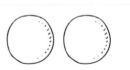         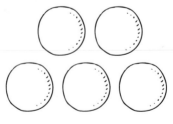

Directions:

1–2. Look for a pattern. Write the missing number.

3. Look for a pattern. Draw a picture in the box for the missing number.

Name _____

Practice at Home

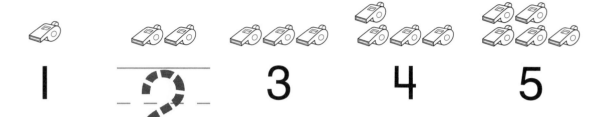

1   2   3   4   5

Directions:
1. Look for a pattern. Write the missing number.
2–3. Look for a pattern. Draw a picture in the box for the missing number.

Vocabulary and English Language Development

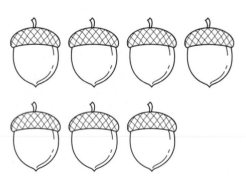 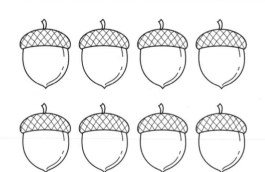

ACTIVITY Gather small blocks or cereal pieces. Ask students to place five items in a column. Then ask students to place four items in a second column. Ask: "Which has **fewer**?" (four) Repeat, making columns of three, two, one, and zero. Each time asking: "Which has **fewer**?".

WORKSHEET DIRECTIONS For each pair of pictures, circle the group that has fewer items.

Name

Skills Practice

1

6   5   4   2   1

2

7   6   5   _____   3

3

7   6   _____   4   _____

Directions:
1–2. Look for a pattern. Write the missing number.
  3. Look for a pattern. Write the missing numbers.

Name _____

Practice at Home

7 **6** **5** **4** **3**

5 **4** **3** ___ **1**

6 ___ **4** **3** ___

Directions:
1–2. Look for a pattern. Write the missing number.
  3. Look for a pattern. Write the missing numbers.

Math Triumphs

Foldables Study Organizer

Dinah Zike's Foldables

Create a Bound Book Foldable to make a giant addition journal.

1 Fold two sheets of paper like a hamburger. Place the papers on top of each other, leaving less than a $\frac{1}{2}$ inch between the "mountain tops".

2 Mark both folds one-inch from the outer edges. On one of the folded sheets cut from the top and bottom edge to the marked spot on both sides.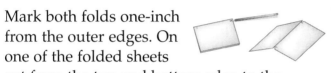

3 On the second folded sheet, start at one of the marked spots and cut the fold between the two marks.

4 Take the cut sheet from step two and fold it like a burrito. Place the burrito through the slit in the other sheet, then open the burrito.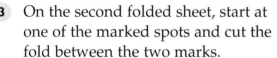

5 Fold the bound pages in half to form an eight page book.

TAKING NOTES

As you read the chapter together, have students use pictures of objects that can be taped or glued into their journal to show ways to model addition by joining groups with sums 1-9.

USING THE FOLDABLE

As students review, have them check their understanding by using manipulatives to model the pictures of objects and their sums in their journal.

USING THE FOLDABLE

In pairs, have students take turns telling stories from their journal that involve joining sets. Guide students to use proper terminology as they describe simple addition problems.

Games and Puzzles
Cover Up

GET READY

- Reproduce and cut out the **Cover Up** domino cards.

- Give each student a **Cover Up** game board.

- Arrange students in pairs or groups of four. Give each pair or group one set of domino cards.

DIRECTIONS:

- Place the domino cards face down in a pile. Decide which player begins. The first player draws a card and adds the dots together. The player states the total number of dots. Then the player places the domino cards on the corresponding number on his or her **Cover Up** game board. Play proceeds to the next player.

- After the first round, play continues as described. If a player draws a certain number of dots more than once, and the corresponding number on his or her **Cover Up** game board is already covered, the student places the card at the bottom of the pile, and draws a new card.

- The first player to cover up all six numbers is the winner.

VARIATION

For students who are ready for a greater challenge, replace the dot cards with addition facts (e.g., 2 + 1 =) and provide manipulatives for the students to solve the problems.

What You Need

- Cover Up domino cards (one set per pair or group)
- Cover Up game board (one per player)

Number of Players

2-4

Game Board
Cover Up

9
8
7
6
5
4
3

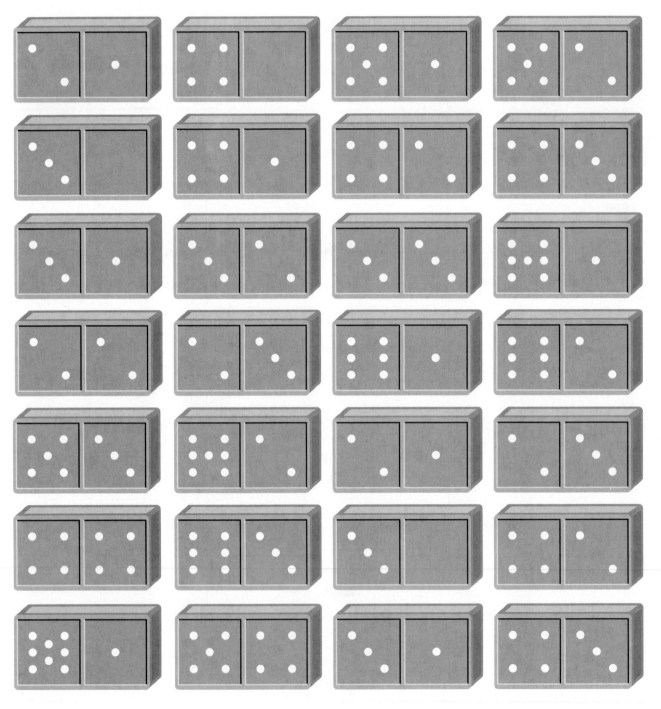

Lesson 3-1

Name

Vocabulary and English Language Development

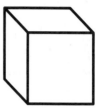

3

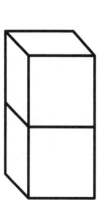

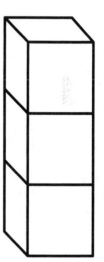

ACTIVITY Gather five stackable building blocks. Place a block on the table. Say: "Let's see how many blocks we can **add** to the stack before it falls." Invite a volunteer to add to the stack. Say: "Add one block to the stack." Count the blocks. Repeat, trying to add four blocks, each time saying: "Add one block."

WORKSHEET DIRECTIONS
1. Draw a square to add one block to the space.
2–4. Draw a square to add one block to the stack.

Math Triumphs

Name _____

Skills Practice

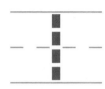

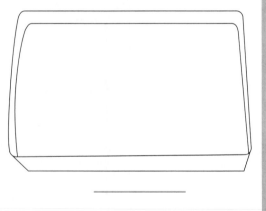

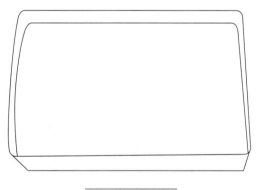

Directions:

1. Grace has 0 apples. The snack helper gives her 1 apple. How many apples does Grace have in all?
2. Chris has 1 apple. The snack helper gives him 1 apple. How many apples does Chris have in all?

3. Draw 1 apple on the tray. Write how many apples in all.
4. Draw 2 apples on the tray. Write how many apples in all.

Name _____

Practice at Home

 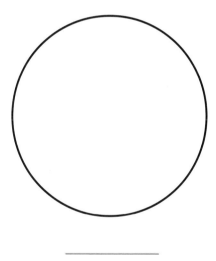

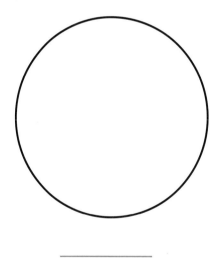

Directions:

1. Seth has 0 marbles. His friend gives him 1 marble. How many marbles does Seth have in all?
2. Arjun has 1 marble. His friend gives him 1 marble. How many marbles does Arjun have in all?
3. Draw 1 marble in the ring. Write how many marbles in all.
4. Draw 2 marbles in the ring. Write how many marbles in all.

Name

Vocabulary and English Language Development

①

②

3

④

5

ACTIVITY Gather two index cards and three colors of beans (or other small counters). On one card, write the number 3, and draw three circles. On the other card, write the number 4, and draw four circles. Start with the 3 card. Choose three beans, representing at least two colors. Place one bean in each of the three circles (e.g., one black bean and two white beans). Say: "There is one black bean and two white beans. There are three beans in all." Repeat the activity with different color combinations. Have a volunteer state the number of each addend (bean) and the total number of beans. Finally, make combinations with the 4 card.

WORKSHEET DIRECTIONS Circle a group of 3 beans. Draw an X on a group of 4 beans.

Name _____

Skills Practice

  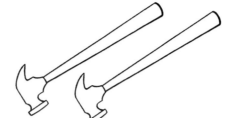

 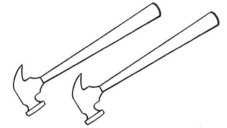 

 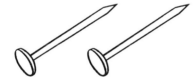

 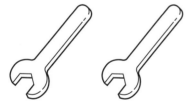 

Directions:

1. Mr. Ruiz has 1 hammer. His friend gives him 2 hammers. How many hammers does Mr. Ruiz have in all?

2. Miss Trong has 2 hammers. She buys 2 screwdrivers. How many tools does she have in all?

3. The toolbox has 2 nails. Mr. Wood puts 1 screw in the toolbox. How many items in all?

4. There are 2 wrenches on the floor. There are 2 more wrenches on the table. How many wrenches in all?

Name

Practice at Home

①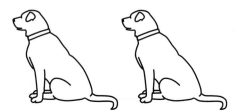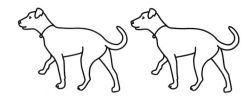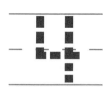

②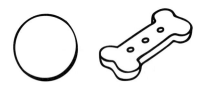

③

④

Directions:

1. There are 2 dogs sitting in the park. Two more dogs come to the park. How many dogs in all?
2. Cullen has 2 dog toys. His brother gives him 1 toy bone. How many dog toys does he have in all?
3. There are 2 dogs in the training class. One more dog joins the class. How many dogs in all?
4. There are 2 leashes on the shelf. There are 2 dog brushes on the next shelf. How many items in all?

Name _____

Vocabulary and English Language Development

①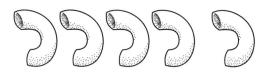

②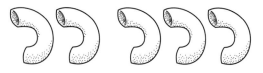

3

④

⑤

⑥

ACTIVITY Gather five pieces of pasta (or small counters), and two index cards. Divide the pasta as follows: one piece and four pieces. Cover the single pasta with one index card and the four pieces with the other index card. Lift off each index card, one at a time. Have students count aloud the number of pieces under each card. Say: "One piece of pasta and four pieces of pasta makes **five** pieces of pasta in all." Repeat the activity, using two pieces of pasta under one card and three pieces of pasta under the second card.

WORKSHEET DIRECTIONS Circle the groups that show five.

Skills Practice

 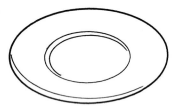 

Directions:

1. There are 4 mugs on the table. Celine places another mug on the table. How many mugs on the table in all?

2. Mom puts 3 forks in the sink. Mia puts 2 spoons in the sink. How many items are in the sink?

3. There is 1 plate in the cabinet. Dad puts 4 glasses in the cabinet. How many items are in the cabinet?

4. There are 0 pieces of silverware in the drawer. Rob puts 5 forks in the drawer. How many forks are in the drawer?

Math Triumphs

Lesson 3-3

Name

Name

Practice at Home

  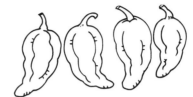 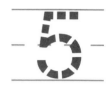

 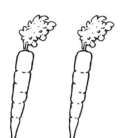 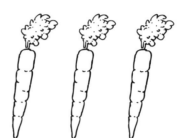

 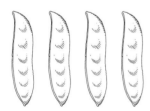

Directions:

1. Mr. Sanders picked 1 head of lettuce. Owen gave him 4 peppers. How many vegetables does Mr. Sanders have in all?
2. Grandma put 2 carrots in the basket. She picked 3 more. How many carrots does she have in all?
3. Tom found 5 ripe tomatoes. He can't find any more. How many tomatoes does he have in all?
4. Susie puts 4 peapods in her basket. Mom gives her a bell pepper. How many vegetables does Susie have in all?

Math Triumphs

Lesson 3-3 A69

Name _____

Vocabulary and English Language Development

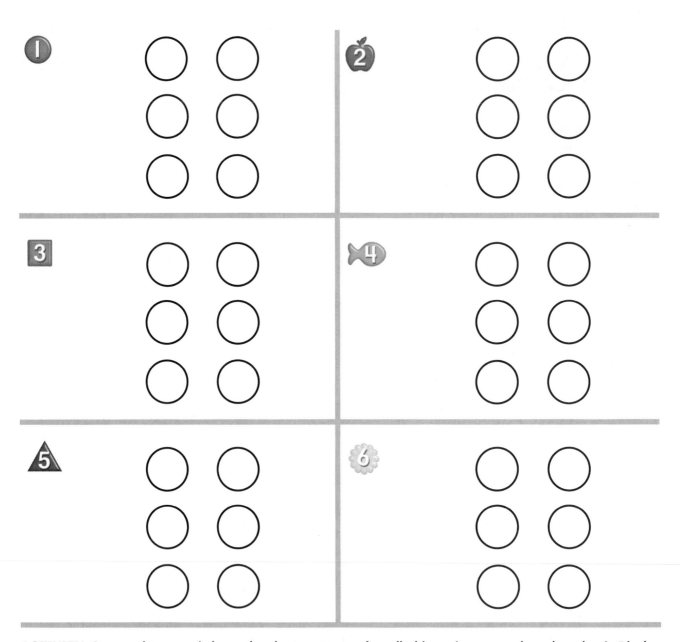

ACTIVITY Cut out six paper circles and gather two types of small objects (e.g., pretzels and crackers). Display the circles on a table. Have students count the circles aloud. Ask a volunteer to place a combination of six objects, one in each circle. Have the student state the combination of items equaling 6. For example, the student might say, "There are two crackers and four pretzels. Two crackers and four pretzels make **six** snacks in all." Repeat, prompting volunteers to make different number combinations.

WORKSHEET DIRECTIONS Use two colors. Color the circles to show two groups equaling 6. Try to make different combinations.

Math Triumphs

Name _____

Skills Practice

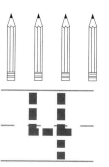 4   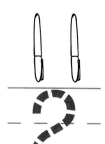 2    6

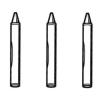

Directions:

1. How many pencils are there? How many markers are there? How many supplies are there in all?
2. Beth puts 3 crayons in her box. She finds 3 more on the floor. How many crayons does she have in all?
3. Mrs. Landers puts 1 glue stick on the art table. She puts 5 glue bottles on another table. How many glues are there in all?
4. You have 4 erasers. Color the number of erasers you need to have 6 erasers in all.

Math Triumphs

Name _____

Practice at Home

 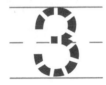 

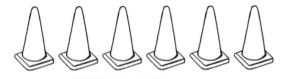

 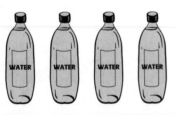 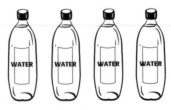

Directions:

1. How many t-shirts are there? How many whistles are there? How many items are there in all?
2. Javier puts 2 shoes into his soccer bag. He puts in 4 socks. How many items are in his soccer bag?
3. The coach put 6 cones on one side of the field. There are 0 cones on the other side of the field. How many cones are there in all?
4. You have 4 water bottles. Shade the number of water bottles you need to have 6 in all.

Name _____

Vocabulary and English Language Development

①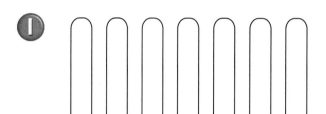

②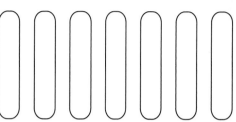

③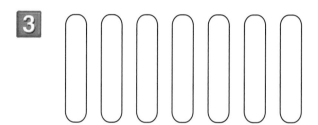

④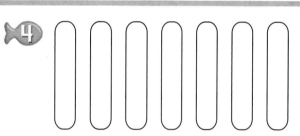

⑤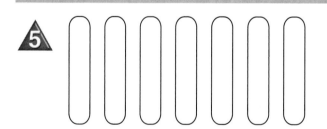

⑥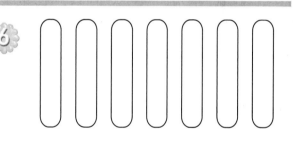

ACTIVITY Gather seven craft sticks. Color one side with a permanent marker. Ask volunteers to make different combinations modeling 7. Have each student state the combination that he or she modeled. For example, the student might say, "There are two white sticks and five blue sticks. That makes **seven** sticks in all."

WORKSHEET DIRECTIONS Use two colors. Color the sticks to show two groups equaling 7. Try to make different combinations.

Name _____

Skills Practice

1

2

3

4

Directions:
1. Draw more ice cream cones to make a total of 7.
2. Jill packed 4 snorkels in a bag. She put in 3 flippers. How many things did she pack in all?
3. Kyle tried on 2 pairs of sunglasses. Then he tried on 5 more. How many pairs did he try on in all?
4. Mom put 1 juice box in the cooler. Color more juice boxes to show 7 juice boxes in all.

Name _____

Practice at Home

 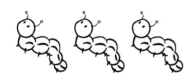 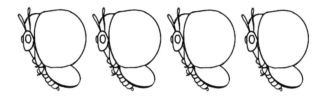

Directions:
1. Draw more bugs to make a total of 7.
2. Ian saw 3 caterpillars in the garden. He saw 4 butterflies. How many bugs did he see in all?
3. Ellie saw 1 grasshopper in the grass. Then, she saw 6 bees. How many bugs did she see in all?
4. Steve collected 1 beetle from the yard. Color more beetles to show 7 beetles in all.

Chapter 3

Name _____

Vocabulary and English Language Development

 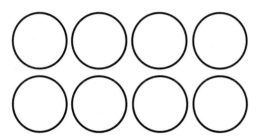

 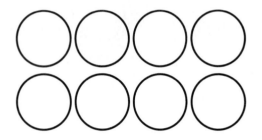

 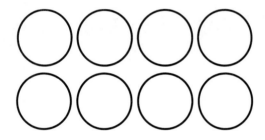

 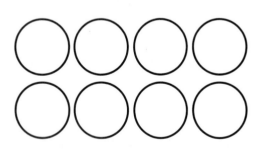

 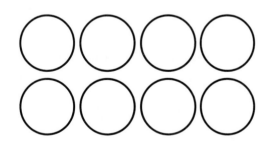

ACTIVITY Gather eight 2-sided counters (or place masking tape on pennies and color one side red and the other blue). Spill the counters onto the table. Ask a volunteer to describe the combination of counters. For example, the student might say, "There are two red and six blue counters. That makes **eight** counters in all." Repeat, making different number combinations.

WORKSHEET DIRECTIONS Use two colors. Color the circles to show two groups equaling 8. Try to make different combinations.

Name _____

Skills Practice

Directions:

1. Dahlia placed 6 toy rockets on the table. She put 2 toy cars next to them. How many toys in all?

2. Doug saw 5 jack-in-the-box toys at the toy store. Then, he saw 3 robots. How many toys did he see in all?

3. Shelby put 4 paintbrushes and 4 paint palettes on the shelf. How many paint supplies in all?

4. Draw more kites to show 8 kites in all.

Math Triumphs

Name _____

Practice at Home

Directions:

1. Scott put 6 baseball bats in his locker. Then he put in 2 baseball mitts. How many items are in Scott's locker?

2. There are 4 ice skates at the sports store. There are 4 skateboards. How many are there in all?

3. The coach put 7 baseballs in his bag. He put in 1 baseball cap. How many items are in the bag?

4. Draw more pennants to show 8 in all.

Name _____

Vocabulary and English Language Development

①

②

③

④

⑤

⑥

ACTIVITY Gather two sheets of paper and nine toy cars. Have students pretend the sheets of paper are parking lots. Ask volunteers to make a combination of nine in the two "parking lots." Prompt students to describe the number combinations equaling nine. For example, the student might say, "There are three cars in one lot and six cars in another lot. That makes **nine** cars in all."

WORKSHEET DIRECTIONS Circle the groups that show 9 cars.

Name

Skills Practice

Directions:

1. There were 6 snails by the pond. Three more snails came. How many snails are there in all?
2. There were 2 fish by the shore. Seven more fish swam over. How many fish are there in all?
3. Four snakes slithered to the pond. Draw more snakes to show 9 snakes in all.
4. Six frogs jumped onto a giant lily pad. Color more frogs to show 9 frogs in all.

Name

Practice at Home

Directions:

1. There are 4 bananas in the fruit bowl. Dad puts 5 more bananas in. How many bananas are there in all?

2. There are 3 carrots in the salad. There are 6 broccoli crowns. How many vegetables are there?

3. Jake put 2 strawberries in the fruit salad. Draw more strawberries to show 9 strawberries in all.

4. Sarika bought 5 apples at the store. Color more apples to show 9 apples in all.

Foldables Study Organizer

Dinah Zike's Foldables

Create a Bound Book Foldable to make a giant subtraction journal.

1 Fold two sheets of paper like a hamburger. Place the papers on top of each other, leaving less than a $\frac{1}{2}$ inch between the "mountain tops".

2 Mark both folds one-inch from the outer edges. On one of the folded sheets cut from the top and bottom edge to the marked spot on both sides.

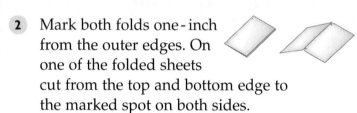

3 On the second folded sheet, start at one of the marked spots and cut the fold between the two marks.

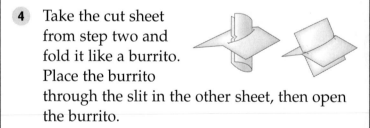

4 Take the cut sheet from step two and fold it like a burrito. Place the burrito through the slit in the other sheet, then open the burrito.

5 Fold the bound pages in half to form an eight page book.

TAKING NOTES

As you read the chapter together, have students use pictures that can be taped or glued into their journal to show ways to model subtraction and taking away or separating sets 1-9.

 **USING THE FOLDABLE**

As students review, have them check their understanding by using a number line to model the subtraction picture in their journal.

 **USING THE FOLDABLE**

In pairs, have students take turns telling subtraction stories from their journal. Guide students to use proper terminology as they describe simple subtraction problems.

Games and Puzzles
Cherry Take Away

GET READY

- Cut apart the **Cherry Take Away** game pieces.
- Count out 20 game pieces for each student and place them in a zip-top bag.
- Arrange students in pairs or groups of four.

DIRECTIONS:

- Roll the number cube. The player with the lowest number goes first.
- Players place their cherries on their game board buckets. The first player rolls the number cube and removes, from his or her bucket, the number of cherries indicated by the number cube. This ends the first player's turn.
- Play continues to the right, as described. The first player to remove all of his or her cherries from the bucket is the winner. Players do not need to roll an exact number to win.

VARIATIONS

- Play as described, but the player must roll an exact number to win.
- For a more challenging game, alter the number cube by writing an addition sign in front of the 1 and 2 and a subtraction sign in front of the 3, 4, 5, and 6. Play is the same, except students either add or subtract cherries according to the number they roll.

What You Need
- Cherry Take Away game board (per student)
- 20 Cherry Take Away game pieces (per student)
- zip-top bag (per student)
- number cube

Number of Players
2–4

Game Pieces
Cherry Take Away

Name _____

Vocabulary and English Language Development

①

②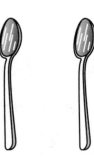

③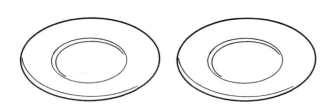

④

ACTIVITY Set a table with two plates, two spoons, and two glasses. Tell students: "We are going to **'take away'** our place settings." Have students count the number of plates (2). Say: "Take away one plate." Have students count the remaining plates (1). Continue having students take away one or two items, emphasizing the phrase *take away*.

WORKSHEET DIRECTIONS
1. Draw an X to take away one.
2. Draw Xs to take away two.
3. Draw Xs to take away two.
4. Draw an X to take away one.

Math Triumphs

Name

Skills Practice

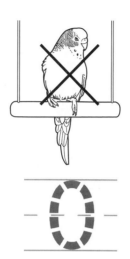

Chapter 4

Directions:

1. There was 1 bird swinging. Then 1 flew away. How many birds are left on the swing?

2. There were 2 birds flying. Then 1 bird landed. How many birds are left flying?

3. There were 2 birds flying. Then 2 birds landed to eat seeds. How many birds are left flying?

4. There were 2 eggs in nests. Then 1 egg hatched. How many eggs are left in nests?

Name _____

Practice at Home

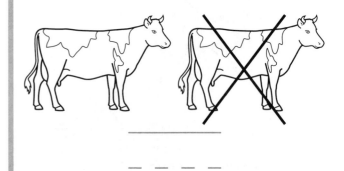

Directions:

1. There were 2 chickens in the pen. The farmer took 1 to the vet. How many chickens are left in the pen?

2. There was 1 goat eating grass in the field. The farmer put it back in the barn. How many goats are left in the field?

3. There were 2 horses in the barn. The farmer took 1 out to ride. How many horses are left in the barn?

4. There were 2 cows in the field. Then 1 cow went to the barn. How many cows are left in the field?

Name

Vocabulary and English Language Development

3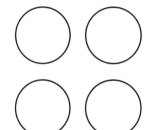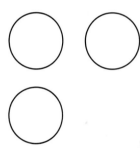

ACTIVITY Gather eight index cards. Write *4* on one index card and *3* on another index card. On the remaining six cards, place dots in various patterns to equal three or four (e.g., three in a row, two in one row and one in the next, and three at random). Put the number cards on the table. Tell students: "This is the number 3," while pointing to the number. Have students count the dots on the dot cards and match them to the number. Encourage the students to say the number (e.g., "There are three dots.").

WORKSHEET DIRECTIONS Count the dots. Circle all the groups that have three. Color all the groups that have four.

Name _____

Skills Practice

  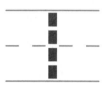

 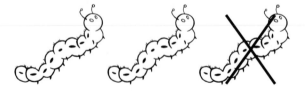 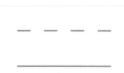

Directions:

1. There were 3 children hunting for butterflies. Then 2 went home. How many children are left?

2. There were 4 butterflies resting on a branch. Then 1 butterfly flew away. How many butterflies are left on the branch?

3. There were 4 butterflies flying. Two butterflies landed. How many butterflies are left flying?

4. There were 3 caterpillars on the leaf. The children took 1 caterpillar to show their teacher. How many caterpillars are left on the leaf?

Name _____

Practice at Home

 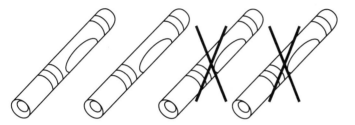

 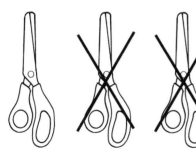 

Chapter 4

Directions:

1. The children made 3 cards. They gave 1 away. How many are left?

2. The children used 4 markers. They threw away 2 dried out markers. How many are left?

3. José had 4 crayons. He gave 1 to his friend. How many crayons does José have left?

4. Jane had 3 scissors. She gave 2 to her friends. How many scissors does Jane have left?

Name _____

Vocabulary and English Language Development

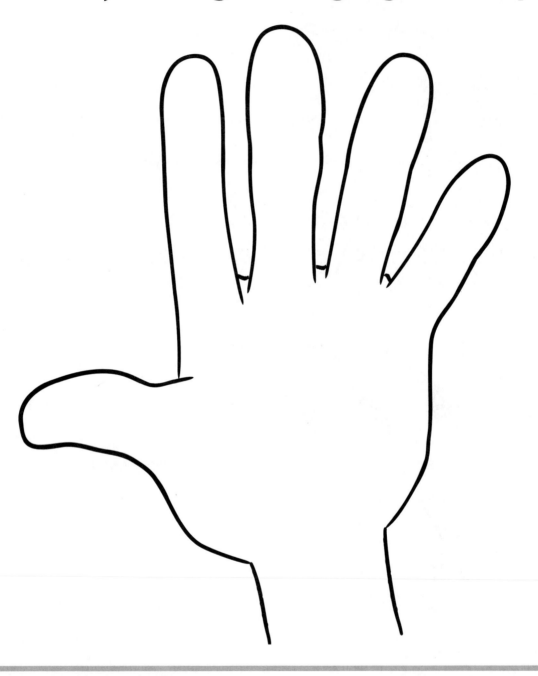

ACTIVITY Trace each student's hand on a blank sheet of paper. Have students count the fingers and write a **5** on the palm. Say: "This is a **five**." Next, have students place one small object (e.g., O-shaped cereal) on each of the hand-drawn fingers, and count them aloud. Have students say: "There are five [rings]."

WORKSHEET DIRECTIONS Draw five rings, one on each finger. Then draw five fingernails, one on each finger.

Math Triumphs

Name

Skills Practice

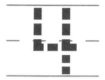

    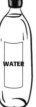

Directions:

1. There were 5 boys playing soccer in the park. Then 1 boy went home. How many boys are left?
2. The coach brought 5 soccer balls. Then 3 balls went flat. How many balls are left?
3. There were 5 shoes. The boys took home 4 shoes. Draw Xs on 4 shoes. How many shoes are left?
4. There were 5 water bottles in the cooler. Then 2 boys drank some water. Draw Xs on 2 bottles. How many bottles are left?

Name

Practice at Home

1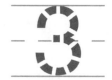

2

3

4

Directions:

1. Mrs. Tang blew up 5 balloons. Then 2 balloons popped. How many balloons are left for the party?
2. There were 5 party hats on the table. Then 4 children put them on. How many hats are left on the table?
3. Sarah got 5 presents. She opened 3 presents. Draw Xs on 3 presents. How many presents does Sarah have left to open?
4. Mrs. Tang made 5 muffins for the party. She dropped 1. Draw an X on 1 muffin. How many muffins are left?

Name _____

Vocabulary and English Language Development

1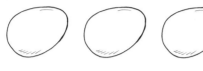

2

3

4

ACTIVITY Gather a half-dozen egg carton, or cut a one-dozen egg carton in half. Place a single bean or small counter in each cup, saying the number—from one to six—as you place each bean. Write the number **6** on the lid, using a permanent marker. Say: "This is a **six**. There are six spaces in the box." Have students repeat the activity, counting other small objects.

WORKSHEET DIRECTIONS Circle the pictures that show six eggs.

Name _____

Skills Practice

3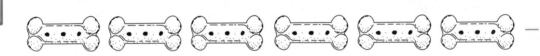

Directions:

1. There were 6 dogs sitting at dog training class. Then 2 dogs got up. How many dogs are left sitting?

2. The instructor brought 6 leashes. She brought 1 that was too small. How many leashes are left?

3. The instructor brought 6 dog biscuits to class. She gave 3 biscuits away. Draw Xs on 3 biscuits. How many biscuits does she have left?

4. The instructor threw 6 balls for the dogs to fetch. The dogs returned 5 balls. Draw Xs on 5 balls. How many balls are left?

Name _____

Practice at Home

 1.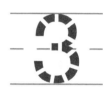

 2.

 3.

 4.

Directions:
1. There were 6 clowns playing in the circus. Then 3 clowns were too sick to play. How many clowns are left for the show?
2. There were 6 dancing bears in the circus. Then 2 bears fell asleep. How many bears are left for the show?
3. There were 6 elephants inside the circus tent. Then 4 elephants went outside the tent. Draw Xs on 4 elephants. How many are left inside the tent?
4. There were 6 monkeys in the show. Then 1 monkey ran away. Draw an X on 1 monkey. How many monkeys are left?

Name _____

Vocabulary and English Language Development

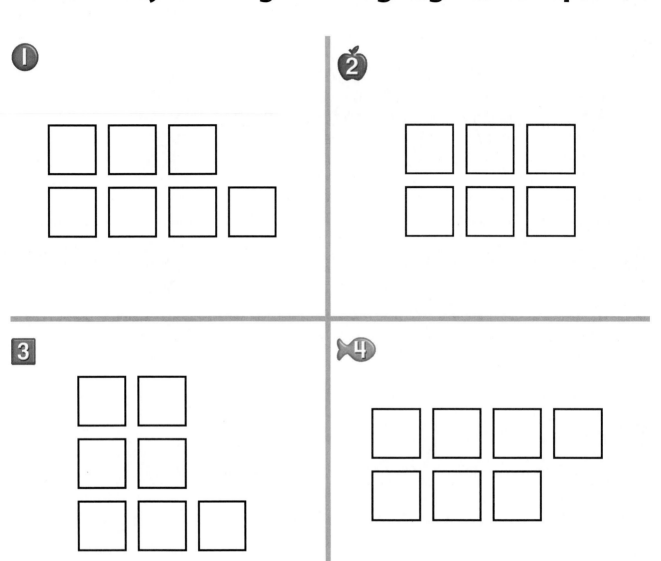

ACTIVITY Draw a large **7** on a blank sheet of paper. Cut seven pieces of colored paper into one-inch squares. Tell students: "This is the number **seven**." Have students use a finger to trace the numeral. Then have students place squares along the line of the numeral, as they count them. Have students tell the number of squares (7).

WORKSHEET DIRECTIONS Circle the groups that show seven squares.

Name _____

Skills Practice

 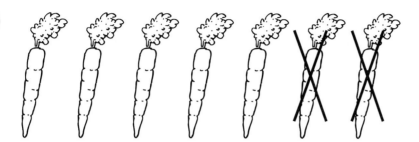

Directions:

1. There were 7 carrots in the garden. Rabbits ate 2 carrots. How many carrots are left?
2. There were 7 tomatoes growing on the vine. The farmer picked 4 tomatoes. How many tomatoes are left?
3. The farmer dug up 7 potatoes. He cooked 5 of them. Draw Xs on 5 potatoes. How many potatoes are left?
4. There were 7 bell peppers in the garden. Birds ate 3 of them. Draw Xs on 3 bell peppers. How many peppers are left?

Math Triumphs

Lesson 4-5   A99

Name

Practice at Home

1

2

3

4

Directions:

1. There were 7 children who wore chef hats to cooking class. Then 6 children took off their hats. How many hats are left?

2. The teacher set out 7 wedges of cheese for pizza. The class used 4 wedges. How many wedges of cheese are left?

3. The students stirred the sauce with 7 spoons. A student dropped a spoon on the floor. Draw an X on 1 spoon. How many spoons are left?

4. The students made 7 pizzas. They ate 5 pizzas. Draw Xs on 5 pizzas. How many pizzas are left?

Name _____

Vocabulary and English Language Development

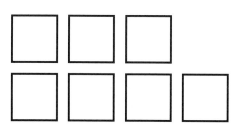

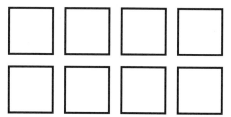

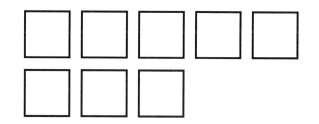

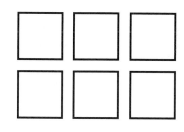

ACTIVITY Cut eight squares out of construction paper, or gather eight square-shaped blocks. Write the number **8** on an index card. Point to the number, and say: "This is the number *eight*." Have students count the squares. Invite students to make different designs, using the squares, and to count them again, saying: "There are eight squares."

WORKSHEET DIRECTIONS Circle the groups that have eight squares.

Name _____

Skills Practice

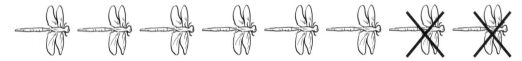

_____

3

_____

_____

Directions:

1. There were 8 frogs on a log. Then 3 frogs jumped off. How many frogs are left on the log?
2. There were 8 dragonflies flying above the pond. Then 2 landed on a lily pad. How many dragonflies are left in the air?
3. There were 8 turtles resting on the bank of the pond. Then 4 turtles entered the water. Draw Xs on 4 turtles. How many turtles are left on the bank?
4. There were 8 fish living in the pond. A bird caught 1 fish. Draw an X on 1 fish. How many fish are left in the pond?

Math Triumphs

Name

Practice at Home

1

2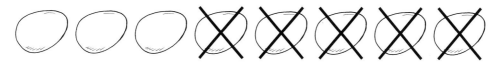

3

4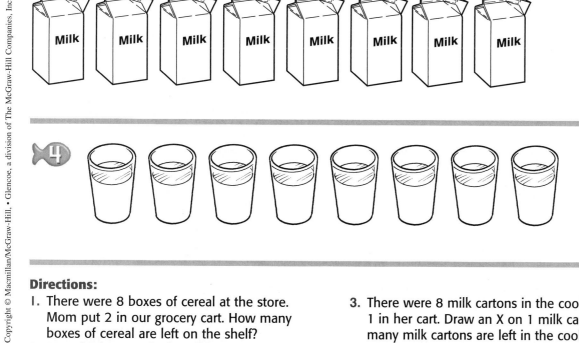

Directions:

1. There were 8 boxes of cereal at the store. Mom put 2 in our grocery cart. How many boxes of cereal are left on the shelf?
2. Mom had 8 eggs in the refrigerator. She used 5 eggs for breakfast. How many eggs are left in the refrigerator?

3. There were 8 milk cartons in the cooler. Mom put 1 in her cart. Draw an X on 1 milk carton. How many milk cartons are left in the cooler?
4. Mom set the table with 8 glasses of milk. Then 2 glasses got knocked over. Draw Xs on 2 glasses. How many glasses are left?

Math Triumphs

Name _____

Vocabulary and English Language Development

1

2

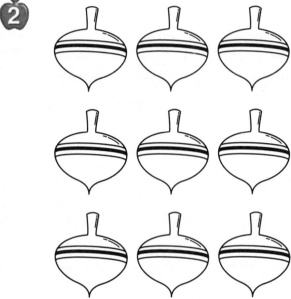

3

4

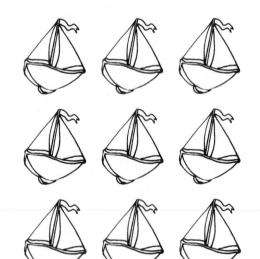

ACTIVITY Place nine empty water bottles to resemble bowling pins (four in the back row, three in the middle row, and two in the front row). Have students count the bottles. Say: "There are **nine** bottles." Then, have students roll a ball to knock down the bottles. Have students reset and recount the bottles after each turn.

WORKSHEET DIRECTIONS Place Xs on nine toys.

Name _____

Skills Practice

1

2

 3

4

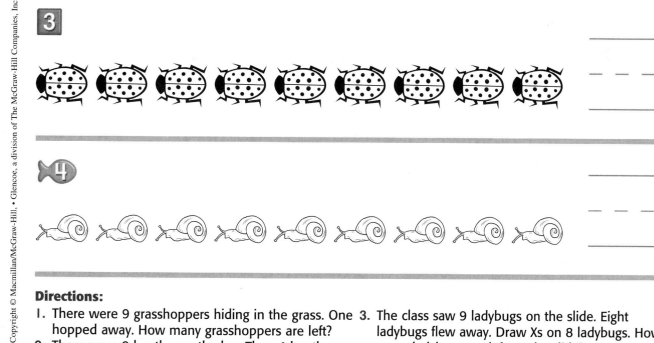

Directions:

1. There were 9 grasshoppers hiding in the grass. One hopped away. How many grasshoppers are left?

2. There were 9 beetles on the log. Then 4 beetles crawled away. How many beetles are left on the log?

3. The class saw 9 ladybugs on the slide. Eight ladybugs flew away. Draw Xs on 8 ladybugs. How many ladybugs are left on the slide?

4. There were 9 snails crawling on the gate. Then 3 snails slid onto the sidewalk. Draw Xs on 3 snails. How many snails are left on the gate?

Math Triumphs

Lesson 4-7   A105

Name _____

Practice at Home

 1

 2

3

 4

Directions:

1. The cafeteria made 9 sandwiches. Then 6 sandwiches were sold. How many sandwiches are left?

2. The cafeteria had 9 yogurts for sale. A student spilled 2 yogurts. How many yogurts are left for sale?

3. There were 9 children who brought bag lunches. Then 5 children threw away their paper bags. Draw Xs on 5 paper bags. How many paper bags are left?

4. There were 9 apples in a basket in the cafeteria. Then 7 students bought apples. Draw Xs on 7 apples. How many apples are left?

Math Triumphs

Foldables Study Organizer

Dinah Zike's Foldables

Create a Standing Cube Foldable to collect information about two-dimensional figures.

1. Use two sheets of the same size paper. Fold each like a hamburger with one side of one $\frac{1}{2}$ inch shorter than the other side.

2. Fold the long side over the short side of both sheets of paper, making tabs.

3. On one of the folded papers, place a small amount of glue along the small folded tab, next to the valley, but not in it.

4. Place the non-folded edge of the second sheet square into the valley and fold the flue-covered tab over this sheet. Press flat until the glue holds. Repeat with the other side.

5. Allow the glue to dry. Then, the cube can be collapsed flat to allow students to work at their desks. The cube can also be folded into fourths for moving it or storing it.
   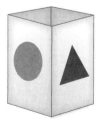

TAKING NOTES

As you read the chapter together, have students find a picture of a circle, square, rectangle, and a triangle and glue them to the four sides of their Foldable. Next, have students make cutouts of circle(s), triangle(s), rectangle(s), and square(s). Then, have them place the figures in their Foldable.

 **USING THE FOLDABLE**

As students review, have them check their understanding by taking a figure from Foldable and describing its features.

USING THE FOLDABLE

In pairs, have students work together using their cutouts to make new figures.

Games and Puzzles
Figure Find

GET READY

- Reproduce a **Figure Find** game board and game cube for each pair of students. Use transparent tape to assemble the game cube.
- Arrange students in pairs, and give each pair a game board, game cube, and game pieces.

DIRECTIONS:

- Players decide who goes first. Both players put their game pieces on START.
- The first player tosses the game cube and moves his or her game piece to the next space showing that figure. If the figures match, the player stays on that space. If the figures do not match, the player goes back to the space from which he or she started.
- The second player then takes a turn. The game is done when a student lands on FINISH and wins the game.
- Emphasize to players that some figures, especially triangles, may look different on the game board than on the game cube, but the goal is to match the figures: triangles to triangles, circles to circles, rectangles to rectangles, and squares to squares.

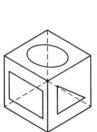

Game Board

Figure Find

Game Cube
Figure Find

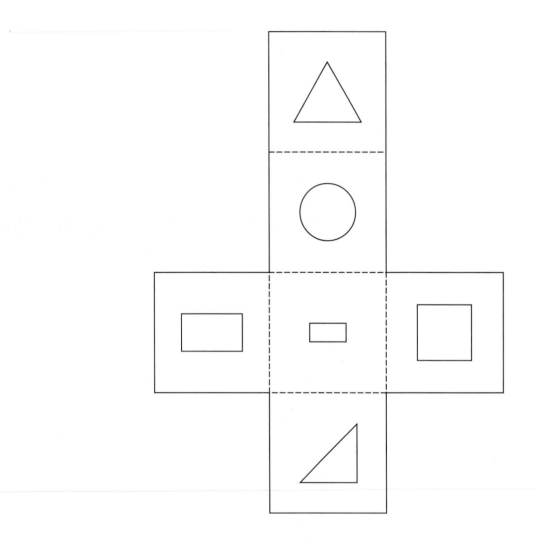

Math Triumphs

Name

Vocabulary and English Language Development

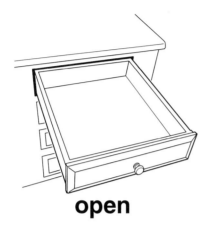

open

closed

1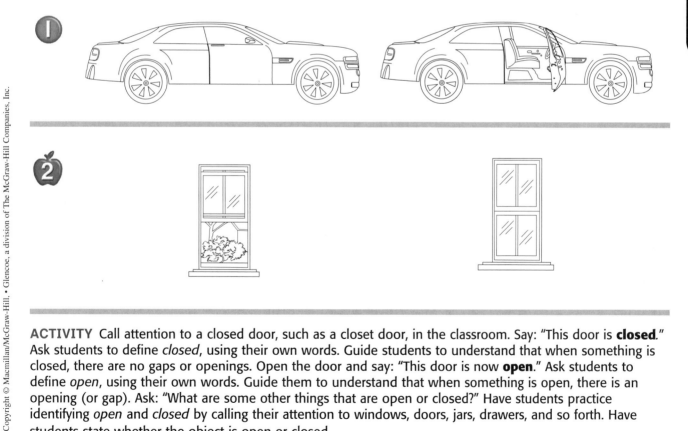

2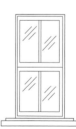

ACTIVITY Call attention to a closed door, such as a closet door, in the classroom. Say: "This door is **closed**." Ask students to define *closed*, using their own words. Guide students to understand that when something is closed, there are no gaps or openings. Open the door and say: "This door is now **open**." Ask students to define *open*, using their own words. Guide them to understand that when something is open, there is an opening (or gap). Ask: "What are some other things that are open or closed?" Have students practice identifying *open* and *closed* by calling their attention to windows, doors, jars, drawers, and so forth. Have students state whether the object is open or closed.

WORKSHEET DIRECTIONS
1. Draw an X on the car with an open door.
2. Circle the window that is closed.

Math Triumphs

Name _____

Skills Practice

  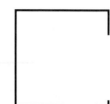 

 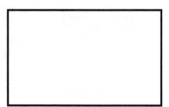 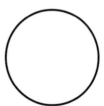 

3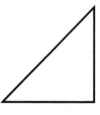

Directions:
1. Circle the closed figure.
2–3. Draw an X on the open figure.

4. Draw a closed figure.

Name _____

Practice at Home

Copyright © Macmillan/McGraw-Hill, • Glencoe, a division of The McGraw-Hill Companies, Inc.

1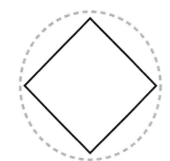

2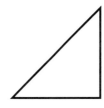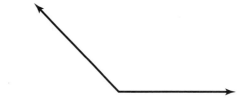

3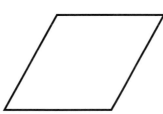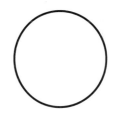

4

Chapter 5

Directions:
1. Circle the closed figure.
2–3. Draw an X on the open figure.

4. Draw a closed figure.

Name _____

Vocabulary and English Language Development

curved   straight

1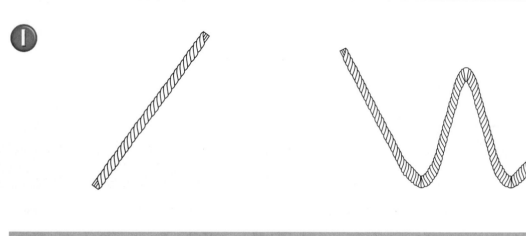

2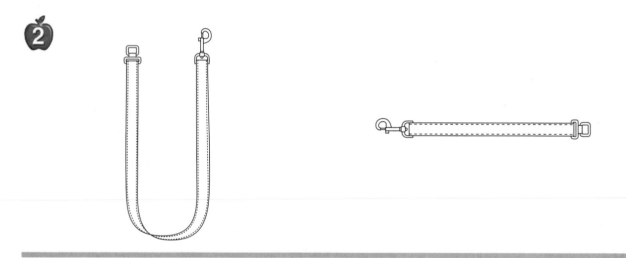

ACTIVITY Have students come to the front of the class, where they usually line up, and say: "Form a **straight** line." Guide students as they line up to ensure the line is straight. Ask: "How do you know this line is straight?" Reposition some students so the line is curved. Say: "This line is **curved**." Ask: "What is the difference between the straight line and the curved line?" Help students brainstorm about times when they have heard or used the words *straight* and *curved*. Help students relate real-life uses of the words *curved* and *straigh*t to help them differentiate between curved and straight lines in this lesson.

WORKSHEET DIRECTIONS Circle the object that is straight.

Name

Skills Practice

   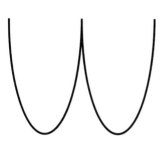

  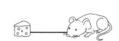 

Chapter 5

Directions:
1–2. Circle the straight line.
   3. Draw an X on the curved lines.

4. Trace the straight line with red. Trace the curved line with blue.

Math Triumphs

Name

Practice at Home

 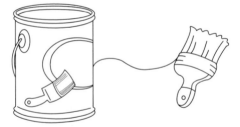 

B

Directions:

1–2. Circle the straight line.

3. Draw an X on the curved lines.

4. Trace the straight line with red. Trace the curved line with blue.

Name _____

Vocabulary and English Language Development

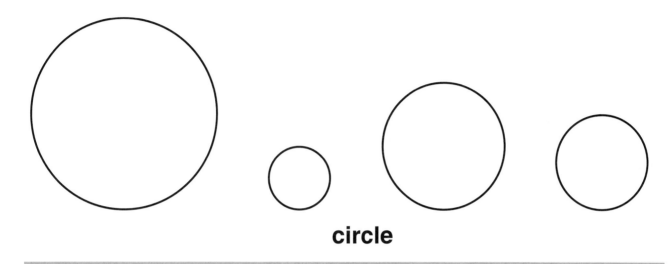

circle

 1

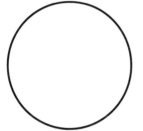

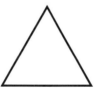

 2

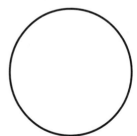

ACTIVITY Show students pictures of several circle-shaped objects, such as a plate, a car tire, a flying disk, and a pizza pie. Use a black marker to trace the circle outline of the object in each picture. Ask: "Are these lines curved or straight?" (curved) "Are these figures open or closed?" (closed) Guide students to understand that a **circle** is a closed figure made of a single curved line. Point out that circles occur in all different sizes. Ask: "What circles do you see in the classroom?" (Accept all reasonable responses.)

WORKSHEET DIRECTIONS Draw an X on the circle.

Name _____

Skills Practice

   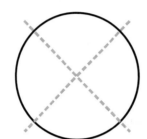

 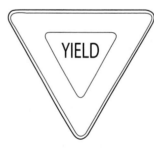 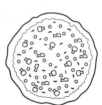

Directions:

1. Draw an X on the circle.
2. Write the number of sides.
3. Draw an X on the circles.
4. Draw an X on the stickers that are circles.

Math Triumphs

Name _____

Practice at Home

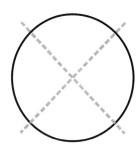

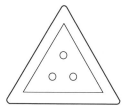
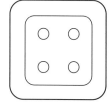
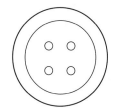

Directions:
1. Draw an X on the circle.
2. Write the number of sides.
3. Draw an X on the circles.
4. Draw an X on the buttons that are circles.

Math Triumphs

Name _____

Vocabulary and English Language Development

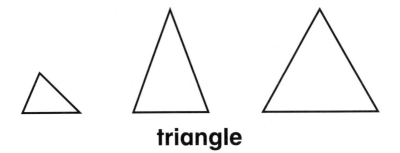

triangle

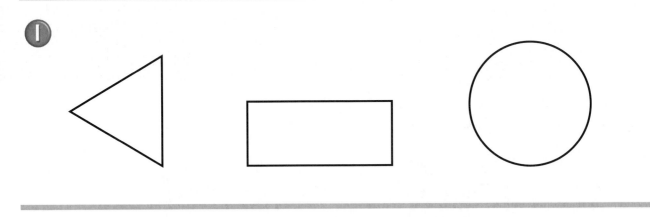

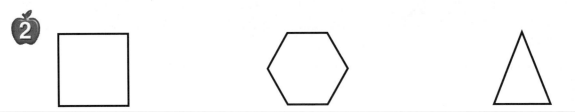

ACTIVITY On the board or overhead, draw several different triangles—show triangles that are different sizes, with different sides and angles. Call students attention to each triangle. Use chalk or a black marker to trace over the figure's sides. Ask: "Are these lines curved or straight?" (straight) "Are these figures open or closed?" (closed) "How many sides are there?" (three) Guide students to understand that a **triangle** is a closed figure made of three straight lines. Ask: "What triangles do you see in the classroom?" (Accept all reasonable responses.)

WORKSHEET DIRECTIONS Draw an X on the triangle.

Name _____

Skills Practice

 1

 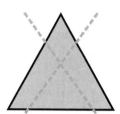

2

3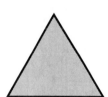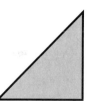

4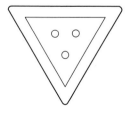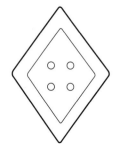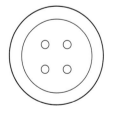

Directions:
1. Draw an X on the triangle.
2. Write the number of sides.

3. Draw an X on the figures with 3 corners.
4. Draw an X on the button that is a triangle.

Name _____

Practice at Home

1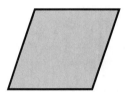

2

3

4

Directions:
1. Draw an X on the triangle.
2. Write the number of sides.

3. Draw an X on the figures with 3 corners.
4. Draw an X on the sticker that is a triangle.

Math Triumphs

Name _____

Vocabulary and English Language Development

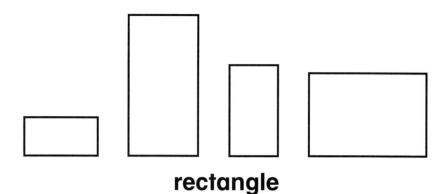

rectangle

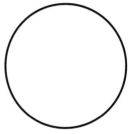 

 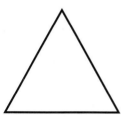

ACTIVITY Show students pictures of several rectangle-shaped objects, such as a notebook, a shoe box, a cereal box, and a flag. Use a black marker to trace the rectangle outline of the object in each picture. Ask: "Are these figures open or closed?" (closed); "Are these lines curved or straight?" (straight); ask "How many sides are there?" (four). Guide students to understand that a rectangle is a closed figure made of four straight lines. Two lines are long and two lines are short. Point out that the lines meet at square corners, which look like the corners of a sheet of paper. Ask: "What rectangles do you see in the classroom?" (Accept all reasonable responses.)

WORKSHEET DIRECTIONS Draw an X on the rectangle.

Name _____

Skills Practice

 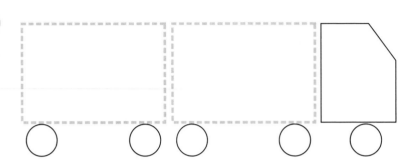

   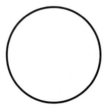

Directions:

1. Trace the rectangles to make a truck.
2. Draw an X on the rectangle.
3. Write the number of sides.
4. Draw an X on the shapes with 4 corners.

Name _____

Practice at Home

1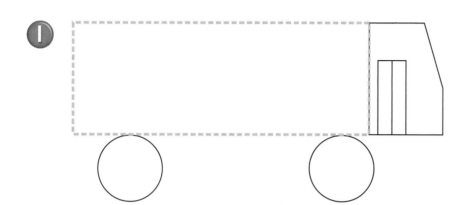

2

3

4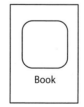

Directions:
1. Trace the rectangle to make a school bus.
2. Draw an X on the rectangle.
3. Write the number of sides.
4. Draw an X on the shapes with 4 corners.

Math Triumphs

Name _____

Vocabulary and English Language Development

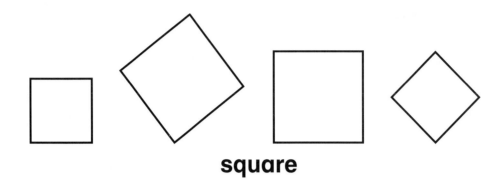

square

 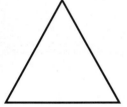 

  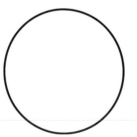

ACTIVITY On the board or overhead, draw several different squares—show squares that are different sizes, with different sides and angles. Call attention to each square. Use chalk or a black marker to trace over the sides. Ask: "Are these lines curved or straight?" (straight); "Are these figures open or closed?" (closed); and, "How many sides are there?" (four). Guide students to understand that a square is a closed figure made of four straight lines. Explain that the four sides of a **square** are the same length. Ask: "What squares do you see in the classroom?" (Accept all reasonable responses.)

WORKSHEET DIRECTIONS Draw an X on the square.

Name

Skills Practice

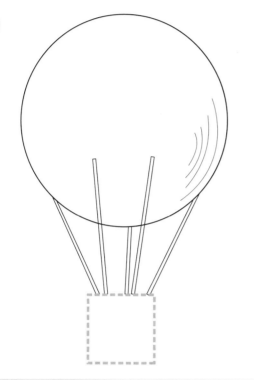

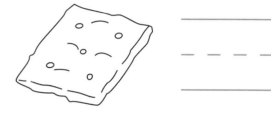

3

4

Directions:
1. Trace the square to make a hot air balloon.
2. Write the number of corners.

3–4. Draw an X on the square.

Name

Practice at Home

①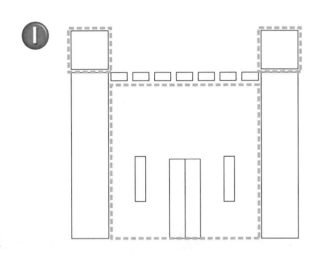

②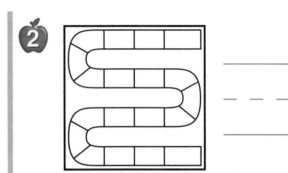

3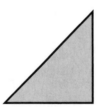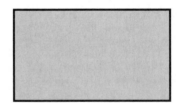

④

Directions:

1. Trace the squares to make a castle.

2. Write the number of sides.

3–4. Draw an X on the square.

Math Triumphs

Name _____

Vocabulary and English Language Development

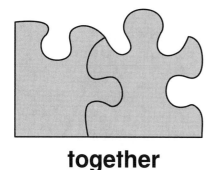

together

apart

1

2

Chapter 5

ACTIVITY Show students two pattern block squares, or squares of construction paper. Hold them apart and say: "The squares are **apart**." Ask: "How can you tell they are apart?" (Sample answer: They are not touching.) Then hold the squares so two sides are touching, and say: "The squares are **together**." Ask: "How can you tell they are together?" (Sample answer: They are touching.) Show students other classroom items that can be together or apart, and have them call out "together" or "apart" to describe the items.

WORKSHEET DIRECTIONS Circle the pieces that are together.

Name

Skills Practice

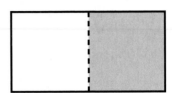

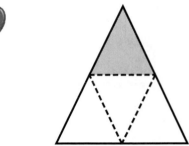

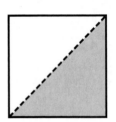

 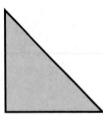

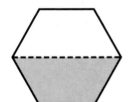

Directions:

1. Draw an X on the shape that is used to make the rectangle.

2. Draw an X on the shape that is used to make the triangle.

3. Draw an X on the shape that is used to make the square.

4. Draw an X on the shape that is used to make the figure.

Name _____

Practice at Home

①
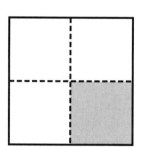

②

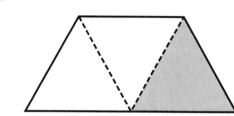

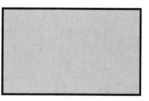 

③

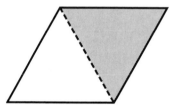

 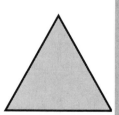

④

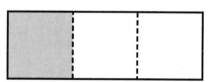

Directions:
1. Draw an X on the shape that is used to make the square.
2. Draw an X on the shape that is used to make the figure.
3. Draw an X on the shape that is used to make the triangle.
4. Draw an X on the shape that is used to make the rectangle.

Foldables Study Organizer

Dinah Zike's Foldables

Create a Standing Cube Foldable to collect information about three-dimensional figures.

1. Use two sheets of the same size paper. Fold each like a hamburger with one side of one $\frac{1}{2}$ inch shorter than the other side.

2. Fold the long side over the short side of both sheets of paper, making tabs.

3. On one of the folded papers, place a small amount of glue along the small folded tab, next to the valley, but not in it.

4. Place the non-folded edge of the second sheet square into the valley and fold the glue-covered tab over this sheet. Press flat until the glue holds. Repeat with the other side.

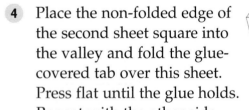

5. Allow the glue to dry. Then, the cube can be collapsed flat to allow students to work at their desks. The cube can also be folded into fourths for moving it or storing it.

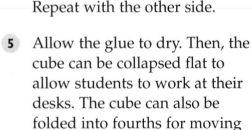

TAKING NOTES

As you read the chapter together, have students find a picture of a sphere, cylinder, rectangular prism, and cube and glue them to the four sides of their Foldable. Have students make cutouts of a sphere, cylinder, rectangular prism, and cube. Then, have them place the figures in their Foldable.

USING THE FOLDABLE

As students review, have them check their understanding by taking a figure from their Foldable and describing its features.

USING THE FOLDABLE

Have students work in pairs, and use their figure cards: circle, rectangle square, cube, rectangular prism, and cylinder from their Foldable to take turns matching the figures with the solid.

Games and Puzzles
Shape Up

GET READY

- Put students in groups of two to four.
- Give each student a copy of the **Shape Up** robot. Give each pair or group one **Shape Up** spinner, a paper clip, and a pencil.

DIRECTIONS:

- Determine the first player and the order of turns.
- Use the paper clip and pencil tip to create a spinner. Place the pencil tip in the center of the spinner diagram to start the game.
- The first player spins and names the shape indicated by the spinner. The player then colors the corresponding shape on the robot.
- Play rotates to the next player. If no shape is available for coloring on the robot, the play progresses to the next player.
- The first player to color the entire robot is the winner.

VARIATION

Create a new three-quadrant spinner to include a square, a rectangle, and a circle. Play is the same, except students color each face on the geometric solid that matches the two-dimensional shape on the spinner. For example, if a student spins a rectangle, he or she could color one face of the rectangular prism on the robot's leg.

What You Need
- Shape Up robot
- Shape Up spinner
- paper clip
- pencil

Number of Players
2–4

Chapter 6

Robot

Shape Up

Math Triumphs

Spinner
Shape Up

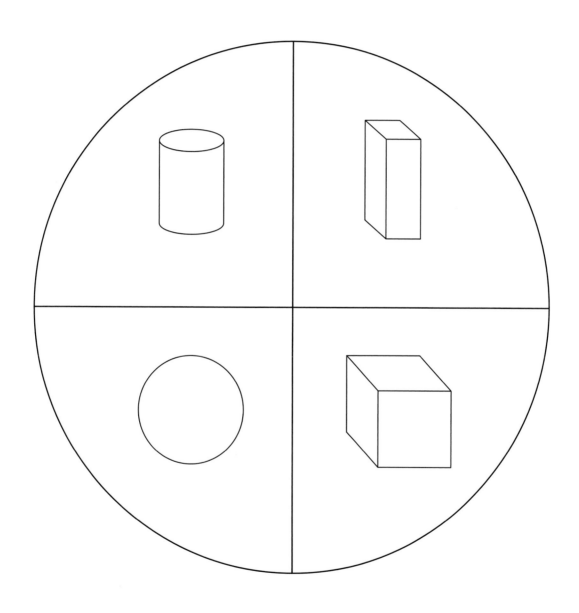

Name _____

Vocabulary and English Language Development

 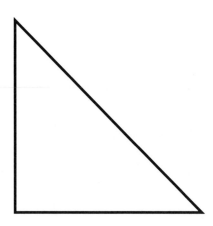

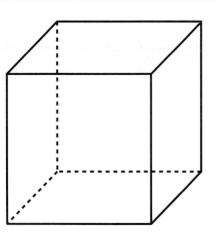 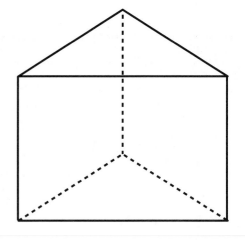

ACTIVITY Display a rectangular sheet of paper or some other two-dimensional **shape.** Ask students to touch the **sides.** Remind students that a **side** is a straight line in a closed figure. Next, display a cereal box, a tissue box, or some other geometric solid. Ask students to touch the **faces.** Remind students that the **faces** are the flat part of a **solid** figure.

WORKSHEET DIRECTIONS
1–2. Trace the sides with a blue crayon.
3–4. Color one face with a red crayon.

Name _____

Skills Practice

 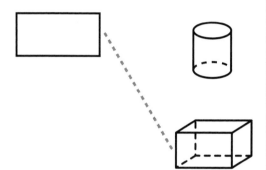

 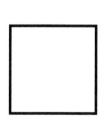 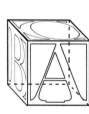 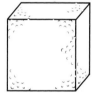

Directions:

1. Draw a line from the rectangle to the solid that has a rectangle as one of its faces.

2. Draw a line from the square to the solid that has a square as one of its faces.

3. Draw a line from the square to the object that has a square as one of its faces.

4. Draw an X on the object that has a circle as one of its faces.

Name _____

Practice at Home

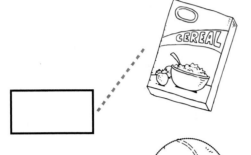

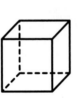

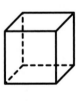

Directions:

1. Draw a line from the rectangle to the object that has a rectangle as one of its faces.
2. Draw an X on the object that has a square as one of its faces.

3. Draw a line from the circle to the solid that has a circle as one of its faces.
4. Draw a line from the square to the solid that has a square as one of its faces.

Name _____

Vocabulary and English Language Development

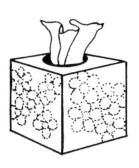

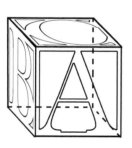

Chapter 6

ACTIVITY With students, talk about objects that **roll** (soccer ball, bike, skateboard) and objects that **stack** (blocks, dishes). Gather several objects that are spheres, cubes, or rectangular prisms (a ball, a block, a tissue box). For each object, ask: "Can a _____ roll? Can a _____ stack?" Have students verify either rolling or stacking for each object.

WORKSHEET DIRECTIONS Circle the things that will roll. Draw an X on the things that will stack.

Name _____

Skills Practice

 1

 2

 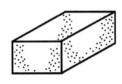 

 3

  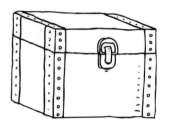

 4

Directions:
1. Circle the object that can be stacked.
2. Circle the object that can be rolled.
3. Draw an X on the object that can be stacked.
4. Draw an X on the object that can be rolled and stacked.

Name _____

Practice at Home

1

2

3

4

Directions:

1. Draw an X on the object that can be rolled.
2. Draw an X on the object that can be stacked.
3. Circle the object that can be rolled.
4. Circle the object that can be rolled and stacked.

Math Triumphs

Chapter 6

Name

Vocabulary and English Language Development

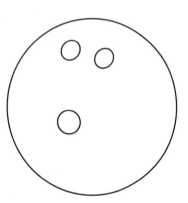 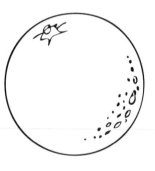

ACTIVITY Gather several examples of **spheres** (a ball, a marble, an orange) and circular shapes that are not spheres (a paper plate, quarter). Show students a ball. Say: "This is a sphere. It is shaped like a ball." Ask students to try to choose the objects that are spheres. Lead them to see that a circle is flat, while a sphere is not.

WORKSHEET DIRECTIONS Color the objects that are spheres.

Name

Skills Practice

①

②

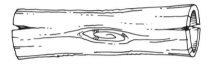

③

④

Chapter 6

Directions:
1–2. Draw an X on the sphere.
3–4. Draw a line from one sphere to the other sphere.

Math Triumphs

Name

Practice at Home

1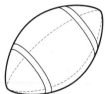

2

3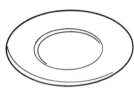

4

Directions:

1–2. Draw an X on the sphere.

3–4. Draw a line from one sphere to the other sphere.

Math Triumphs

Name _____

Vocabulary and English Language Development

Chapter 6

1

2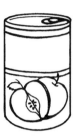

3

4

5

6

ACTIVITY Show students a **cylinder.** Have students find the **circles** on the ends and the curved face. Have students search for cylinders in the classroom (e.g., cans, jars, cups, etc.).

WORKSHEET DIRECTIONS Circle the objects that are cylinders.

Name _____

Skills Practice

1

2

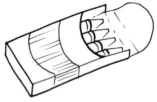

3

4

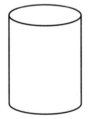

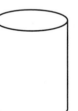

Directions:
1–2. Circle the cylinder.
3–4. Draw a line from one cylinder to the other cylinder.

Name

Practice at Home

1

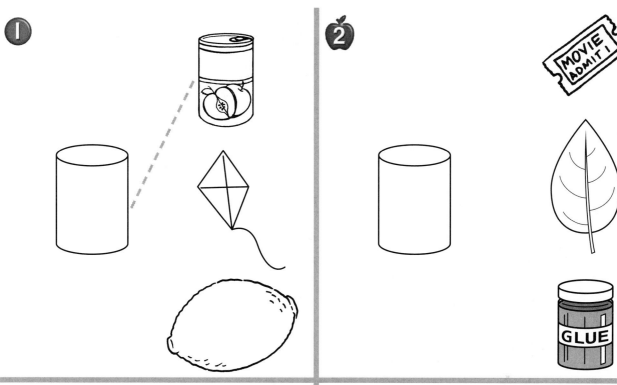

2

3

4

Chapter 6

Directions:
1–2. Draw a line from one cylinder to the other cylinder.
3–4. Circle the cylinder.

Name _____

Vocabulary and English Language Development

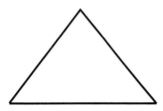

ACTIVITY Take out three straws. Cut one exactly in half. Guide students in using the two long straws and the two short pieces to make a **rectangle.** Ask students to describe the sides on a rectangle. (Two sides are long and two sides are short.) Have students look for examples of rectangles in the classroom (e.g., the cover of a book, a chalkboard eraser, a picture frame).

WORKSHEET DIRECTIONS Trace the rectangles with a red crayon.

Math Triumphs

Name _____

Skills Practice

 1

   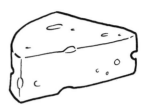

 2

 3

 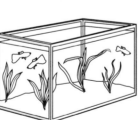

4

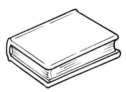

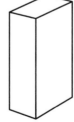 

Chapter 6

Directions:
1–2. Draw an X on the rectangular prism.
3–4. Draw a line from one rectangular prism to the other rectangular prism.

Name _____

Practice at Home

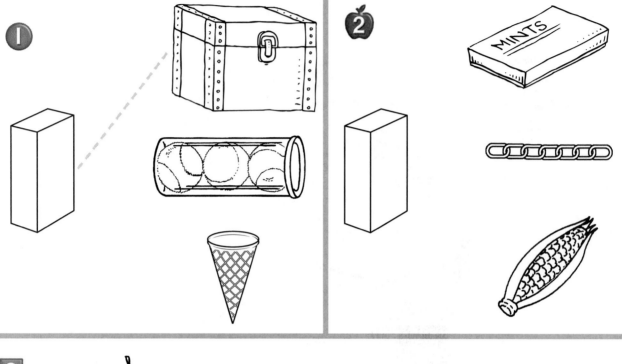

  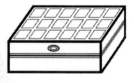

 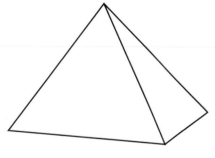 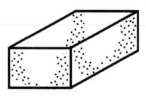 

Directions:

1–2. Draw a line from one rectangular prism to the other rectangular prism.

3–4. Draw an X on the rectangular prism.

Name

Vocabulary and English Language Development

 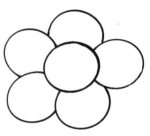

 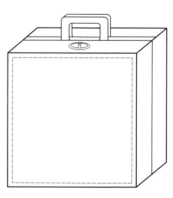

Chapter 6

ACTIVITY Give students four craft sticks. Ask them to use the sticks to make a **square**. Have students count the **sides**. Cut out pictures from a magazine. Have students identify any squares in the pictures.

WORKSHEET DIRECTIONS Color the squares.

Name _____

Skills Practice

 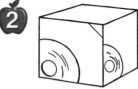

 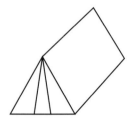

 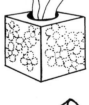

Directions:

1–2. Draw an X on the cube.

3–4. Draw a line from one cube to the other cube.

Math Triumphs

Name

Practice at Home

1

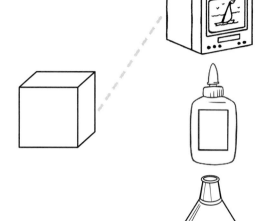

2

3

4

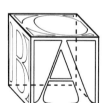

Directions:
1–2. Draw a line from one cube to the other cube.
3–4. Draw an X on the cube.

Lesson 6-7

Name

Vocabulary and English Language Development

1 3	2 4
3 6	4 8

ACTIVITY Give students three craft sticks. Ask: "Can you make a **figure** with three sticks?" Ask students to name the figures they have just made. If they do not know, give them the figure's name. Repeat with four, six, and eight sticks.

WORKSHEET DIRECTIONS Draw a figure with the number of sides shown.

Name

Skills Practice

1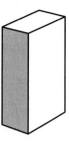

2

3

4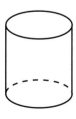

Chapter 6

Directions:

1. Draw an X on the shape that is a face of the rectangular prism.
2. Draw an X on the shape that is a face of the cube.
3. Draw an X on the shape that is a face of the box.
4. Draw an X on the shapes that make a cylinder.

Name

Practice at Home

1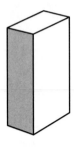

2

3

4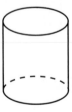

Directions:
1. Draw an X on the shape that is a face of the rectangular prism.
2. Draw an X on the shape that is a face of the box.
3. Draw an X on the shape that is a face of the cube.
4. Draw an X on the shapes that make a cylinder.

Math Triumphs

Foldables Study Organizer

Dinah Zike's Foldables

Create three Pocket Foldables for describing objects' space and position.

1 Fold an $8\frac{1}{2}$" × 11" sheet of paper in half like a hamburger.

2 Open the folded paper and fold one of the long sides up two inches to form a pocket. Refold along the hamburger fold so that the newly formed pockets are on the inside.

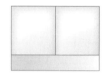

3 Glue the outer edges of the two-inch fold with a small amount of glue.

4 Make three sets of Pocket Foldables (enough for each lesson). Glue pockets together to form a Pocket Book.

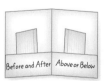 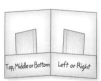

TAKING NOTES

As you read the chapter together, record the lesson titles on the pockets, and have students find pictures of objects that can be glued or taped onto their index cards in group that corresponds with the title of the pocket.

 USING THE FOLDABLE

As students review, have them check their understanding by placing a counter on the objects that corresponds with the title on the pocket.

 USING THE FOLDABLE

In pairs, have students take turns using their Foldable to identify the picture that corresponds with the title on the pocket.

Games and Puzzles
Position It

GET READY

- Reproduce the **Position It** game board and **Position It** spinner on cardstock. You will need one game board and one spinner for each pair of students.

- Arrange students in pairs, and give each pair a game board, a spinner and paper clip, two game pieces, and one cube of each color: red, green, blue, and yellow.

DIRECTIONS:

- Players put together the spinner, using a pencil and paper clip. Players put their game pieces on START and determine who will play first.

- Players take turns spinning. Each player moves his or her piece on the game board, according to the number of squares indicated by the spinner. The player then uses cubes to model the configuration described on the game board square. The other player checks his or her work.

- If the model is correct, the player remains on the square. If the model is not correct, the player moves back one square.

- The first player to reach FINISH wins the game.

What You Need

- Position It game board
- Position It spinner
- cardstock
- paper clip for spinner
- counters for game pieces
- red, green, blue, and yellow cubes (one each per pair)
- pencil

Number of Players

2

START	A blue cube is to the right of a red cube.	A green cube is in the middle of a tower.	A red cube is inside your desk.	A yellow cube is before a green cube.
				A green cube is to the left of a blue cube.
A green cube is to the right of a yellow cube.	A red cube is after a blue cube.	A yellow cube is outside your pencil box.	A yellow cube is to the right of a blue cube.	A blue cube is at the top of a tower.
A red cube is at the bottom of a tower.				
A blue cube is in the middle of a tower.	A green cube is inside the coat closet.	A green cube is before a yellow cube.	A yellow cube is to the left of a red cube.	A yellow cube is in the middle of a tower.
				A green cube is at the bottom of a tower.
FINISH	A blue cube is outside your backpack.	A green cube is to the right of a red cube.	A yellow cube is after a green cube.	A red cube is at the top of a tower.

Game Board

Position It

START	A blue cube is to the right of a red cube.	A green cube is in the middle of a tower.	A red cube is inside your desk.	A yellow cube is before a green cube.
				A green cube is to the left of a blue cube.
A green cube is to the right of a yellow cube.	A red cube is after a blue cube.	A yellow cube is outside your pencil box.	A yellow cube is to the right of a blue cube.	A blue cube is at the top of a tower.
A red cube is at the bottom of a tower.				
A blue cube is in the middle of a tower.	A green cube is inside the coat closet.	A green cube is before a yellow cube.	A yellow cube is to the left of a red cube.	A yellow cube is in the middle of a tower.
				A green cube is at the bottom of a tower.
FINISH	A blue cube is outside your backpack.	A green cube is to the right of a red cube.	A yellow cube is after a green cube.	A red cube is at the top of a tower.

Spinner

Position It

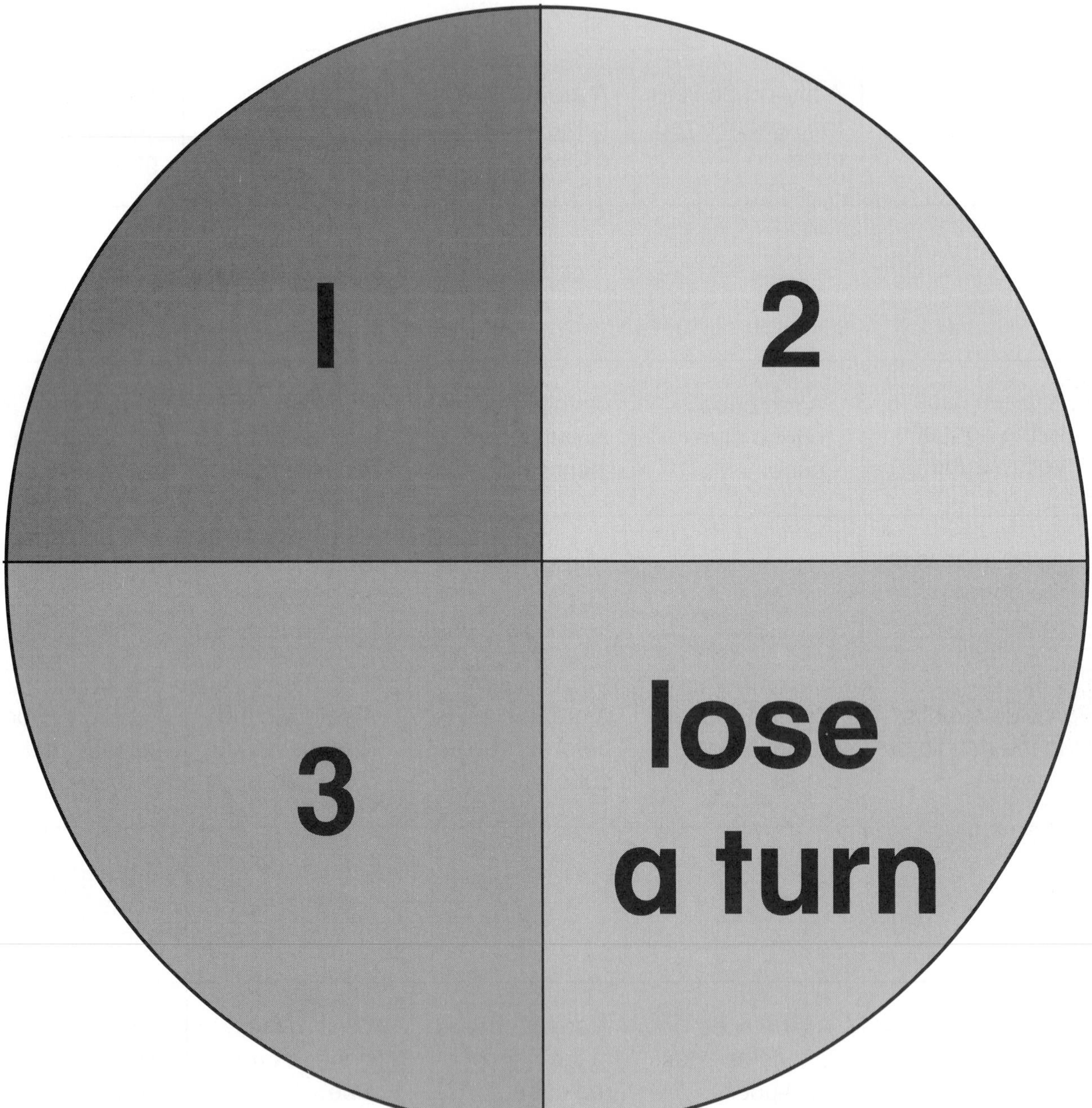

Name _____

Vocabulary and English Language Development

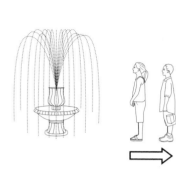

 is before

 is after

①

②

③

④

ACTIVITY Have two students stand, one in front of the other, facing the chalkboard. Point to the first student and say: "(first student's name) is **before** (second student's name)." Then point to the second student and say: "(second student's name) is **after** (first student's name)." Have those students sit down and ask three other students to form a line, facing the chalkboard. Point to the middle student in the line and ask: "Who is before (middle student's name)?" or: "Who is after (middle student's name)?" Continue for each student in line. Then, have students switch places, and repeat the questioning.

WORKSHEET DIRECTIONS

1. Find the bear before the gray bear. Color it blue.
2. Find the bear after the gray bear. Color it red.
3. Find the bear before the gray bear. Color it green.
4. Find the bear after the gray bear. Color it orange.

Lesson 7-1

Name _____

Skills Practice

1

2

3

4

Directions:

1. Circle the marble before the gray-and-black marble.

2. Circle the marble before the white-and-black marble.

3. Draw an X on the marble after the gray-and-black marble.

4. Draw an X on the marble after the white-and-black marble.

Math Triumphs

Name _____

Practice at Home

Chapter 7

Directions:
1. Circle the star before the white star.
2. Circle the star before the gray star.
3. Draw an X on the star after the gray star.
4. Draw an X on the star after the striped star.

Name _____

Vocabulary and English Language Development

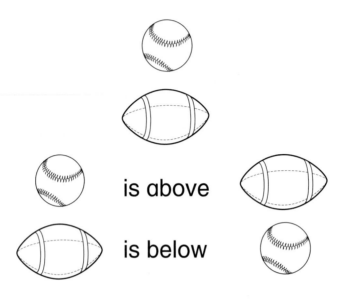

is above

is below

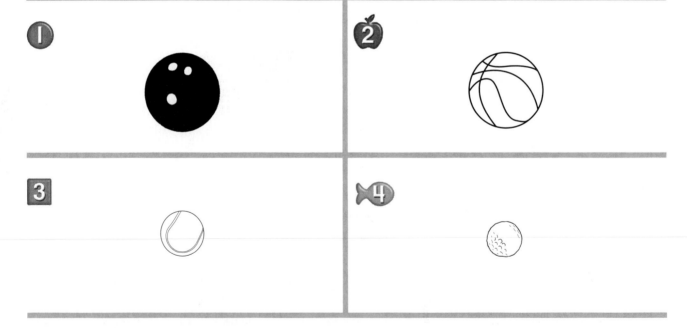

ACTIVITY Make a tower by placing a blue cube below a red cube. Tell students: "The blue cube is **below** the red cube." Point out that *below* means *under*. Then say, "The red cube is **above** the blue cube." Tell students that *above* means *over*. Hand out blue, green and red cubes to small groups of students. Have them build towers. Then, invite them to describe their towers to the class, using the words *below* and *above*.

WORKSHEET DIRECTIONS

1–2. Draw an X above each ball.   3–4. Draw an X below each ball.

Math Triumphs

Name _____

Skills Practice

1

2

3

4

Chapter 7

Directions:
1. Draw an X below the boat.
2. Draw an X above the airplane.

3. Circle the object below the helicopter.
4. Circle the object above the wagon.

Name _____

Practice at Home

1

2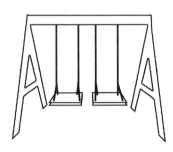

3

4

Directions:

1. Draw an X above the slide.
2. Draw an X below the swing set.

3. Circle the object above the teeter-totter.
4. Circle the object below the monkey bars.

Name

Vocabulary and English Language Development

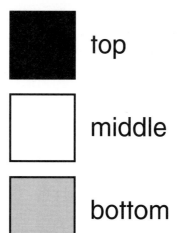

top

middle

bottom

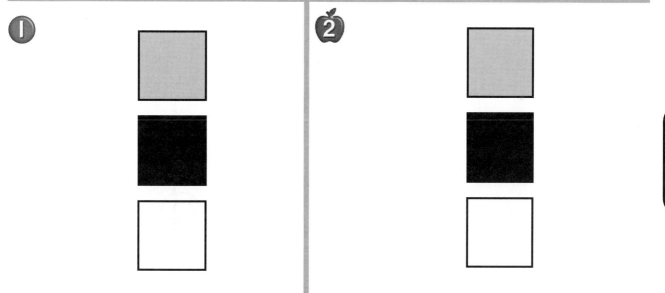

① ②

ACTIVITY Make a tower by placing a red cube at the top, a yellow cube in the middle, and a blue cube at the bottom. Show students which cubes are the **top**, **bottom**, and **middle** cubes. As you do, explain that the top is the highest, the bottom is the lowest, and the middle is in between. Then, distribute differently colored cubes to small groups of students. Let them build their own towers and describe them to the class, using the words *top*, *middle*, and *bottom*.

WORKSHEET DIRECTIONS
1. Circle the square at the bottom.
2. Circle the square in the middle.

Math Triumphs

Name _____

Skills Practice

1

2

3

4

Directions:
1. Circle the object in the middle.
2. Circle the object at the top.

3. Circle the object at the bottom.
4. Draw a circle at the top. Draw an X at the bottom.

Name _____

Practice at Home

1

2

3

4

Chapter 7

Directions:
1. Circle the object at the bottom.
2. Circle the object in the middle.
3. Circle the object at the top.
4. Draw a circle at the top. Draw an X at the bottom.

Math Triumphs

Name

Vocabulary and English Language Development

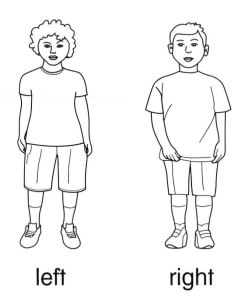

left   right

1

2

ACTIVITY Hand out one yellow and one green cube to each student. Using your own, place the yellow cube to the right (the students' right) of the green cube, and say: "The yellow cube is to the **right** of the green cube. The green cube is to the **left** of the yellow cube." Then, have students work together to set up their own two-cube arrangements. Invite them to describe their setups to the class, using the words *left* and *right*.

WORKSHEET DIRECTIONS
1. Circle the student on the right.
2. Circle the student on the left.

Name _____

Skills Practice

1

2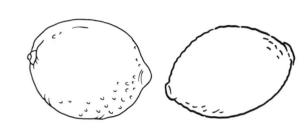

3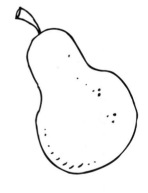

4

Chapter 7

Directions:
1. Circle the apple on the left.
2. Circle the lemon on the right.
3. Draw a circle to the right of the pear.
4. Draw a square to the right of the strawberry.
   Draw a triangle to the left of the strawberry.

Math Triumphs

Name _____

Practice at Home

1

2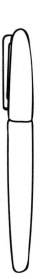

3

4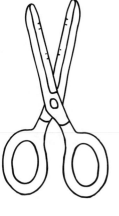

Directions:
1. Circle the crayon on the right.
2. Circle the marker on the left.

3. Draw a circle to the left of the glue.
4. Draw a triangle to the right of the scissors.
   Draw a square to the left of the scissors.

Name _____

Vocabulary and English Language Development

front

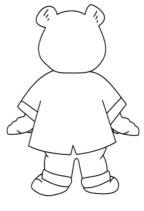

back

1

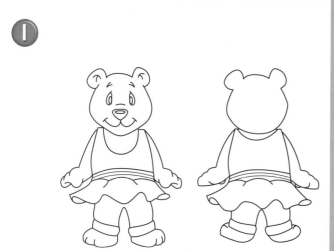

2

Chapter 7

ACTIVITY Show students the front of a stuffed animal. Ask: "What do you see on the **front**?" (eyes, a face, a belly, etc.) Show students the **back**. Ask: "What do you see on the back?" (a tail, etc.) Discuss with students how the front and back of the stuffed animal are alike and different. Then, show students the front and back of other objects, such as a cereal box or a book. Have them determine if you are showing the front or the back of the object. Ask students to explain their choices.

WORKSHEET DIRECTIONS
1. Circle the picture of the front of the bear.
2. Circle the picture of the back of the bunny.

Math Triumphs

Name

Skills Practice

Directions:
1. Circle the picture of the front of the bunny.
2. Circle the picture of the back of the dog.
3. Draw an X on the back of the frog.
4. Draw an X on the front of the gerbil.
5. Circle the pictures that show the back of a bear.

Name _____

Practice at Home

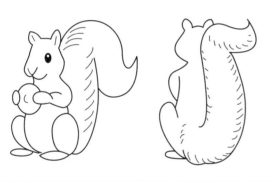

Chapter 7

Directions:

1. Circle the picture of the back of the kitten.
2. Circle the picture of the front of the lion.
3. Draw an X on the front of the squirrel.
4. Draw an X on the back of the bear.
5. Circle the pictures that show the back of a bunny.

Name _____

Vocabulary and English Language Development

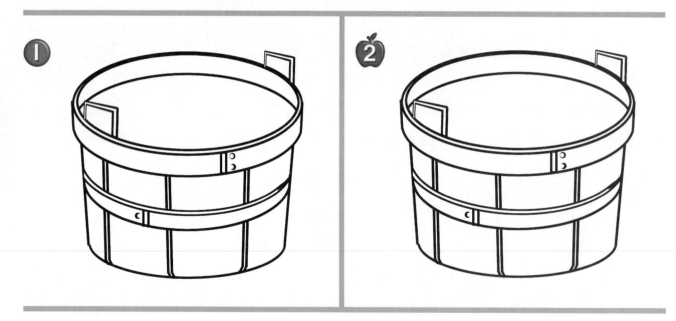

ACTIVITY Place a cube inside a box. Tell students, "The cube is **inside** the box." Remove the cube from the box and set it outside the box. Say: "Now the cube is **outside** the box." Give small groups of students a box and a cube. Have each group member place the cube inside or outside the box and describe the cube's position to group members, using the words *inside* or *outside*.

WORKSHEET DIRECTIONS
1. Draw an X inside the basket.
2. Draw an X outside the basket.

Name _____

Skills Practice

1

2

3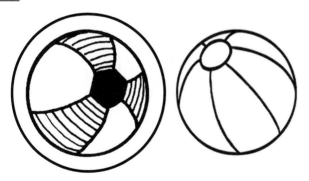

4

Chapter 7

Directions:

1. Draw an X outside the birdcage.
2. Draw an X inside the bathtub.
3. Draw an X on the ball that is inside the circle.
4. Draw an X on the book that is outside the circle.

Name

Practice at Home

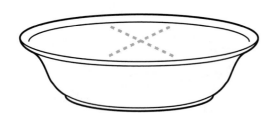 

Directions:

1. Draw an X inside the bowl.
2. Draw an X outside the bucket.

3. Draw an X on the juice box that is outside the circle.
4. Draw an X on the toy that is inside the circle.

Name

Vocabulary and English Language Development

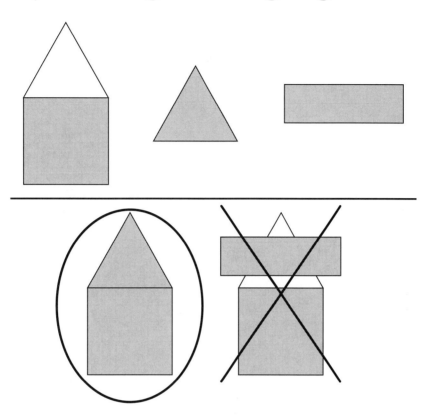

ACTIVITY Draw the outline of a rectangle on the board. Hold up a congruent construction paper rectangle and a square, and ask students: "Which object will fill the space?" (rectangle) Demonstrate trying to fit both pieces, saving the correct one for last. Repeat with other outlines on the board and other congruent paper shapes.

WORKSHEET DIRECTIONS Circle the object that fits in the blank space.

Math Triumphs

Chapter 7

Name _____

Skills Practice

  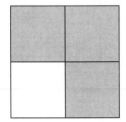 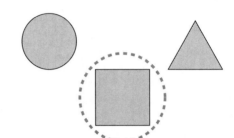

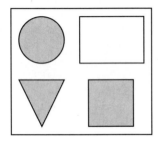 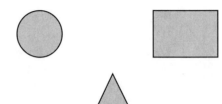

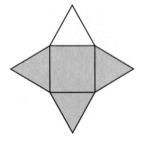 

  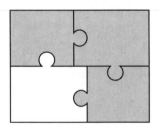

Directions:
1–4. Circle the object that fits in the blank space.

Math Triumphs

Name

Practice at Home

1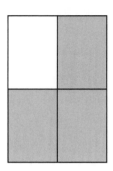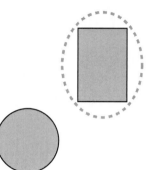

2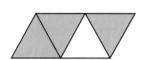

3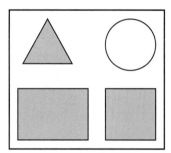

4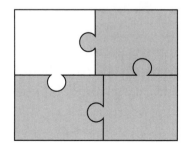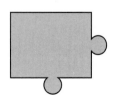

Chapter 7

Directions:

1–4. Circle the object that fits in the blank space.

Math Triumphs

Foldables Study Organizer

Dinah Zike's Foldables

Create a Display Case Foldable to sort objects by attributes.

1 Make a four-door book out of a shutter fold.

2 Fold the two inside corners back to the outer edges (mountains) of the shutter fold. This will result in two tacos that will make the four-door book look like it has a shirt collar. Do the same thing to the bottom of the four-door book.

3 Form a 90-degree angle and overlap the folder triangles to make a display case that does not use staples or glue. Or, as illustrated, cut off all four triangles, and staple or glue the sides.

4 Place two of the same object(s) in one display case and two different objects in the second display case.

TAKING NOTES

As you read the chapter together, have students make separate word cards for the following terms:

- Same or Different
- Equal or Unequal
- More or Less
- Long or Short
- Tall or Short
- Heavy or Light
- Full or Empty

 USING THE FOLDABLE

As students review, have them check their understanding by using the display cases to sort objects by the attributes that were written on the word cards. For example, place the word card same in one display case and dfferent in another display case. Then, have students place two of the same objects in the correctly labeled display case and two different objects in the correctly labeled display case.

USING THE FOLDABLE

Have students work in pairs, and take turns sorting objects by attribute by placing them in the display cases and labeling them with a word card.

Games and Puzzles
Match Game

GET READY

- Reproduce the **Match Game** cards on cardstock. You will need one set of cards for each pair of students.

- Pair up students and give each pair a set of shuffled game cards and a coin. Guide them to arrange the cards facedown in an array.

DIRECTIONS:

- Players flip a coin to decide who goes first.

- The first player turns over two cards. If they are alike in color, shape, and size, the player keeps the two cards. If the cards are different, the player turns them facedown.

- The other player then takes a turn. The game is over when all of the cards are matched.

- The player with the greater number of cards wins.

What You Need
- Match Game cards
- cardstock
- coin

Number of Players
2

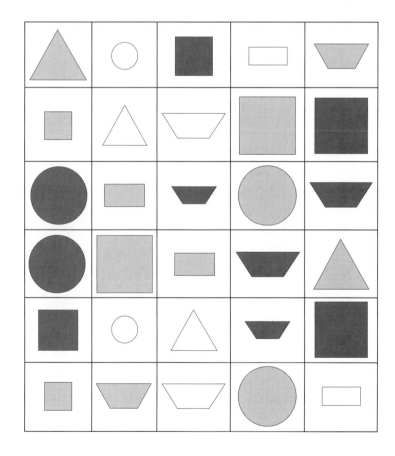

Chapter 8

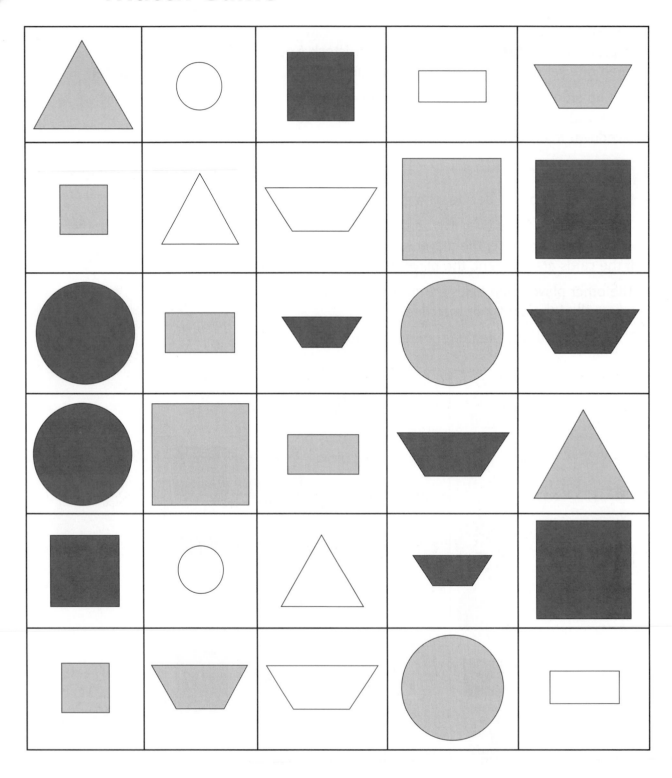

Math Triumphs

Name _____

Vocabulary and English Language Development

same

different

Chapter 8

ACTIVITY Show students two paper circles that are the same size and color. Say: "These circles are the **same** because they are the same size and color." Then hold up two circles that are different sizes and colors. Say: "These circles are **different** because they are not the same sizes or the same colors." Provide children with paper and circular objects, such as jar lids. Have them trace and color two circles that are the same and two circles that are different.

WORKSHEET DIRECTIONS Circle the squirrels that are the same. Draw an X on the squirrels that are different.

Name

Skills Practice

1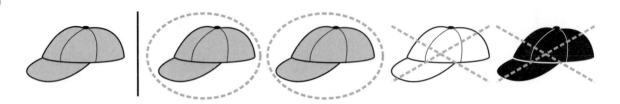

2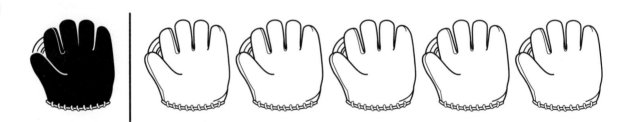

3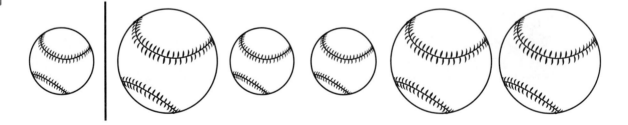

Directions:

1. Look at the first cap. Circle all of the caps that are the same color. Draw an X on the caps that are a different color.
2. Look at the first mitt. Color three mitts the same color. Color the other mitts a different color.
3. Look at the first ball. Circle the balls that are the same size as the first ball. Draw an X on the balls that are a different size.

Math Triumphs

Name

Practice at Home

3

Chapter 8

Directions:

1. Look at the first bunch of grapes. Circle all of the bunches of grapes that are the same color. Draw an X on the bunches of grapes that are a different color.

2. Look at the first apple. Color two apples the same color. Color the other apples a different color.

3. Look at the first orange. Circle the oranges that are the same size as the first orange. Draw an X on the oranges that are a different size.

Name _____

Vocabulary and English Language Development

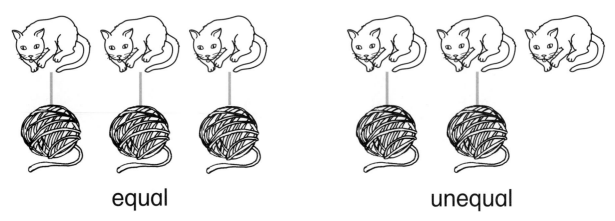

equal   unequal

1   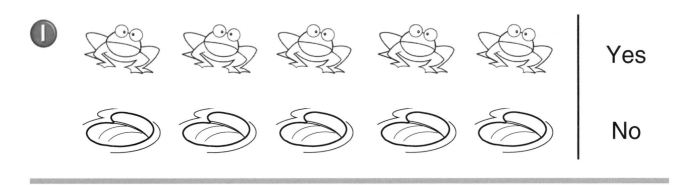   Yes

No

2      Yes

No

ACTIVITY Show students four pencils and three erasers. Count the items in each group. Ask: "Is the number of pencils **equal** to the number of erasers?" (no) Point out that there are more pencils than erasers. Say: "The groups are **unequal**." Add another eraser to the group. Re-count the items in each group. Ask: "Is the number of pencils **equal** to the number of erasers?" (yes) Provide students with a group of crayons and a group of markers, and ask them to make one equal group and one unequal group.

WORKSHEET DIRECTIONS Draw lines to match. Circle *Yes* if the sets are equal. Circle *No* if the sets are unequal.

_____
_ _ _ _ _ _ _ _ _ _ _ _ _ _ _ _ _ _ _ _

Name _____

Skills Practice

1

2

3

Chapter 8

Directions:

1. Draw lines to match the horses and the horseshoes. Circle them if they are equal or draw an X on them if they are unequal.
2. Draw lines to match the sheep and the cows. Circle them if they are equal or draw an X on them if they are unequal.
3. Draw lines to match the chickens and the eggs. Circle them if they are equal or draw an X on them if they are unequal.

Name

Practice at Home

 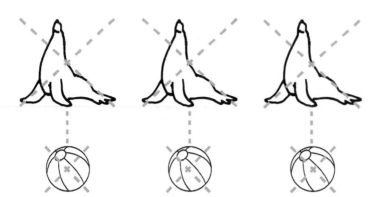

Directions:

1. Draw lines to match the seals and the beach balls. Circle them if they are equal or draw an X on them if they are unequal.

2. Draw lines to match the rabbits and the turtles. Circle them if they are equal or draw an X on them if they are unequal.

3. Draw lines to match the ducks and the ponds. Circle them if they are equal or draw an X on them if they are unequal.

Name _____

Vocabulary and English Language Development

holds **more** than

holds **less** than

 1

 2

ACTIVITY Show students two bowls of different sizes. Ask: "Which bowl holds more?" (the larger one) Guide students to relate **more** to *bigger* and **less** to *smaller*. Illustrate this concept by filling the small bowl with dry beans or rice. Ask: "What will happen if I pour the rice into the larger bowl?" (The larger bowl will not be filled.) Pour the rice from the smaller bowl to the larger bowl. Repeat this process with several other pairs of containers. Ask students to first identify which container holds more (or less), and then test the prediction by pouring dry beans or rice from one bowl to the other.

WORKSHEET DIRECTIONS
1. Circle the container that holds more.
2. Draw an X on the container that holds less.

Math Triumphs

Chapter 8

Name

Skills Practice

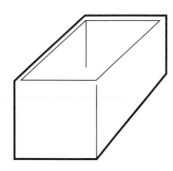

MILK

Directions:

1. The box holds 50 connecting cubes. The glass holds 5 connecting cubes. Draw an X on the container that holds less.

2. One person can have a serving of milk from the carton. Twelve people can have a serving of milk from the jug. Circle the container that holds more.

3. April is packing old clothing in a bag. She is using the bag shown. Draw a bag that will hold less clothing than April's bag.

_____

Name _____

Practice at Home

Directions:

1. The bowl holds 3 eggs. The bucket holds 30 eggs. Circle the container that holds more.
2. One person can have a serving of juice from the glass. Eight people can have a serving of juice from the pitcher. Draw an X on the container that holds less.
3. Roy is playing in the water at the beach. He is using the pail shown. Draw a pail that will hold more water than Roy's pail.

Math Triumphs

Lesson 8-3   A193

Chapter 8

Name _____

Vocabulary and English Language Development

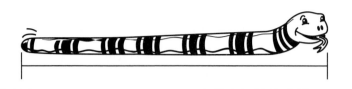 **long**

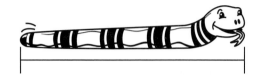 **short**

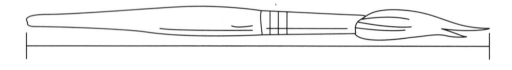

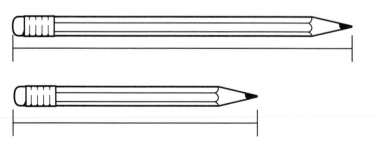

ACTIVITY Show students two connecting cube trains—one made with six blue cubes and the other made with four red cubes. Align the trains one above the other and ask: "Which train is long?" (blue) "How can you tell?" (Accept all reasonable responses.) Discuss with students the meaning of **long** and **short**. Show students a classroom object, such as a yardstick or board eraser, and invite them to find other objects that are short or long when compared to the given object.

WORKSHEET DIRECTIONS
1. Circle the long paintbrush.
2. Draw an X on the short pencil.

Math Triumphs

Name

Skills Practice

(1)

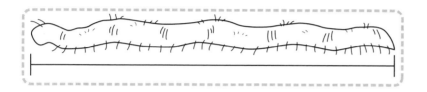

(2)

3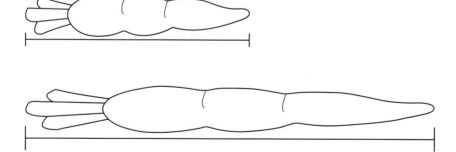

Chapter 8

Directions:

1. Circle the long bug.

2. Draw an X on the short loaf of bread.

3. Circle the long carrot.

Math Triumphs

Name

Practice at Home

1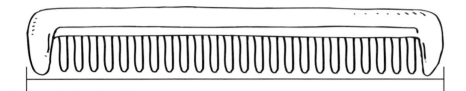

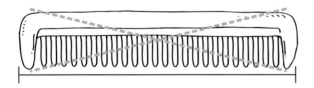

2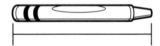

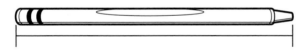

3

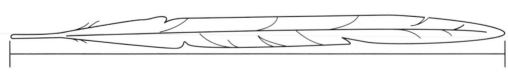

Directions:
1. Draw an X on the short comb.
2. Circle the long crayon.

3. Draw an X on the short feather.

Name _____

Vocabulary and English Language Development

short   **tall**

1

2

ACTIVITY Invite a student to stand next to you at the front of the room. Say: "[Name of student] is **short** and I am **tall**." Find other things around the classroom that are short and tall. Then, have students look through books or magazines and cut out pairs of images that represent *short* and *tall*. Encourage them to share their pictures with their classmates.

WORKSHEET DIRECTIONS
1. Circle the tall building.
2. Draw an X on the short tree.

Chapter 8

Name

Skills Practice

 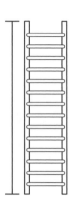

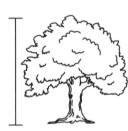 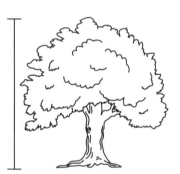

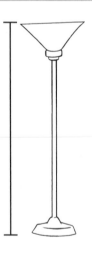 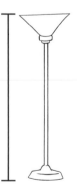

Directions:

1. Draw an X on the short ladder.

2. Circle the tall tree.

3. Draw an X on the short lamp.

Math Triumphs

Name _____

Practice at Home

1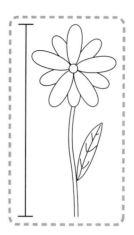

2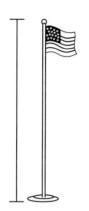

3

Chapter 8

Directions:

1. Circle the tall flower.
2. Draw an X on the short flagpole.

3. Circle the tall giraffe.

Name _____

Vocabulary and English Language Development

light

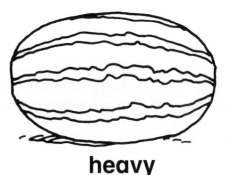

heavy

1

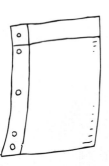

2

ACTIVITY Ask students to take out their math books and a sheet of paper. Have students lift each object. Then ask: "Which object was **heavy**?" (the book) "Which object was **light**?" (the paper) Invite volunteers to explain why the book was heavy and the paper was light. Have students feel the weight of a classroom object, such as a regular stapler or pencil box, and invite them to find other objects that are heavy or light when compared to the given object.

WORKSHEET DIRECTIONS
1. Circle the light object.
2. Draw an X on the heavy object.

Name _____

Skills Practice

1

2

3

Chapter 8

Directions:
1–4. Circle the light object. Draw an X on the heavy object.

Math Triumphs

Lesson 8-6   A201

Name

Practice at Home

  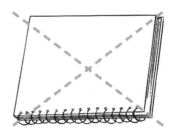

  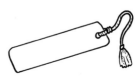

Directions:

1–4. Circle the light object. Draw an X on the heavy object.

Name _____

Vocabulary and English Language Development

empty

full

ACTIVITY Show students a small jar that is **full** of marbles. Point out that that the jar is full—there is no more room to add marbles to the jar. Pour out all of the marbles and show students the **empty** jar. Explain that the jar is empty because there is nothing in it. Ask students to use the words *full* and *empty* in sentences that express their meanings.

WORKSHEET DIRECTIONS
1. Circle the full treasure chest.
2. Draw an X on the empty jar.

Chapter 8

Name

Skills Practice

1

2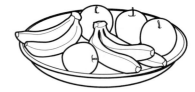

3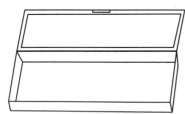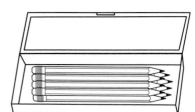

4

Directions:

1–4. Circle the objects that are full. Draw an X on the objects that are empty.

Math Triumphs

Name _____

Practice at Home

 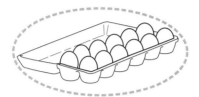 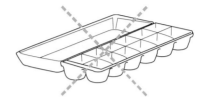

 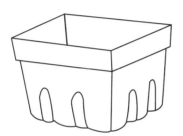 

Chapter 8

Directions:
1–4. Circle the objects that are full. Draw an X on the objects that are empty.

Math Triumphs

Foldables Study Organizer

Dinah Zike's Foldables

Create a Display Case Foldable to order objects by attributes.

1. Make a four-door book out of a shutter fold.

2. Fold the two inside corners back to the outer edges (mountains) of the shutter fold. This will result in two tacos that will make with four door book look like it has a shirt collar. Do the same thing to the bottom of the four-door book.

3. Form a 90-degree angle and overlap the folder triangles to make a display case that does not use staples or glue. Or, as illustrated cut off all four triangles, and staple or glue the sides.

4. Place objects in the display case to be ordered by the attributes that were written on the word cards.

long, longer, longest

TAKING NOTES

As you read the chapter together, have students make word cards for the following terms:

- long, loger, longest
- tall, taller, tallest
- short, shorter, shotest
- heavy or heavier
- light or lighter
- more and most
- less and least

USING THE FOLDABLE

As students review, have them check their understanding by using the display cases to order objects by the attributes that were written on the word cards. For example, place the word card long, longer, and longest in the display case. Then, have students place the three objects in the display case in the correct order.

USING THE FOLDABLE

Have students work in pairs, and take turns ordering objects by attribute by placing them in the display case and labeling them with the correct word card.

Games and Puzzles
Can of Worms

GET READY

- Arrange students in pairs. Give each pair a **Can of Worms** game board and spinner.

- Cut yarn into 20 different lengths. (Make sure that no two are equal.) Make a set for each pair of players.

DIRECTIONS:

- Demonstrate how to use the spinner by placing the paper clip on the point of the pencil, and then placing the pencil point on the spinner. Hold the pencil in one hand and spin the paper clip with the other.

- Place the lengths of yarn in the "can," on the game board. Play begins with each student selecting a "worm." The students place the worms side by side and compare their lengths.

- The students take turns spinning the spinner. If the student spins "shorter," the shorter worm wins. If the student spins "longer," the longer worm wins.

- The winner takes both lengths of yarn and places them inside his or her cup. After all the "worms" have been chosen, the students count the worms in their individual cups. The player with the most worms wins.

VARIATION

Have the first student take a "worm" out of his or her cup, place it on the game board, and spin the spinner. If the spinner lands on "shorter," the second player must find a worm that is shorter than the first player's worm. If the spinner lands on "longer," the second player must find a worm that is longer. If the second player is successful, he or she receives 1 point. The players then switch turns. At the end of the game, the player with the most tally marks wins.

What You Need

- Can of Worms game board
- Can of Worms spinner
- pencil
- paper clip
- 2 small plastic cups
- brown yarn
- scissors

Number of Players

2

Game Board
Can of Worms

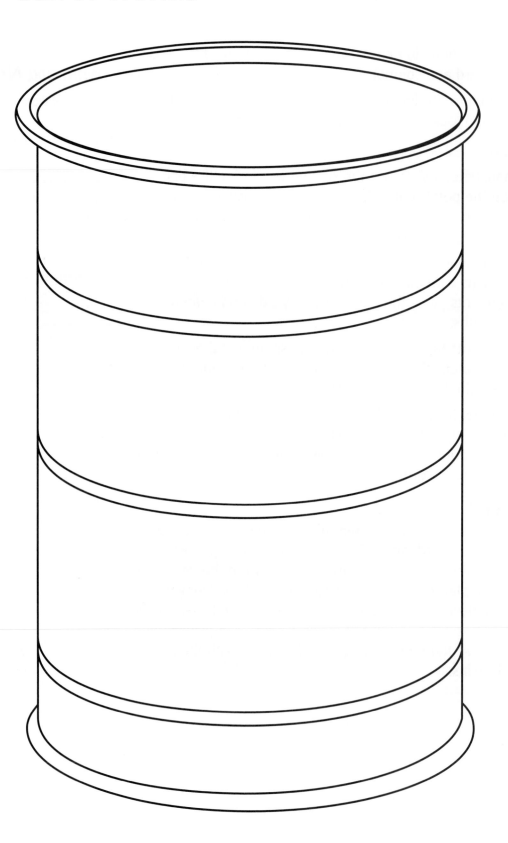

Math Triumphs

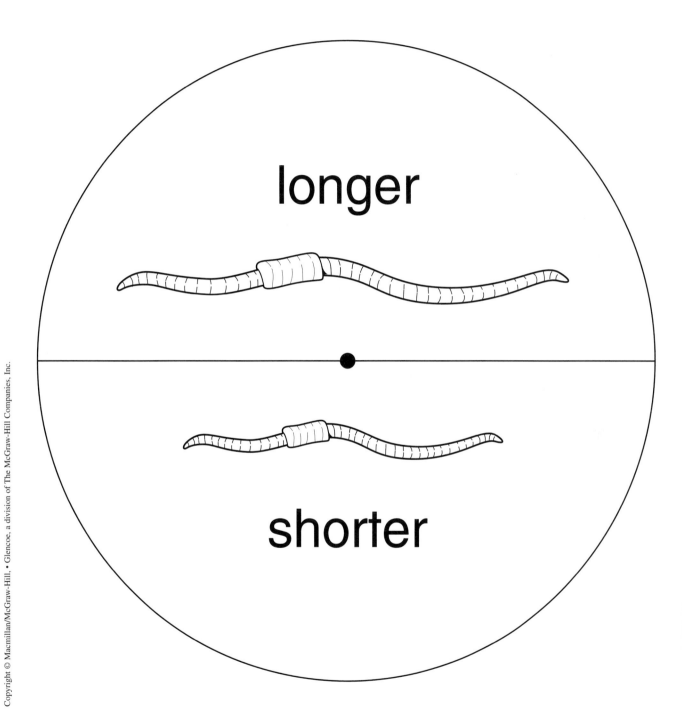

Chapter 9

Name _____

Vocabulary and English Language Development

1

2

3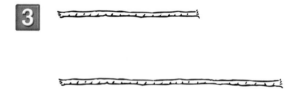

ACTIVITY Cut three strings of different lengths. Invite students to order the strings by increasing length, pointing to each string and saying: **"long, longer, longest."**

WORKSHEET DIRECTIONS

1–2. Draw a string that is longer.

   3. Draw a string that is the longest.

Math Triumphs

Name

Skills Practice

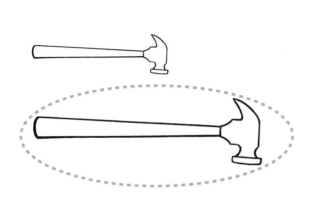

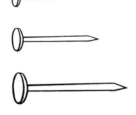

3

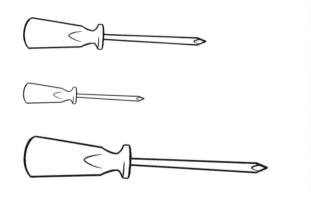

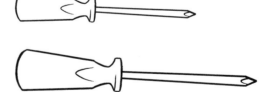

Chapter 9

Directions:
1. Circle the hammer that is longer.
2. Circle the longest nail.
3. Circle the group that shows the lengths in order from long to longest.

Name

Practice at Home

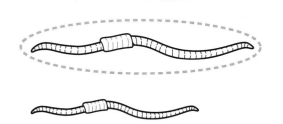

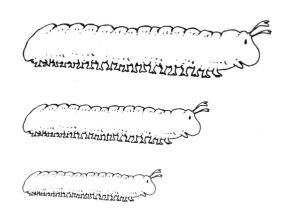

3

Directions:
1. Circle the worm that is longer.
2. Circle the longest caterpillar.
3. Circle the group that shows the lengths in order from long to longest.

Math Triumphs

Name _____

Vocabulary and English Language Development

1

2

3

ACTIVITY Have the students look for objects that are taller than they are. Then, have the students order the objects by identifying each one as **tall, taller,** and **tallest.**

WORKSHEET DIRECTIONS
1–2. Draw a tree that is taller.   3. Draw a tree that is tallest.

Math Triumphs   **Lesson 9-2   A213**

Name

Skills Practice

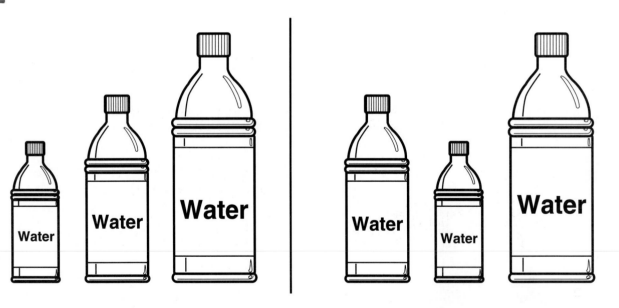

Directions:
1. Circle the container that is taller.
2. Circle the tallest container.
3. Circle the group that is in order from tall to tallest.

Name

Practice at Home

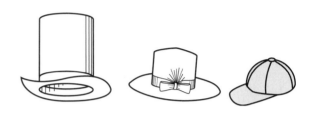

Directions:
1. Circle the hat that is taller.
2. Circle the tallest hat.
3. Circle the group that is in order from tall to tallest.

Math Triumphs

Chapter 9

Name _____

Vocabulary and English Language Development

ACTIVITY Gather magazine pictures of haircuts to demonstrate *short, shorter, shortest.* Show the students pictures of two haircuts. Ask: "Which is the shorter haircut?" Then add the third picture and ask: "Which is the shortest haircut?" Have the students point to each picture and say, **"short, shorter,** and **shortest."**

WORKSHEET DIRECTIONS Draw short hair on the first picture. Draw shorter hair on the second picture. Draw the shortest hair on the third picture.

Name

Skills Practice

 1

2

3

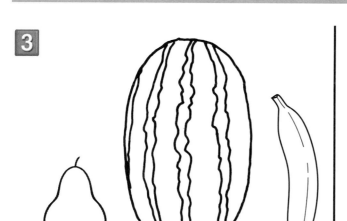 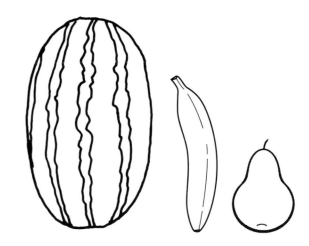

Directions:
1. Circle the shorter fruit.
2. Circle the shortest fruit.
3. Circle the group that is in order from short to shortest.

Math Triumphs

Chapter 9

Name

Practice at Home

1

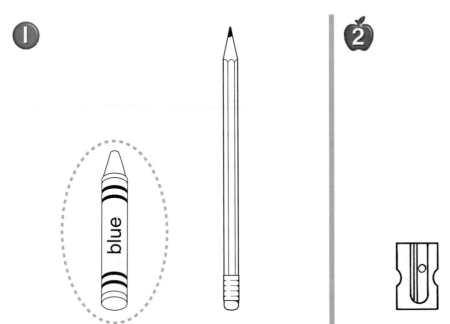

3

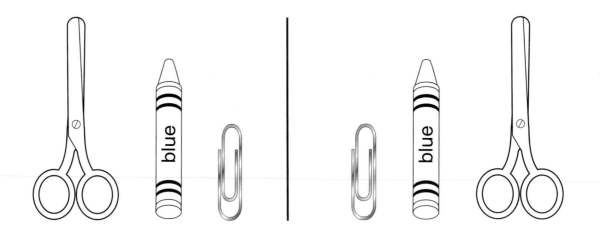

Directions:

1. Circle the shorter object.
2. Circle the shortest object.
3. Circle the group that is in order from short to shortest.

Name _____

Vocabulary and English Language Development

1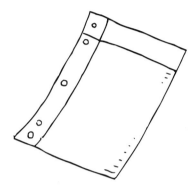

2

3

ACTIVITY Gather a medium-weight book and a heavyweight book. Ask a volunteer to hold up the medium-weight book. Say: "The book is **heavy**." Then ask the same student to hold up the heavyweight book. Ask: "Which book is **heavier**?" Repeat with other objects, having students identify each object as *heavy* and *heavier*.

WORKSHEET DIRECTIONS
1–3. Draw an X on the object that is heavier.

Math Triumphs

Name

Skills Practice

Directions:

1–2. Circle the heavier animal.

3. Circle the animal that is heavier than the tiger.

Math Triumphs

Name

Practice at Home

Directions:
1–2. Circle the heavier object.
   3. Circle the object that is heavier than the television.

Chapter 9

Name _____

Vocabulary and English Language Development

1

2

3

4

ACTIVITY Gather a kickball and a balloon. Have a volunteer toss the kickball up in the air. Then have the student toss a balloon up in the air. Ask: "Which is **lighter**?" Have volunteers find objects that are lighter than the ball.

WORKSHEET DIRECTIONS Draw an X on the objects that are lighter than a kickball.

Name _____

Skills Practice

1

2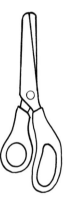

3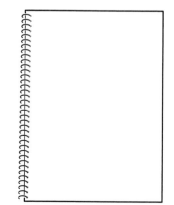

Directions:

1–2. Circle the school supply that is lighter.

3. Circle the school supply that is lighter than the eraser.

Math Triumphs

Chapter 9

Name _____

Practice at Home

 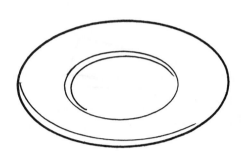 

Directions:

1–2. Circle the object that is lighter.

3. Circle the object that is lighter than the soup bowl.

Name

Vocabulary and English Language Development

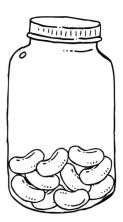

Chapter 9

ACTIVITY Gather three containers of graduated size and enough beans or rice to fill the smallest container. Hold up two of the containers. Ask: "Which will hold **more**?" Have a volunteer fill the smaller container with beans or rice and pour it into the larger container to demonstrate which holds more. Show all three containers. Ask: "Which holds the **most**?" Have a volunteer fill the containers to confirm.

WORKSHEET DIRECTIONS
1–2. Draw an X on the container that holds more.
   3. Draw an X on the container that holds the most.

Math Triumphs

Name _____

Skills Practice

1

2

3

4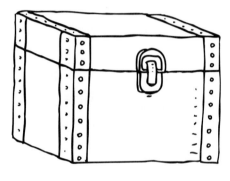

Directions:
1–2. Circle the object that holds more.
3–4. Circle the object that holds the most.

Name

Practice at Home

①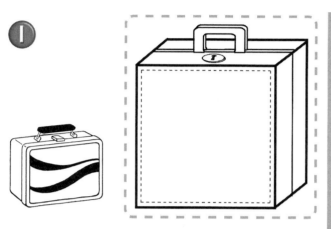

②

③

④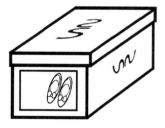

Chapter 9

Directions:
1–2. Circle the object that holds more.
3–4. Circle the object that holds the most.

Name _____

Vocabulary and English Language Development

1

2

3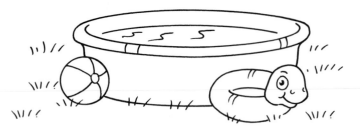

ACTIVITY Gather three containers of graduated size, and enough beans or rice to fill the smallest container. Hold up two of the containers. Ask: "Which will hold **less**?" Have a volunteer fill the smaller container with beans or rice and pour it into the larger container to demonstrate which holds less. Show all three containers. Ask: "Which holds the **least**?" Have a volunteer fill the containers to confirm.

WORKSHEET DIRECTIONS
1–2. Draw an X on the container that holds less.
  3. Draw an X on the container that holds the least.

Math Triumphs

Name _____

Skills Practice

1

2

3

4

Chapter 9

Directions:

1–2. Circle the object that holds less.

3–4. Circle the object that holds the least.

Math Triumphs

Name

Practice at Home

Directions:
1–2. Circle the object that holds less.
3–4. Circle the object that holds the least.

Foldables Study Organizer

Dinah Zike's Foldables

Create a Flashcard Holder Foldable for making patterns.

1 Fold a sheet of $8\frac{1}{2}$" × 11" paper in half like a hamburger. Open the hamburger and fold the two outer edges toward the valley, forming a shutter fold.

2 Fold one of the edges of the shutter back to the outside fold, forming a floppy "L."

3 Glue the floppy L-tab down to the base so that it forms a strong, straight L-tab. Glue the other shutter side to the front of this L-tab. This forms a tent that is backboard for displaying flashcards.

4 Fold the edge of the L-tab up one quarter to on half. This will form a lip that will keep the student work from slipping off the holder.

TAKING NOTES

As you read the chapter together, model sequential patterns for the students. Then, have students copy the pattern on their flashcard holder, and recognize what type of pattern they have made.

 USING THE FOLDABLE

As students review, have them check their understanding by creating a variety of patterns independently. Encourage students to use shapes or something they prefer to use.

 USING THE FOLDABLE

In pairs, have one student in each pair start any sequential pattern with one pattern unit. Have the other student copy the pattern, and extend the pattern two or more times. Then, have the second student start a different pattern and repeat the activity.

Games and Puzzles
Pattern Builder

GET READY

- Reproduce a **Pattern Builder** game sheet for each pair of students.
- Put students in pairs. Give each pair a game sheet, 15 counters, and a paper bag with ten pattern blocks: five squares and five triangles.

DIRECTIONS:

- Players look at the pattern blocks in their bag and make an AB, ABB, or AAB pattern, using two or three of the blocks. Using a pencil, students trace the pattern at the top of the game sheet.
- Players decide who goes first. The first player pulls a pattern block from the paper bag. If it is the piece needed to start the pattern at the top of the game sheet, the player traces it on the game board and receives a counter. If it is not the correct piece, the player's turn is over.
- The pattern block is returned to the bag and the other player takes a turn. The game continues with players pulling pattern blocks from the bag and tracing those that are next in the pattern. Players receive a counter for each pattern block that he or she traces.
- The game is over when the **Pattern Builder** game sheet is complete. The player who has the most counters wins the game.

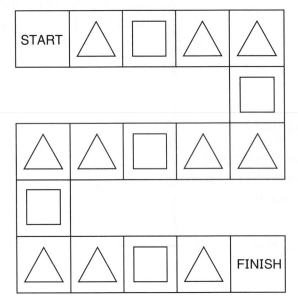

Math Triumphs

Game Board
Pattern Builder

pattern

game board

START				

				FINISH

Name _____

Vocabulary and English Language Development

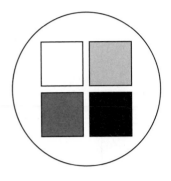

alike

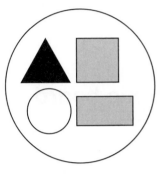

different

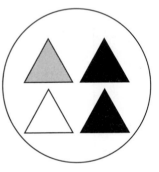

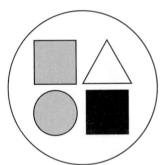

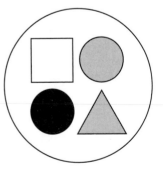

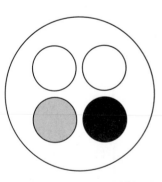

ACTIVITY Show students three squares of different colors. Ask: "How are the shapes **alike?**" (all squares) "How are the shapes **different?**" (different colors) Show students a triangle, a circle, and a rectangle. Ask: "Are these shapes alike or different?" (different) Explain that shapes that are alike are the *same* in some way, and shapes that are different are *not the same*. Give students a variety of shapes. Ask them to make a group of shapes that are alike, and a group of shapes that are different.

WORKSHEET DIRECTIONS Draw an X on the group that is alike.

Name _____

Skills Practice

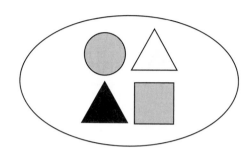 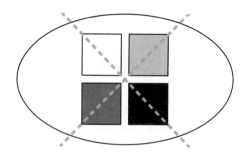

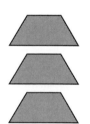   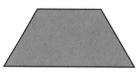

Directions:

1. Draw an X on the group that shows figures of the same shape and size.
2. Circle the figure that belongs in the group.
3. Draw and color a figure that is the same size and shape as those shown.
4. Circle the triangles. Draw an X on the rectangles.

Math Triumphs **Lesson 10-1 A235**

Chapter 10

Name

Practice at Home

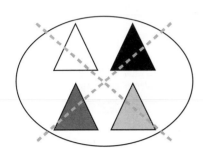   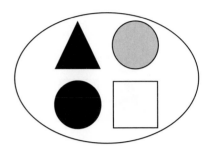

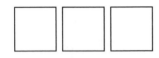

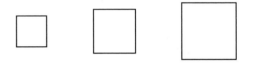

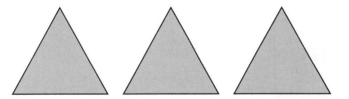

Directions:

1. Draw an X on the group that shows figures of the same shape and size.
2. Circle the figure that belongs in the group.

3. Draw and color a figure that is the same size and shape as those shown.
4. Circle the squares. Draw an X on the circles.

Name

Vocabulary and English Language Development

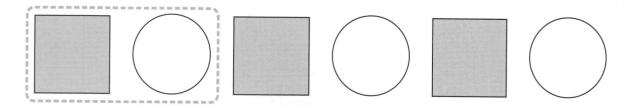

AB pattern

①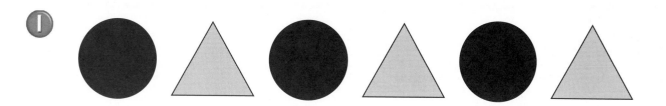

②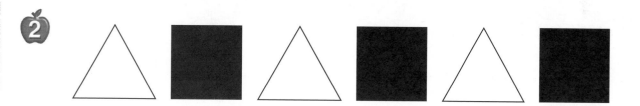

ACTIVITY Lead students in a pattern exercise in which they raise their hands above their heads and then place their hands on their hips. Have students repeat the pattern several times, then ask: "What will you do next?" After students respond, discuss with them how they knew what to do next. Guide students to understand that a **pattern** repeats in a predictable way. Ask: "What are the two actions in the pattern?" (hands up, hands on hips) Emphasize that those two actions are repeated over and over. Tell students this is an **AB pattern** because the part that repeats is two different actions.

WORKSHEET DIRECTIONS Circle the part of the pattern that repeats.

Chapter 10

Math Triumphs

Name _____

Skills Practice

1

  |

2

3    |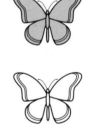

4

Directions:
1. Circle the insect that comes next in the pattern.
2. Draw an X on the animal that does not belong.
3. Circle the butterfly that comes next in the pattern.
4. Draw and color the caterpillar that comes next.

Math Triumphs

Name _____

Practice at Home

1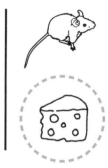

2

3

4

Directions:
1. Circle what comes next in the pattern.
2. Draw an X on the insect that does not belong.
3. Circle the frog that comes next in the pattern.
4. Draw and color the ant that comes next.

Chapter 10

Name _____

Vocabulary and English Language Development

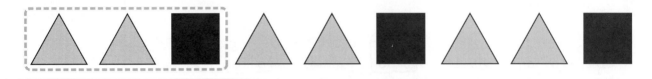

AAB pattern

---

①

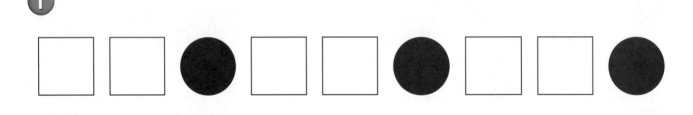

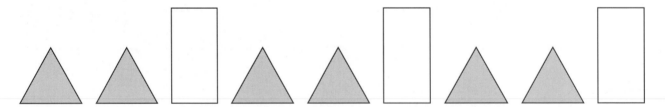

ACTIVITY Review AB patterns with students by doing a clap-tap pattern together. Then, alter the pattern to make it a clap-clap-tap pattern. Lead the students in four cycles of the pattern, then ask: "What part of the pattern **repeats?"** (clap, clap, tap) Point out that this part repeats to make the **AAB pattern.** Have students continue the clap-clap-tap pattern. Guide them to understand that the **order** of the pattern is important. Invite volunteers to lead the class in a sound or motion AAB pattern. After each pattern, have students identify the part that repeats.

WORKSHEET DIRECTIONS Circle the part of the pattern that repeats.

Name

Skills Practice

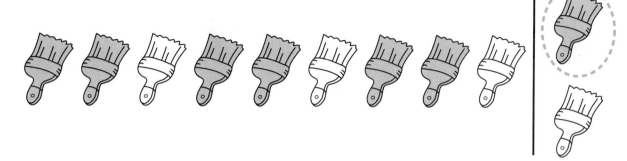

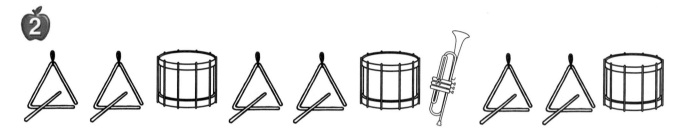

Chapter 10

Directions:

1. Circle the brush that comes next.
2. Draw an X on the instrument that does not belong.
3. Circle the school supply that comes next.
4. Draw and color the notebook that comes next.

Math Triumphs

Lesson 10-3   A241

Name _____

Practice at Home

  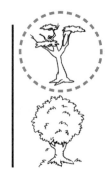

Directions:

1. Circle the tree that comes next.
2. Draw an X on the leaf that does not belong.

3. Circle the flower that comes next.
4. Draw and color the pumpkin that comes next.

Math Triumphs

Name _____

Vocabulary and English Language Development

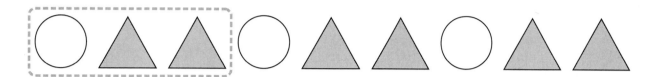

ABB pattern

ACTIVITY Show students an ABB pattern, using triangle and trapezoid blocks. Work with students to find the part of the pattern that repeats. Guide students to understand that this type of repeating pattern is an **ABB pattern.** Review with students that the order of the blocks is important in the pattern. Give small groups of students pattern blocks and have them build ABB patterns. As each pattern is built, ask: "What part of the pattern repeats?"

WORKSHEET DIRECTIONS Circle the part of the pattern that repeats.

Chapter 10

Math Triumphs

Name _____

Skills Practice

1

2

3

4

Directions:

1. Circle the object that comes next.
2. Draw an X on the drink that does not belong.

3. Circle the object that comes next.
4. Draw the object that comes next.

Math Triumphs

Name

Practice at Home

1

2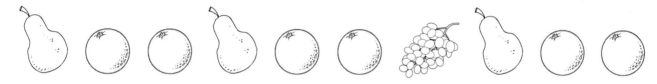

3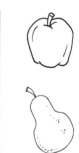

 4

Directions:

1. Circle the fruit that comes next.
2. Draw an X on the fruit that does not belong.
3. Circle the fruit that comes next.
4. Draw the fruit that comes next.

Math Triumphs

Chapter 10

Name _____

Vocabulary and English Language Development

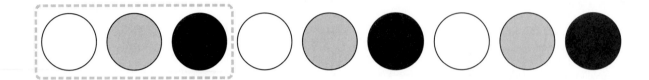

ABC pattern

ACTIVITY Show students a red, blue, green color pattern, using construction paper circles. Work with students to find how the pattern repeats (color) and what part of the pattern repeats (red, blue, green). Guide students to understand that this type of repeating pattern is an **ABC pattern.** Distribute three colors of cubes to small groups of students. Have them make ABC patterns. For each pattern, ask: "What part repeats?"

WORKSHEET DIRECTIONS Circle the part of the pattern that repeats.

Math Triumphs

Name

Skills Practice

1

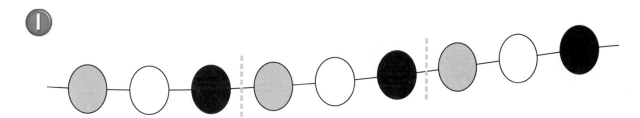

2

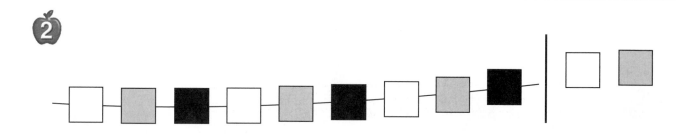

3

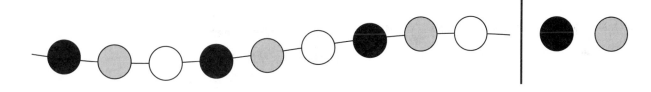

4

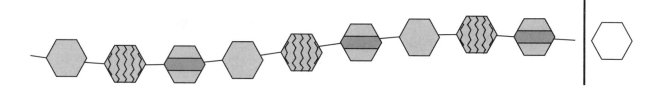

Directions:
1. Draw a line to show where the pattern starts over, or repeats.
2–3. Circle the bead that comes next in the pattern.
4. Color the white bead to show what comes next.

Math Triumphs

Name

Practice at Home

1

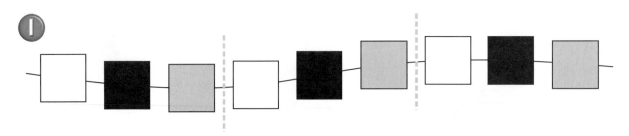

2

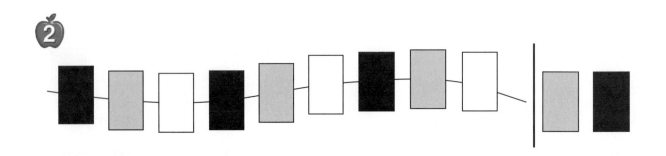

3

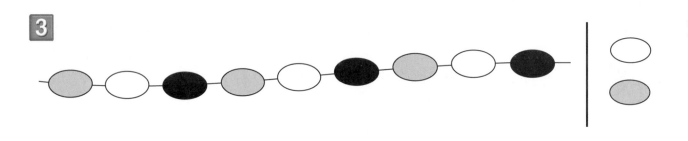

4

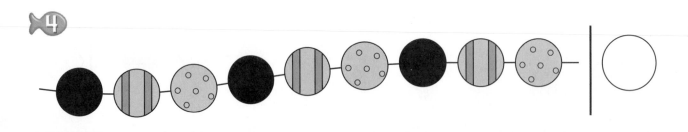

Directions:
1. Draw a line to show where the pattern starts over, or repeats.
2–3. Circle the bead that comes next in the pattern.
4. Color the white bead to show what comes next.

Name

Vocabulary and English Language Development

next

ACTIVITY Begin a discussion about a series of daily behaviors, in order to model and emphasize the word *next*. Say, for example: "I put on my socks; **next,** I put on my shoes." Explain to students that **next** is when something happens after something else. Suggest a sentence starter, including the word *next*; then call on a volunteer to complete the sentence. For example, "I put toothpaste on my toothbrush; next,…; "I pour cereal in a bowl; next,…". Finally, have students make a drawing of something that happens *first* and *next* in their daily lives.

WORKSHEET DIRECTIONS Circle the picture that shows what happens next.

Math Triumphs

Chapter 10

Name

Skills Practice

1

2

3

4

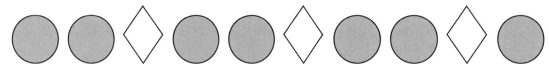

Directions:
1–4. Look at the pattern. Draw and color the next figure.

Math Triumphs

Name _____

Practice at Home

①

②

③

④

Directions:

1–4. Look at the pattern. Draw and color the next figure.

Chapter 10

Name _____

Vocabulary and English Language Development

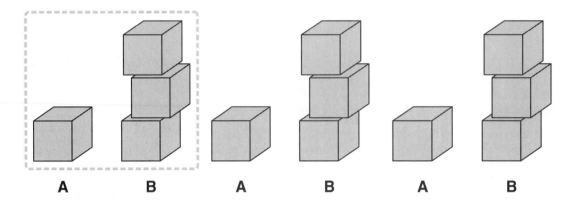

A   B   A   B   A   B

1

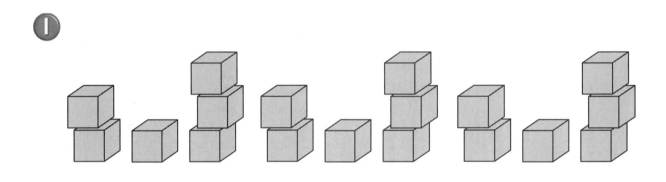

2

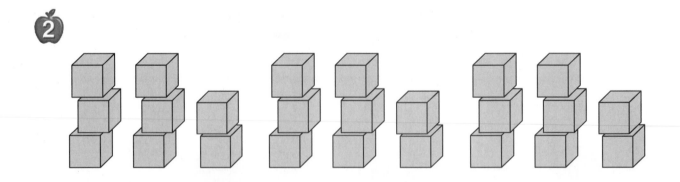

ACTIVITY Have six volunteers come to the front of the class. Ask the second, fourth, and sixth student to kneel, and the rest to stand. Point out that the students are making an AB pattern. Have students come up with other positions that will also make an AB pattern. (Example: hands up/hands down; sitting/standing). Extend the activity by helping students create AAB and ABC patterns. Encourage them to make their own patterns by drawing squares on their notebooks.

WORKSHEET DIRECTIONS Circle the part of the pattern that repeats.

Name _____

Skills Practice

| P | Q | P | Q | | | | |

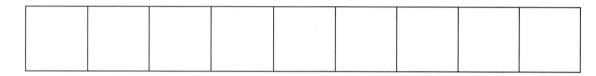

Directions:
1. Use the letters P and Q to make a pattern.
2. Choose two numbers. Make an ABB pattern.

3. Choose three figures. Make an ABC pattern.
4. Choose a letter, a number, and a figure. Draw a pattern in the boxes. Use one letter, number, or figure in each box.

Chapter 10

Name

Skills Practice

1

D E D E

2

3

4

Directions:

1. Use the letters D and E to make a pattern.
2. Choose two numbers. Make an ABB pattern.
3. Choose three figures. Make an ABC pattern.
4. Choose a letter, a number, and a figure. Draw a pattern in the boxes. Use one letter, number, or figure in each box.

Answer Key (Lesson 1-1 and 1-2)

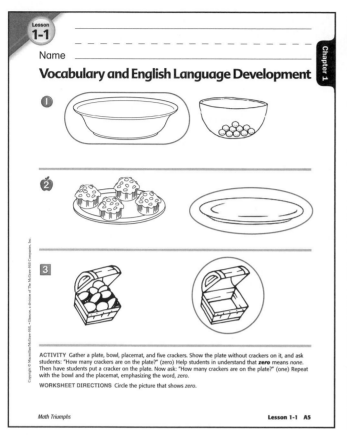

Lesson 1-1

Name

Chapter 1

Vocabulary and English Language Development

ACTIVITY Gather a plate, bowl, placemat, and five crackers. Show the plate without crackers on it, and ask students: "How many crackers are on the plate?" (zero) Help students in understand that *zero* means *none*. Then have students put a cracker on the plate. Now ask: "How many crackers are on the plate?" (one) Repeat with the bowl and the placemat, emphasizing the word, *zero*.

WORKSHEET DIRECTIONS Circle the picture that shows *zero*.

Math Triumphs   **Lesson 1-1   A5**

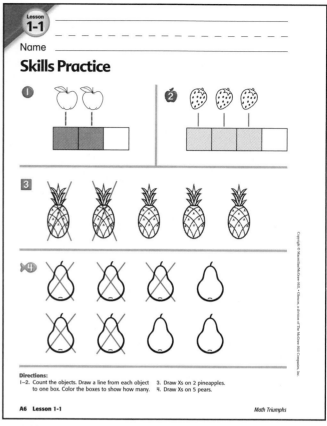

Lesson 1-1

Name

Skills Practice

Directions:
1–2. Count the objects. Draw a line from each object to one box. Color the boxes to show how many.
3. Draw Xs on 2 pineapples.
4. Draw Xs on 5 pears.

A6 Lesson 1-1   *Math Triumphs*

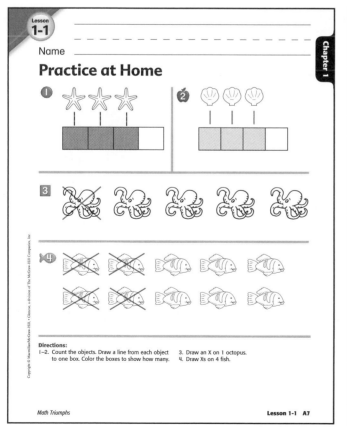

Lesson 1-1

Name

Chapter 1

Practice at Home

Directions:
1–2. Count the objects. Draw a line from each object to one box. Color the boxes to show how many.
3. Draw an X on 1 octopus.
4. Draw Xs on 4 fish.

Math Triumphs   **Lesson 1-1   A7**

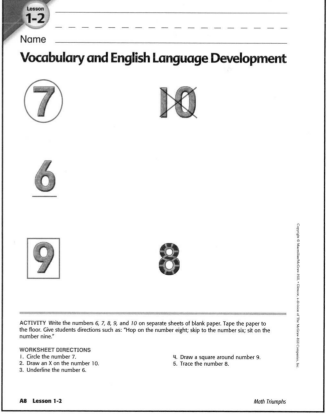

Lesson 1-2

Name

Vocabulary and English Language Development

ACTIVITY Write the numbers 6, 7, 8, 9, and 10 on separate sheets of blank paper. Tape the paper to the floor. Give students directions such as: "Hop on the number eight; skip to the number six; sit on the number nine."

WORKSHEET DIRECTIONS
1. Circle the number 7.
2. Draw an X on the number 10.
3. Underline the number 6.
4. Draw a square around number 9.
5. Trace the number 8.

A8 Lesson 1-2   *Math Triumphs*

Answer Key (Lesson 1-2 and 1-3)

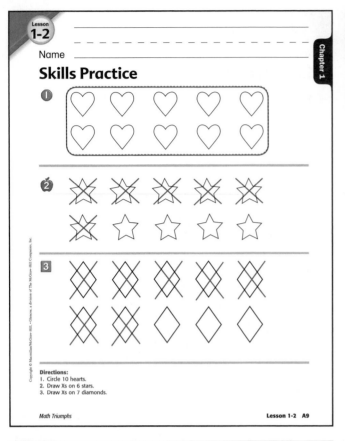

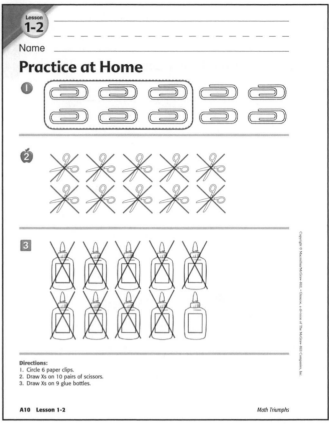

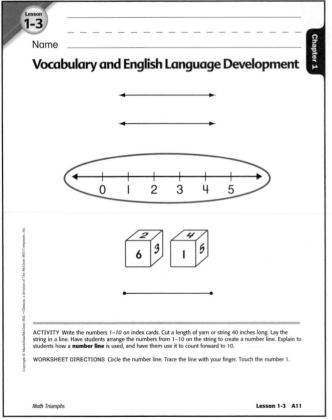

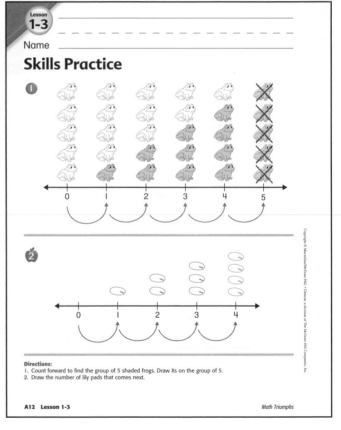

Answer Key (Lesson 1-3 and 1-4)

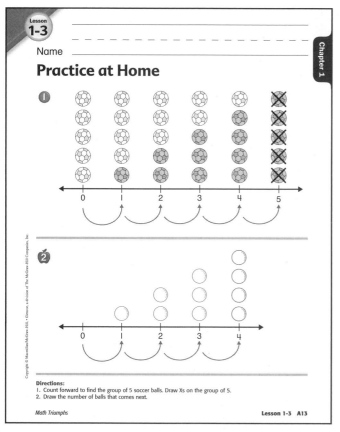

Directions:
1. Count forward to find the group of 5 soccer balls. Draw Xs on the group of 5.
2. Draw the number of balls that comes next.

Math Triumphs Lesson 1-3 **A13**

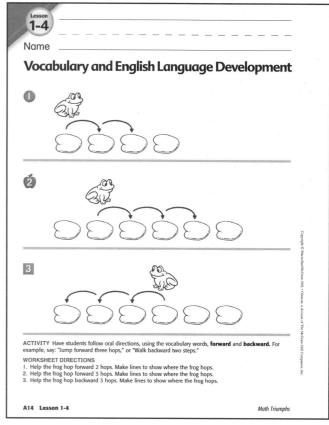

ACTIVITY Have students follow oral directions, using the vocabulary words, **forward** and **backward.** For example, say: "Jump forward three hops," or "Walk backward two steps."

WORKSHEET DIRECTIONS
1. Help the frog hop forward 2 hops. Make lines to show where the frog hops.
2. Help the frog hop forward 3 hops. Make lines to show where the frog hops.
3. Help the frog hop backward 3 hops. Make lines to show where the frog hops.

A14 Lesson 1-4 *Math Triumphs*

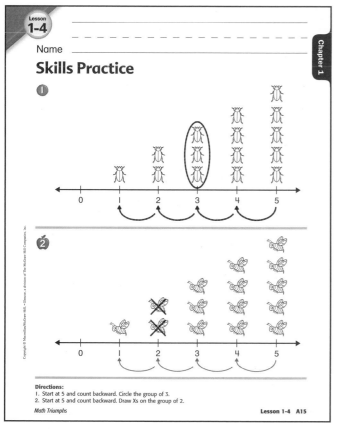

Directions:
1. Start at 5 and count backward. Circle the group of 3.
2. Start at 5 and count backward. Draw Xs on the group of 2.

Math Triumphs Lesson 1-4 **A15**

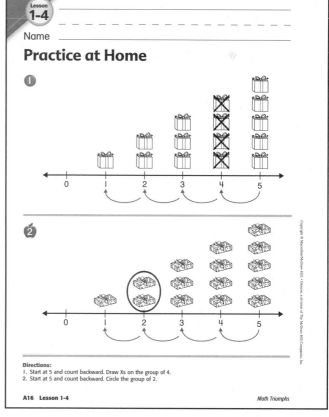

Directions:
1. Start at 5 and count backward. Draw Xs on the group of 4.
2. Start at 5 and count backward. Circle the group of 2.

A16 Lesson 1-4 *Math Triumphs*

Math Triumphs **Lesson 1-3 and 1-4   A257**

Answer Key (Lesson 1-5 and 1-6)

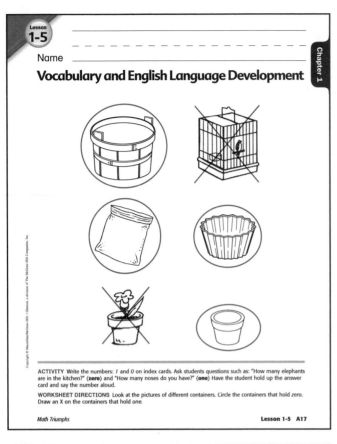

ACTIVITY Write the numbers: *1* and *0* on index cards. Ask students questions such as: "How many elephants are in the kitchen?" (**zero**) and "How many noses do you have?" (**one**) Have the student hold up the answer card and say the number aloud.

WORKSHEET DIRECTIONS Look at the pictures of different containers. Circle the containers that hold *zero*. Draw an X on the containers that hold *one*.

Math Triumphs   Lesson 1-5   **A17**

Directions:
Here are some things you might see at a park.

1. How many sandboxes are there? Trace the number. Then write the number two times.
2. How many slides are there? Trace the number. Then write the number two times.
3. How many basketball hoops are there? Trace the number. Then write the number three times.
4. How many swings are there? Trace the number. Then write the number three times.

A18   Lesson 1-5   *Math Triumphs*

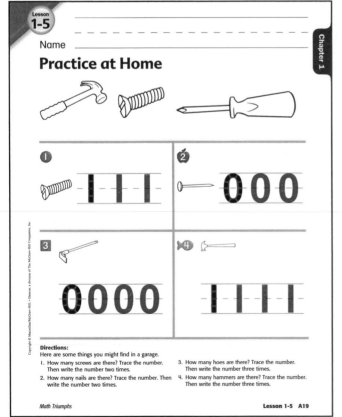

Directions:
Here are some things you might find in a garage.

1. How many screws are there? Trace the number. Then write the number two times.
2. How many nails are there? Trace the number. Then write the number two times.
3. How many hoes are there? Trace the number. Then write the number three times.
4. How many hammers are there? Trace the number. Then write the number three times.

Math Triumphs   Lesson 1-5   **A19**

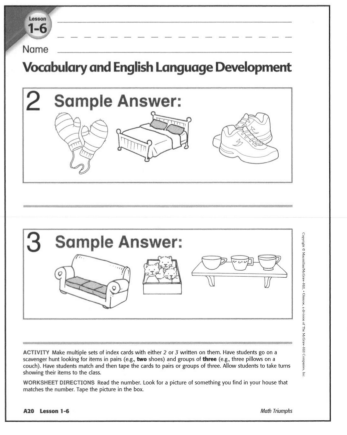

ACTIVITY Make multiple sets of index cards with either *2* or *3* written on them. Have students go on a scavenger hunt looking for items in pairs (e.g., **two** shoes) and groups of **three** (e.g., three pillows on a couch). Have students match and then tape the cards to pairs or groups of three. Allow students to take turns showing their items to the class.

WORKSHEET DIRECTIONS Read the number. Look for a picture of something you find in your house that matches the number. Tape the picture in the box.

A20   Lesson 1-6   *Math Triumphs*

Answer Key (Lesson 1-6 and 1-7)

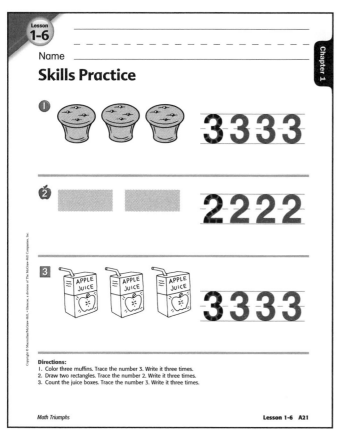

Lesson 1-6

Name

Skills Practice

Chapter 1

1. 3 3 3 3

2. 2 2 2 2

3. 3 3 3 3

Directions:
1. Color three muffins. Trace the number 3. Write it three times.
2. Draw two rectangles. Trace the number 2. Write it three times.
3. Count the juice boxes. Trace the number 3. Write it three times.

Math Triumphs   **Lesson 1-6   A21**

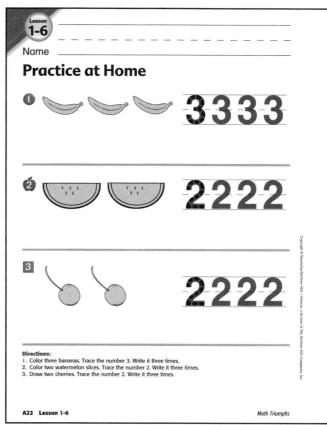

Lesson 1-6

Name

Practice at Home

1. 3 3 3 3

2. 2 2 2 2

3. 2 2 2 2

Directions:
1. Color three bananas. Trace the number 3. Write it three times.
2. Color two watermelon slices. Trace the number 2. Write it three times.
3. Draw two cherries. Trace the number 2. Write it three times.

A22   Lesson 1-6   *Math Triumphs*

Lesson 1-7

Name

Vocabulary and English Language Development

Chapter 1

ACTIVITY Ask students: "Have you played with a group of friends on the playground? Have you joined a group or club? Have you ever seen a group of birds?" Explain that a **group** is more than two things that are together. Have students identify groups of objects in the classroom (e.g., a group of pencils).

WORKSHEET DIRECTIONS Circle the objects that are in groups.

Math Triumphs   **Lesson 1-7   A23**

Lesson 1-7

Name

Skills Practice

1. 5 5 5 5

2. 4 4 4 4

3. 4 4 4 4

Directions:
1. Count the dogs. Trace the number 5. Write it three times.
2. Draw 4 dog balls. Trace the number 4. Write it three times.
3. Circle the group of 4. Trace the number 4. Write it three times.

A24   Lesson 1-7   *Math Triumphs*

Answer Key (Lesson 1-7 and 1-8)

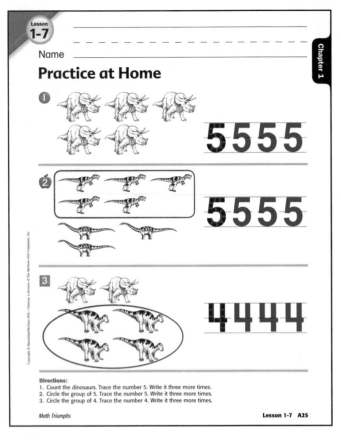

Lesson 1-7

Name

Practice at Home

Directions:
1. Count the dinosaurs. Trace the number 5. Write it three more times.
2. Circle the group of 5. Trace the number 5. Write it three more times.
3. Circle the group of 4. Trace the number 4. Write it three more times.

Math Triumphs   Lesson 1-7 A25

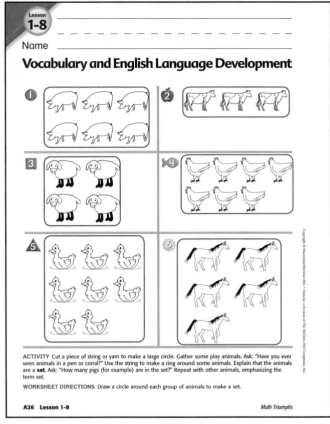

Lesson 1-8

Name

Vocabulary and English Language Development

ACTIVITY Cut a piece of string or yarn to make a large circle. Gather some play animals. Ask: "Have you ever seen animals in a pen or corral?" Use the string to make a ring around some animals. Explain that the animals are a **set**. Ask: "How many pigs (for example) are in the set?" Repeat with other animals, emphasizing the term *set*.

WORKSHEET DIRECTIONS Draw a circle around each group of animals to make a set.

A26 Lesson 1-8   *Math Triumphs*

Lesson 1-8

Name

Skills Practice

Directions:
1. Circle the group of 6. Trace the number 6. Write it three times.
2. Draw Xs on 7 balloons. Trace the number 7. Write it three times.
3. Color 8 marbles. Trace the number 8. Write it three times.
4. Color 9 teddy bears. Trace the number 9. Write it three times.
5. Color 3 more balls to make 10. Trace the number 10. Write it 3 times.

Math Triumphs   Lesson 1-8 A27

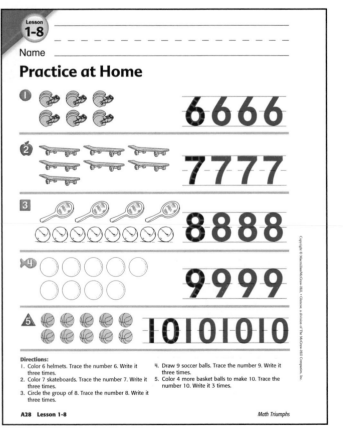

Lesson 1-8

Name

Practice at Home

Directions:
1. Color 6 helmets. Trace the number 6. Write it three times.
2. Color 7 skateboards. Trace the number 7. Write it three times.
3. Circle the group of 8. Trace the number 8. Write it three times.
4. Draw 9 soccer balls. Trace the number 9. Write it three times.
5. Color 4 more basket balls to make 10. Trace the number 10. Write it 3 times.

A28 Lesson 1-8   *Math Triumphs*

Answer Key (Lesson 2-1 and 2-2)

Lesson 2-1

Vocabulary and English Language Development

Chapter 2

ACTIVITY Talk about a student's day, emphasizing the words *before* and *after*. For example, ask: "What do you do **after** you get up? What do you do **before** you go to bed?" Help students cut out a magazine picture of a child doing an activity (e.g., putting on shoes, picking up toys, sleeping). Have students share their pictures, and ask them: "What do you think happened before this? What do you think happened after this?"

WORKSHEET DIRECTIONS
1. Look at the boy sleeping. Circle the picture that shows what happened before he went to sleep.
2. Look at the girl washing her hands. Circle the picture that shows what will happen after she washes her hands.

Math Triumphs   **Lesson 2-1   A33**

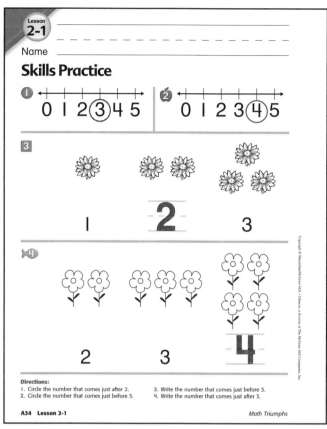

Lesson 2-1

Skills Practice

Directions:
1. Circle the number that comes just after 2.
2. Circle the number that comes just before 5.
3. Write the number that comes just before 3.
4. Write the number that comes just after 3.

A34   Lesson 2-1   *Math Triumphs*

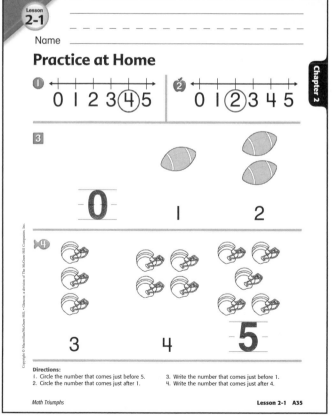

Lesson 2-1

Practice at Home

Chapter 2

Directions:
1. Circle the number that comes just before 5.
2. Circle the number that comes just after 1.
3. Write the number that comes just before 1.
4. Write the number that comes just after 4.

Math Triumphs   **Lesson 2-1   A35**

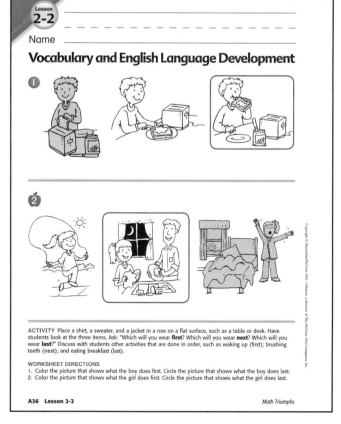

Lesson 2-2

Vocabulary and English Language Development

ACTIVITY Place a shirt, a sweater, and a jacket in a row on a flat surface, such as a table or desk. Have students look at the three items. Ask: "Which will you wear **first**? Which will you wear **next**? Which will you wear **last**?" Discuss with students other activities that are done in order, such as waking up (first); brushing teeth (next); and eating breakfast (last).

WORKSHEET DIRECTIONS
1. Color the picture that shows what the boy does first. Circle the picture that shows what the boy does last.
2. Color the picture that shows what the girl does first. Circle the picture that shows what the girl does last.

A36   Lesson 2-2   *Math Triumphs*

Answer Key (Lesson 2-2 and 2-3)

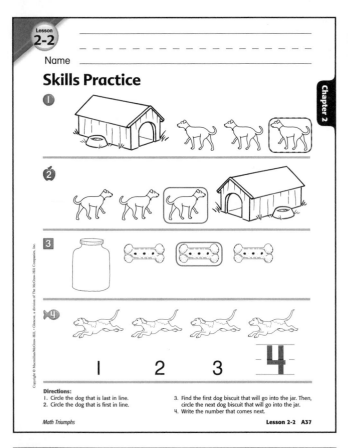

Lesson 2-2

Name

Skills Practice

Directions:
1. Circle the dog that is last in line.
2. Circle the dog that is first in line.
3. Find the first dog biscuit that will go into the jar. Then, circle the next dog biscuit that will go into the jar.
4. Write the number that comes next.

Math Triumphs   **Lesson 2-2   A37**

Lesson 2-2

Name

Practice at Home

Directions:
1. Circle the last train car that the engine is pulling.
2. Circle the first top that will go into the toy box.
3. Circle the last teddy bear that will go into the toy box.
4. Write the number that comes next.

A38   Lesson 2-2   *Math Triumphs*

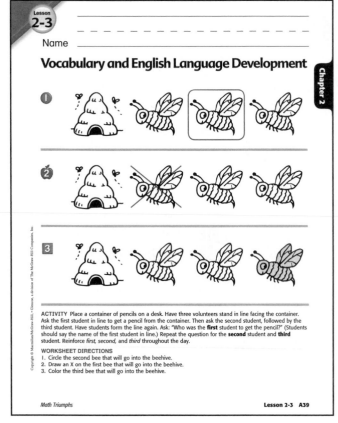

Lesson 2-3

Name

Vocabulary and English Language Development

ACTIVITY Place a container of pencils on a desk. Have three volunteers stand in line facing the container. Ask the first student in line to get a pencil from the container. Then ask the second student, followed by the third student. Have students form the line again. Ask: "Who was the **first** student to get the pencil?" (Students should say the name of the first student in line.) Repeat the question for the **second** student and **third** student. Reinforce *first, second,* and *third* throughout the day.

WORKSHEET DIRECTIONS
1. Circle the second bee that will go into the beehive.
2. Draw an X on the first bee that will go into the beehive.
3. Color the third bee that will go into the beehive.

Math Triumphs   **Lesson 2-3   A39**

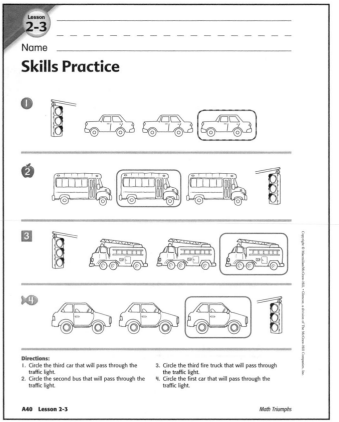

Lesson 2-3

Name

Skills Practice

Directions:
1. Circle the third car that will pass through the traffic light.
2. Circle the second bus that will pass through the traffic light.
3. Circle the third fire truck that will pass through the traffic light.
4. Circle the first car that will pass through the traffic light.

A40   Lesson 2-3   *Math Triumphs*

Answer Key (Lesson 2-3 and 2-4)

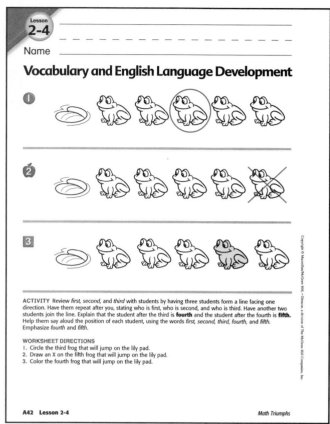

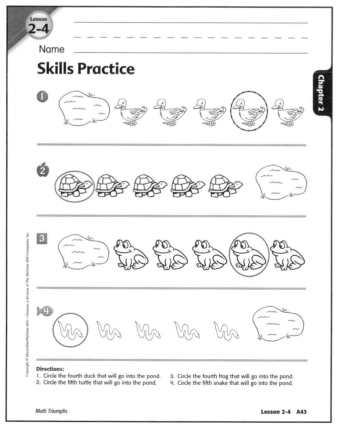

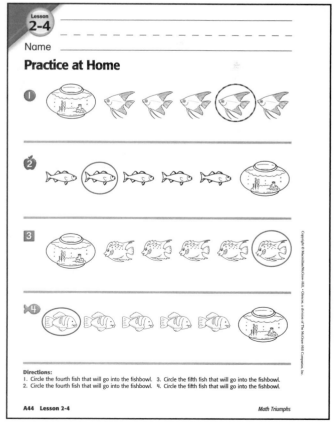

Answer Key (Lesson 2-5 and 2-6)

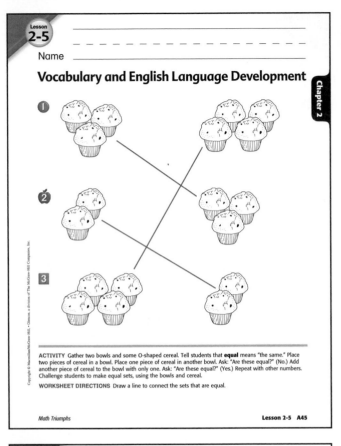

Name

Vocabulary and English Language Development

Chapter 2

ACTIVITY Gather two bowls and some O-shaped cereal. Tell students that **equal** means "the same." Place two pieces of cereal in a bowl. Place one piece of cereal in another bowl. Ask: "Are these equal?" (No.) Add another piece of cereal to the bowl with only one. Ask: "Are these equal?" (Yes.) Repeat with other numbers. Challenge students to make equal sets, using the bowls and cereal.

WORKSHEET DIRECTIONS Draw a line to connect the sets that are equal.

Math Triumphs **Lesson 2-5 A45**

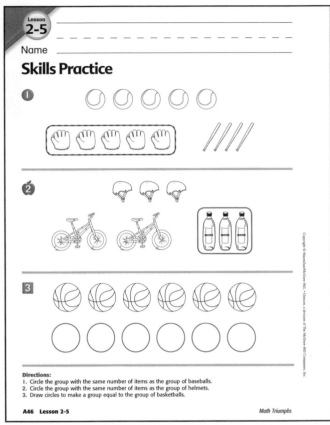

Name

Skills Practice

Directions:
1. Circle the group with the same number of items as the group of baseballs.
2. Circle the group with the same number of items as the group of helmets.
3. Draw circles to make a group equal to the group of basketballs.

A46 Lesson 2-5 *Math Triumphs*

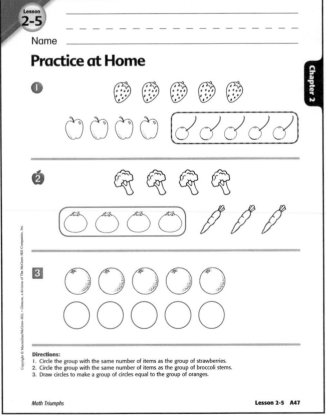

Name

Practice at Home

Chapter 2

Directions:
1. Circle the group with the same number of items as the group of strawberries.
2. Circle the group with the same number of items as the group of broccoli stems.
3. Draw circles to make a group of circles equal to the group of oranges.

Math Triumphs **Lesson 2-5 A47**

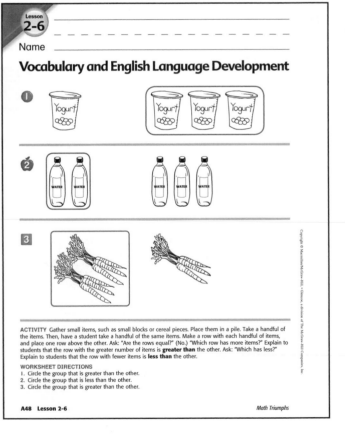

Name

Vocabulary and English Language Development

ACTIVITY Gather small items, such as small blocks or cereal pieces. Place them in a pile. Take a handful of the items. Then, have a student take a handful of the same items. Make a row with each handful of items, and place one row above the other. Ask: "Are the rows equal?" (No.) "Which row has more items?" Explain to students that the row with the greater number of items is **greater than** the other. Ask: "Which has less?" Explain to students that the row with fewer items is **less than** the other.

WORKSHEET DIRECTIONS
1. Circle the group that is greater than the other.
2. Circle the group that is less than the other.
3. Circle the group that is greater than the other.

A48 Lesson 2-6 *Math Triumphs*

Answer Key (Lesson 2-6 and 2-7)

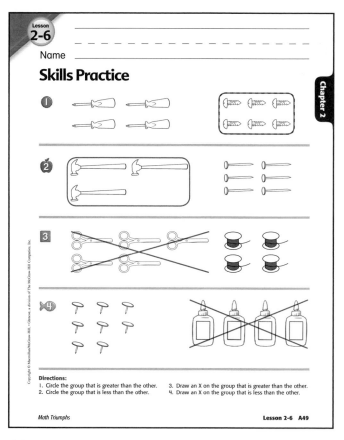

Skills Practice

Directions:
1. Circle the group that is greater than the other.
2. Circle the group that is less than the other.
3. Draw an X on the group that is greater than the other.
4. Draw an X on the group that is less than the other.

Math Triumphs Lesson 2-6 A49

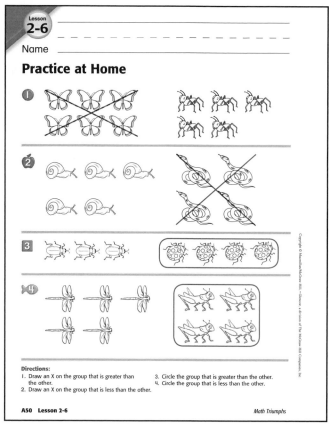

Practice at Home

Directions:
1. Draw an X on the group that is greater than the other.
2. Draw an X on the group that is less than the other.
3. Circle the group that is greater than the other.
4. Circle the group that is less than the other.

A50 Lesson 2-6 *Math Triumphs*

Vocabulary and English Language Development

ACTIVITY Ask: "How tall were you when you were born?" Say: "You are **growing** each year." Remind students that when something **grows**, it gets larger. Have students think of things that grow (e.g., plants, pets).

WORKSHEET DIRECTIONS Circle the items that grow.

Math Triumphs Lesson 2-7 A51

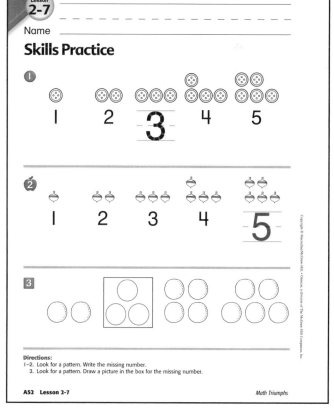

Skills Practice

Directions:
1–2. Look for a pattern. Write the missing number.
3. Look for a pattern. Draw a picture in the box for the missing number.

A52 Lesson 2-7 *Math Triumphs*

Answer Key (Lesson 2-7 and 2-8)

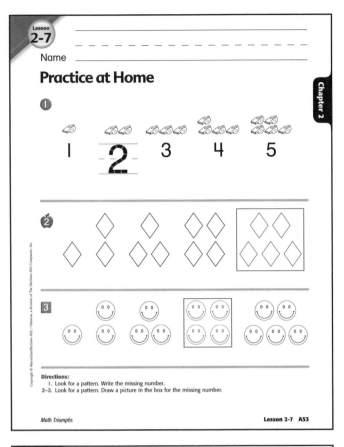

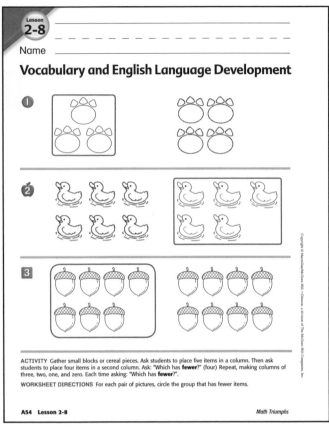

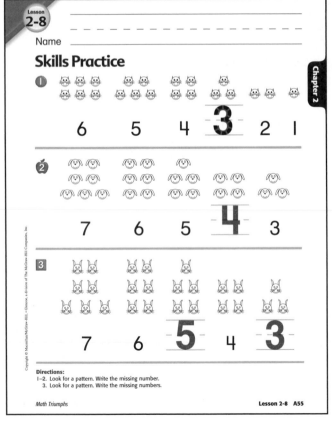

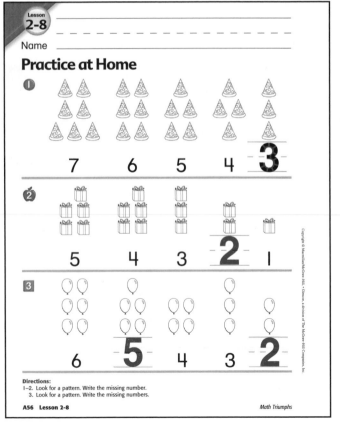

Answer Key (Lesson 3-1 and 3-2)

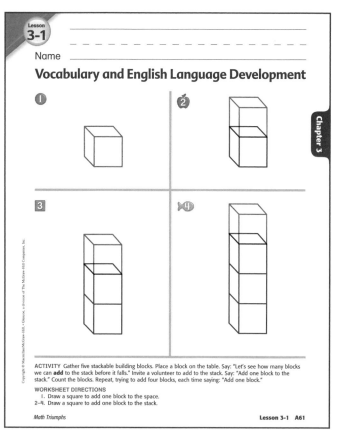

Lesson 3-1

Name

Vocabulary and English Language Development

Chapter 3

ACTIVITY Gather five stackable building blocks. Place a block on the table. Say: "Let's see how many blocks we can **add** to the stack before it falls." Invite a volunteer to add to the stack. Say: "Add one block to the stack." Count the blocks. Repeat, trying to add four blocks, each time saying: "Add one block."

WORKSHEET DIRECTIONS
1. Draw a square to add one block to the space.
2–4. Draw a square to add one block to the stack.

Math Triumphs   **Lesson 3-1   A61**

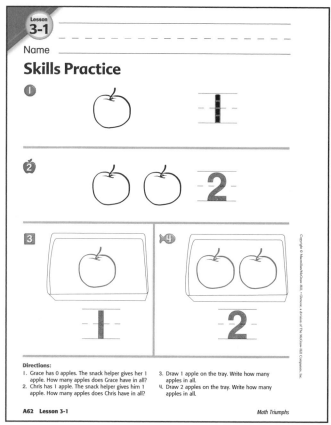

Lesson 3-1

Name

Skills Practice

Directions:
1. Grace has 0 apples. The snack helper gives her 1 apple. How many apples does Grace have in all?
2. Chris has 1 apple. The snack helper gives him 1 apple. How many apples does Chris have in all?
3. Draw 1 apple on the tray. Write how many apples in all.
4. Draw 2 apples on the tray. Write how many apples in all.

A62   Lesson 3-1   *Math Triumphs*

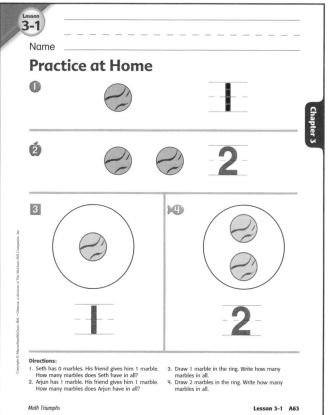

Lesson 3-1

Name

Practice at Home

Chapter 3

Directions:
1. Seth has 0 marbles. His friend gives him 1 marble. How many marbles does Seth have in all?
2. Arjun has 1 marble. His friend gives him 1 marble. How many marbles does Arjun have in all?
3. Draw 1 marble in the ring. Write how many marbles in all.
4. Draw 2 marbles in the ring. Write how many marbles in all.

Math Triumphs   **Lesson 3-1   A63**

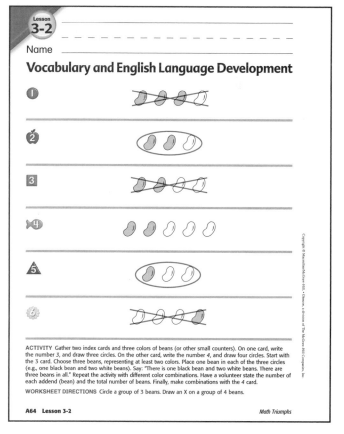

Lesson 3-2

Name

Vocabulary and English Language Development

ACTIVITY Gather two index cards and three colors of beans (or other small counters). On one card, write the number *3*, and draw three circles. On the other card, write the number *4*, and draw four circles. Start with the 3 card. Choose three beans, representing at least two colors. Place one bean in each of the three circles (e.g., one black bean and two white beans). Say: "There is one black bean and two white beans. There are three beans in all." Repeat the activity with different color combinations. Have a volunteer state the number of each addend (bean) and the total number of beans. Finally, make combinations with the *4* card.

WORKSHEET DIRECTIONS Circle a group of 3 beans. Draw an X on a group of 4 beans.

A64   Lesson 3-2   *Math Triumphs*

Answer Key (Lesson 3-2 and 3-3)

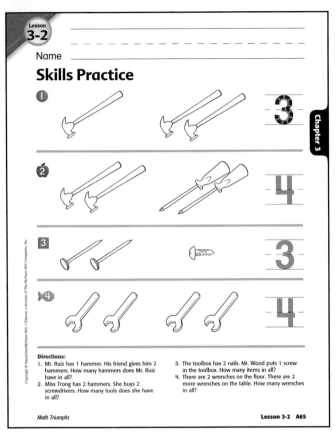

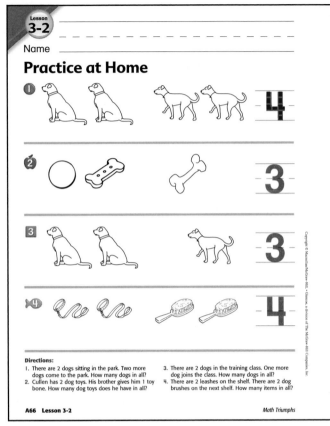

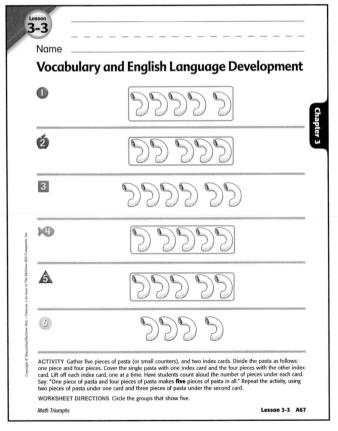

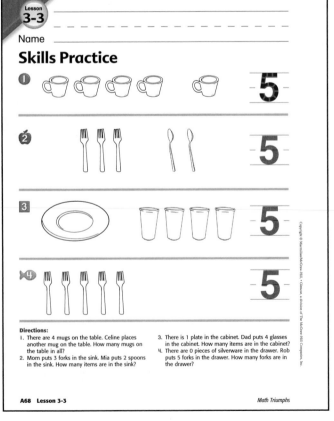

Answer Key (Lesson 3-3 and 3-4)

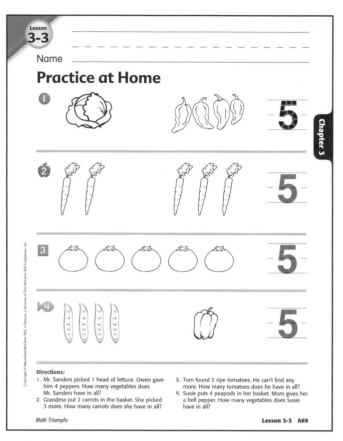

Lesson 3-3

Name _____

Practice at Home

Chapter 3

Directions:
1. Mr. Sanders picked 1 head of lettuce. Owen gave him 4 peppers. How many vegetables does Mr. Sanders have in all?
2. Grandma put 2 carrots in the basket. She picked 3 more. How many carrots does she have in all?
3. Tom found 5 ripe tomatoes. He can't find any more. How many tomatoes does he have in all?
4. Susie puts 4 peapods in her basket. Mom gives her a bell pepper. How many vegetables does Susie have in all?

Math Triumphs   Lesson 3-3   A69

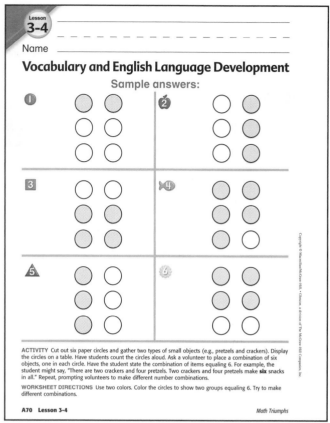

Lesson 3-4

Name _____

Vocabulary and English Language Development
Sample answers:

ACTIVITY Cut out six paper circles and gather two types of small objects (e.g., pretzels and crackers). Display the circles on a table. Have students count the circles aloud. Ask a volunteer to place a combination of six objects, one in each circle. Have the student state the combination of items equaling 6. For example, the student might say, "There are two crackers and four pretzels. Two crackers and four pretzels make **six** snacks in all." Repeat, prompting volunteers to make different number combinations.

WORKSHEET DIRECTIONS Use two colors. Color the circles to show two groups equaling 6. Try to make different combinations.

A70   Lesson 3-4   *Math Triumphs*

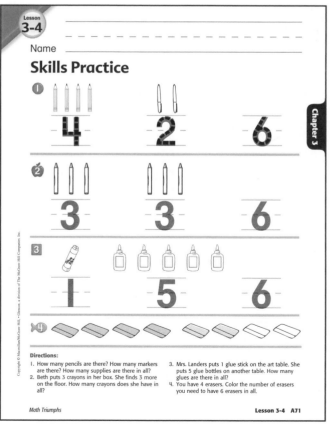

Lesson 3-4

Name _____

Skills Practice

Chapter 3

Directions:
1. How many pencils are there? How many markers are there? How many supplies are there in all?
2. Beth puts 3 crayons in her box. She finds 3 more on the floor. How many crayons does she have in all?
3. Mrs. Landers puts 1 glue stick on the art table. She puts 5 glue bottles on another table. How many glues are there in all?
4. You have 4 erasers. Color the number of erasers you need to have 6 erasers in all.

Math Triumphs   Lesson 3-4   A71

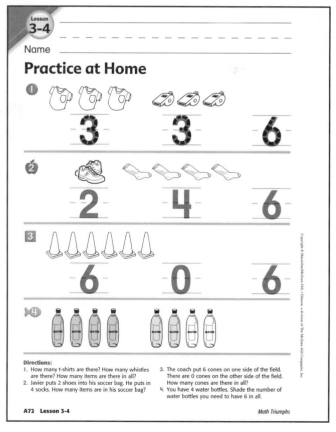

Lesson 3-4

Name _____

Practice at Home

Directions:
1. How many t-shirts are there? How many whistles are there? How many items are there in all?
2. Javier puts 2 shoes into his soccer bag. He puts in 4 socks. How many items are in his soccer bag?
3. The coach put 6 cones on one side of the field. There are 0 cones on the other side of the field. How many cones are there in all?
4. You have 4 water bottles. Shade the number of water bottles you need to have 6 in all.

A72   Lesson 3-4   *Math Triumphs*

Answer Key (Lesson 3-5 and 3-6)

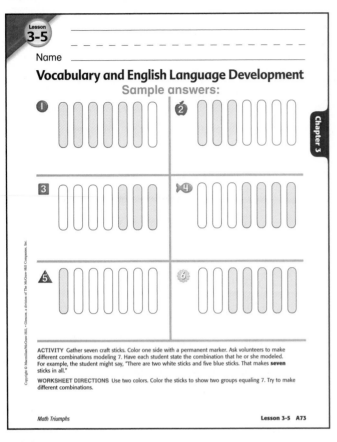

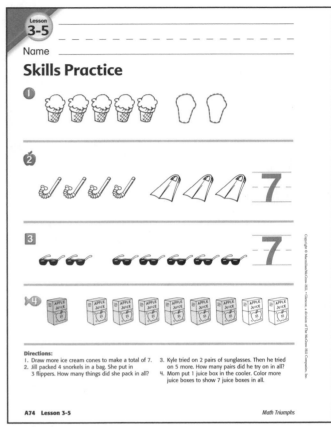

Answer Key (Lesson 3-6 and 3-7)

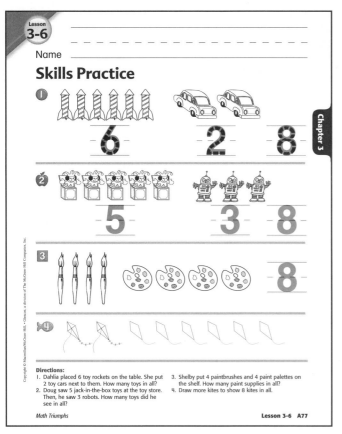

Name

Skills Practice

Directions:
1. Dahlia placed 6 toy rockets on the table. She put 2 toy cars next to them. How many toys in all?
2. Doug saw 5 jack-in-the-box toys at the toy store. Then, he saw 3 robots. How many toys did he see in all?
3. Shelby put 4 paintbrushes and 4 paint palettes on the shelf. How many paint supplies in all?
4. Draw more kites to show 8 kites in all.

Math Triumphs   **Lesson 3-6   A77**

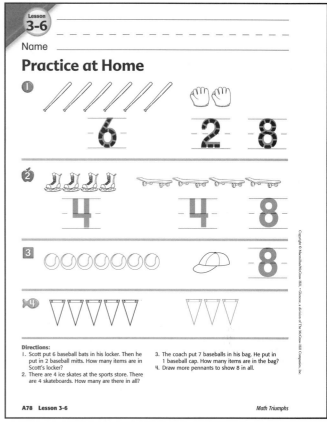

Name

Practice at Home

Directions:
1. Scott put 6 baseball bats in his locker. Then he put in 2 baseball mitts. How many items are in Scott's locker?
2. There are 4 ice skates at the sports store. There are 4 skateboards. How many are there in all?
3. The coach put 7 baseballs in his bag. He put in 1 baseball cap. How many items are in the bag?
4. Draw more pennants to show 8 in all.

A78   Lesson 3-6   *Math Triumphs*

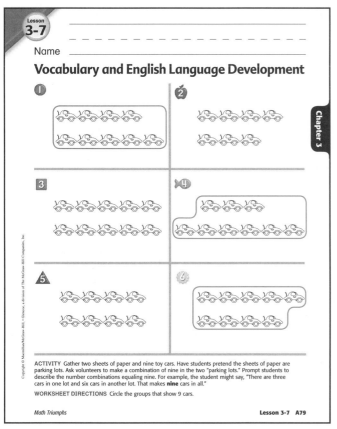

Name

Vocabulary and English Language Development

ACTIVITY Gather two sheets of paper and nine toy cars. Have students pretend the sheets of paper are parking lots. Ask volunteers to make a combination of nine in the two "parking lots." Prompt students to describe the number combinations equaling nine. For example, the student might say, "There are three cars in one lot and six cars in another lot. That makes **nine** cars in all."

WORKSHEET DIRECTIONS Circle the groups that show 9 cars.

Math Triumphs   **Lesson 3-7   A79**

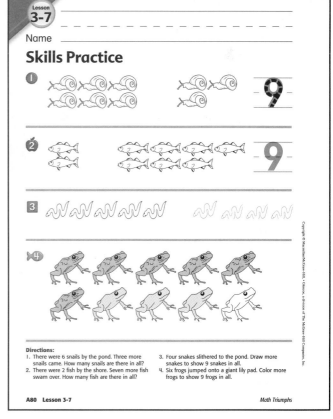

Name

Skills Practice

Directions:
1. There were 6 snails by the pond. Three more snails came. How many snails are there in all?
2. There were 2 fish by the shore. Seven more fish swam over. How many fish are there in all?
3. Four snakes slithered to the pond. Draw more snakes to show 9 snakes in all.
4. Six frogs jumped onto a giant lily pad. Color more frogs to show 9 frogs in all.

A80   Lesson 3-7   *Math Triumphs*

Answer Key (Lesson 3-7 and 4-1)

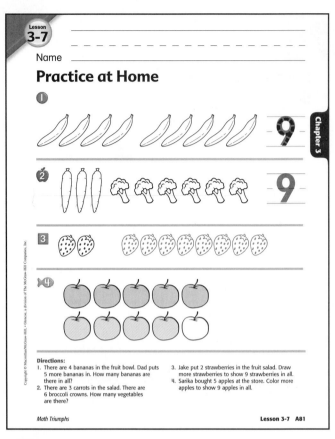

Lesson 3-7

Name

Practice at Home

Directions:
1. There are 4 bananas in the fruit bowl. Dad puts 5 more bananas in. How many bananas are there in all?
2. There are 3 carrots in the salad. There are 6 broccoli crowns. How many vegetables are there?
3. Jake put 2 strawberries in the fruit salad. Draw more strawberries to show 9 strawberries in all.
4. Sarika bought 5 apples at the store. Color more apples to show 9 apples in all.

Math Triumphs   **Lesson 3-7   A81**

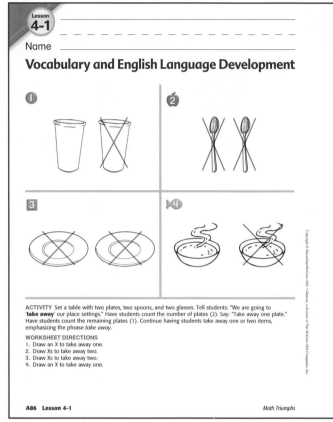

Lesson 4-1

Name

Vocabulary and English Language Development

ACTIVITY Set a table with two plates, two spoons, and two glasses. Tell students: "We are going to '**take away**' our place settings." Have students count the number of plates (2). Say: "Take away one plate." Have students count the remaining plates (1). Continue having students take away one or two items, emphasizing the phrase *take away*.

WORKSHEET DIRECTIONS
1. Draw an X to take away one.
2. Draw Xs to take away two.
3. Draw Xs to take away two.
4. Draw an X to take away one.

A86   Lesson 4-1   *Math Triumphs*

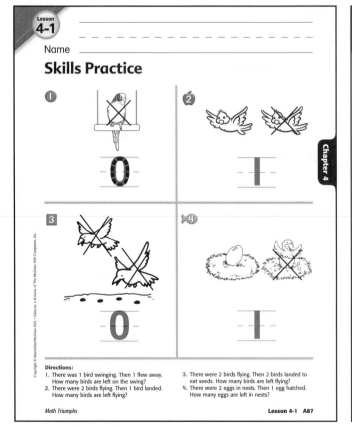

Lesson 4-1

Name

Skills Practice

Directions:
1. There was 1 bird swinging. Then 1 flew away. How many birds are left on the swing?
2. There were 2 birds flying. Then 1 bird landed. How many birds are left flying?
3. There were 2 birds flying. Then 2 birds landed to eat seeds. How many birds are left flying?
4. There were 2 eggs in nests. Then 1 egg hatched. How many eggs are left in nests?

Math Triumphs   **Lesson 4-1   A87**

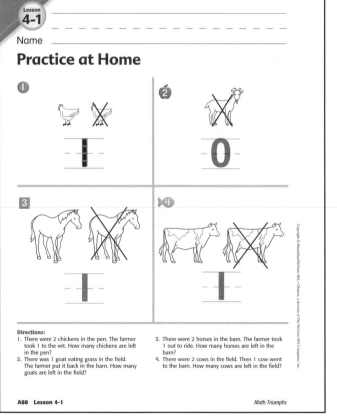

Lesson 4-1

Name

Practice at Home

Directions:
1. There were 2 chickens in the pen. The farmer took 1 to the vet. How many chickens are left in the pen?
2. There was 1 goat eating grass in the field. The farmer put it back in the barn. How many goats are left in the field?
3. There were 2 horses in the barn. The farmer took 1 out to ride. How many horses are left in the barn?
4. There were 2 cows in the field. Then 1 cow went to the barn. How many cows are left in the field?

A88   Lesson 4-1   *Math Triumphs*

Answer Key (Lesson 4-2 and 4-3)

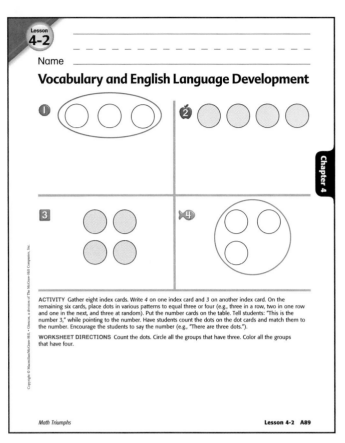

Lesson 4-2

Name

Vocabulary and English Language Development

ACTIVITY Gather eight index cards. Write 4 on one index card and 3 on another index card. On the remaining six cards, place dots in various patterns to equal three or four (e.g., three in a row, two in one row and one in the next, and three at random). Put the number cards on the table. Tell students: "This is the number 3," while pointing to the number. Have students count the dots on the dot cards and match them to the number. Encourage the students to say the number (e.g., "There are three dots.").

WORKSHEET DIRECTIONS Count the dots. Circle all the groups that have three. Color all the groups that have four.

Math Triumphs **Lesson 4-2   A89**

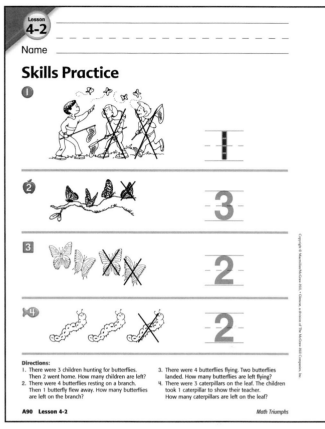

Lesson 4-2

Name

Skills Practice

Directions:
1. There were 3 children hunting for butterflies. Then 2 went home. How many children are left?
2. There were 4 butterflies resting on a branch. Then 1 butterfly flew away. How many butterflies are left on the branch?
3. There were 4 butterflies flying. Two butterflies landed. How many butterflies are left flying?
4. There were 3 caterpillars on the leaf. The children took 1 caterpillar to show their teacher. How many caterpillars are left on the leaf?

A90   Lesson 4-2 *Math Triumphs*

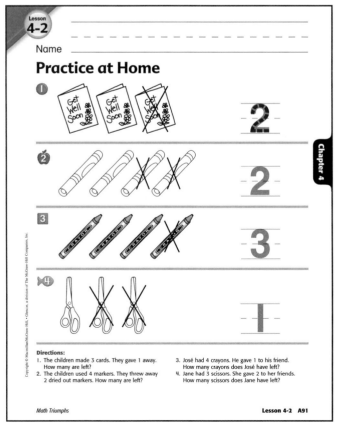

Lesson 4-2

Name

Practice at Home

Directions:
1. The children made 3 cards. They gave 1 away. How many are left?
2. The children used 4 markers. They threw away 2 dried out markers. How many are left?
3. José had 4 crayons. He gave 1 to his friend. How many crayons does José have left?
4. Jane had 3 scissors. She gave 2 to her friends. How many scissors does Jane have left?

Math Triumphs **Lesson 4-2   A91**

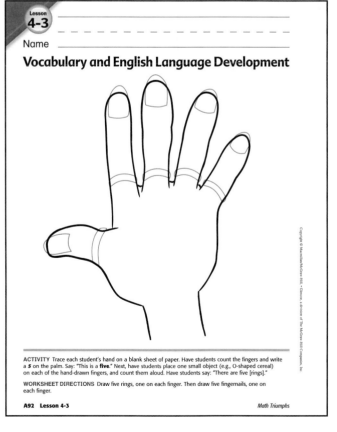

Lesson 4-3

Name

Vocabulary and English Language Development

ACTIVITY Trace each student's hand on a blank sheet of paper. Have students count the fingers and write a *5* on the palm. Say: "This is a **five**." Next, have students place one small object (e.g., O-shaped cereal) on each of the hand-drawn fingers, and count them aloud. Have students say: "There are five [rings]."

WORKSHEET DIRECTIONS Draw five rings, one on each finger. Then draw five fingernails, one on each finger.

A92   Lesson 4-3 *Math Triumphs*

Answer Key (Lesson 4-3 and 4-4)

Lesson 4-3

Name

Skills Practice

Directions:
1. There were 5 boys playing soccer in the park. Then 1 boy went home. How many boys are left?
2. The coach brought 5 soccer balls. Then 3 balls went flat. How many balls are left?
3. There were 5 shoes. The boys took home 4 shoes. Draw Xs on 4 shoes. How many shoes are left?
4. There were 5 water bottles in the cooler. Then 2 boys drank some water. Draw Xs on 2 bottles. How many bottles are left?

Math Triumphs   Lesson 4-3   A93

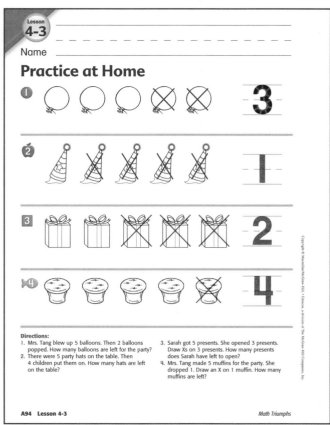

Lesson 4-3

Name

Practice at Home

Directions:
1. Mrs. Tang blew up 5 balloons. Then 2 balloons popped. How many balloons are left for the party?
2. There were 5 party hats on the table. Then 4 children put them on. How many hats are left on the table?
3. Sarah got 5 presents. She opened 3 presents. Draw Xs on 3 presents. How many presents does Sarah have left to open?
4. Mrs. Tang made 5 muffins for the party. She dropped 1. Draw an X on 1 muffin. How many muffins are left?

A94   Lesson 4-3   *Math Triumphs*

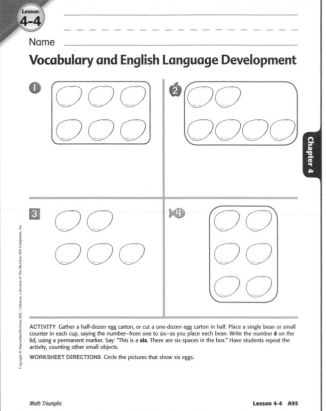

Lesson 4-4

Name

Vocabulary and English Language Development

ACTIVITY Gather a half-dozen egg carton, or cut a one-dozen egg carton in half. Place a single bean or small counter in each cup, saying the number--from one to six--as you place each bean. Write the number **6** on the lid, using a permanent marker. Say: "This is a **six**. There are six spaces in the box." Have students repeat the activity, counting other small objects.

WORKSHEET DIRECTIONS Circle the pictures that show six eggs.

Math Triumphs   Lesson 4-4   A95

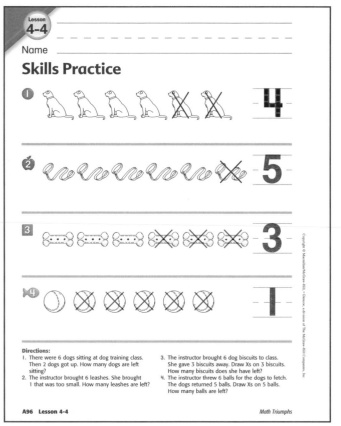

Lesson 4-4

Name

Skills Practice

Directions:
1. There were 6 dogs sitting at dog training class. Then 2 dogs got up. How many dogs are left sitting?
2. The instructor brought 6 leashes. She brought 1 that was too small. How many leashes are left?
3. The instructor brought 6 dog biscuits to class. She gave 3 biscuits away. Draw Xs on 3 biscuits. How many biscuits does she have left?
4. The instructor threw 6 balls for the dogs to fetch. The dogs returned 5 balls. Draw Xs on 5 balls. How many balls are left?

A96   Lesson 4-4   *Math Triumphs*

Answer Key (Lesson 4-4 and 4-5)

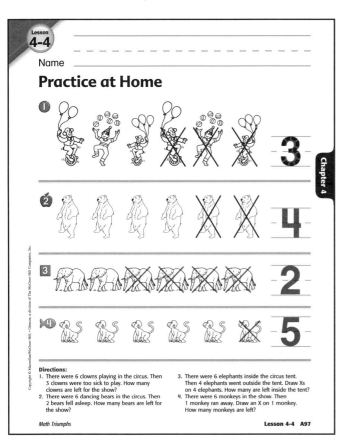

Lesson 4-4

Name

Practice at Home

Chapter 4

Directions:
1. There were 6 clowns playing in the circus. Then 3 clowns were too sick to play. How many clowns are left for the show?
2. There were 6 dancing bears in the circus. Then 2 bears fell asleep. How many bears are left for the show?
3. There were 6 elephants inside the circus tent. Then 4 elephants went outside the tent. Draw Xs on 4 elephants. How many are left inside the tent?
4. There were 6 monkeys in the show. Then 1 monkey ran away. Draw an X on 1 monkey. How many monkeys are left?

Math Triumphs **Lesson 4-4 A97**

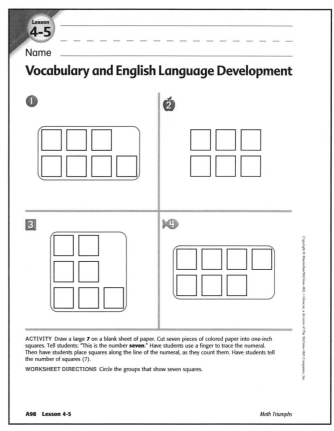

Lesson 4-5

Name

Vocabulary and English Language Development

ACTIVITY Draw a large **7** on a blank sheet of paper. Cut seven pieces of colored paper into one-inch squares. Tell students: "This is the number **seven**." Have students use a finger to trace the numeral. Then have students place squares along the line of the numeral, as they count them. Have students tell the number of squares (7).

WORKSHEET DIRECTIONS Circle the groups that show seven squares.

A98 Lesson 4-5 *Math Triumphs*

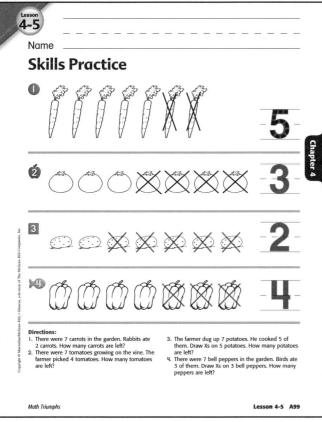

Lesson 4-5

Name

Skills Practice

Chapter 4

Directions:
1. There were 7 carrots in the garden. Rabbits ate 2 carrots. How many carrots are left?
2. There were 7 tomatoes growing on the vine. The farmer picked 4 tomatoes. How many tomatoes are left?
3. The farmer dug up 7 potatoes. He cooked 5 of them. Draw Xs on 5 potatoes. How many potatoes are left?
4. There were 7 bell peppers in the garden. Birds ate 3 of them. Draw Xs on 3 bell peppers. How many peppers are left?

Math Triumphs **Lesson 4-5 A99**

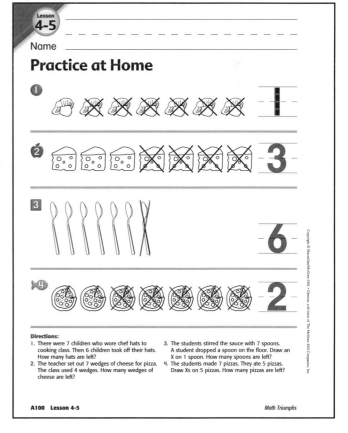

Lesson 4-5

Name

Practice at Home

Directions:
1. There were 7 children who wore chef hats to cooking class. Then 6 children took off their hats. How many hats are left?
2. The teacher set out 7 wedges of cheese for pizza. The class used 4 wedges. How many wedges of cheese are left?
3. The students stirred the sauce with 7 spoons. A student dropped a spoon on the floor. Draw an X on 1 spoon. How many spoons are left?
4. The students made 7 pizzas. They ate 5 pizzas. Draw Xs on 5 pizzas. How many pizzas are left?

A100 Lesson 4-5 *Math Triumphs*

Answer Key (Lesson 4-6 and 4-7)

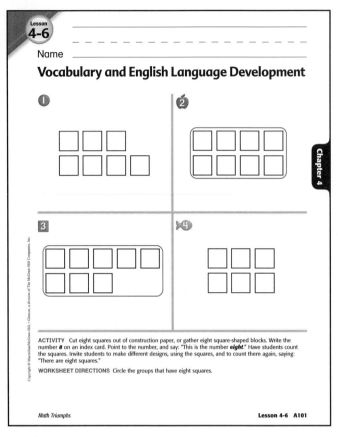

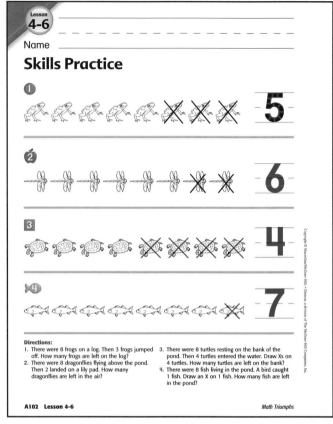

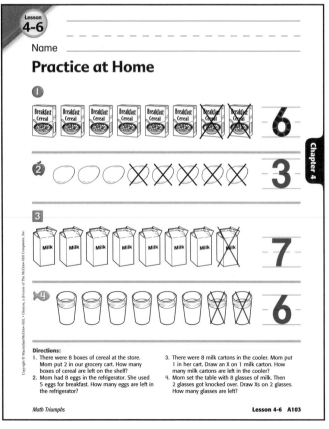

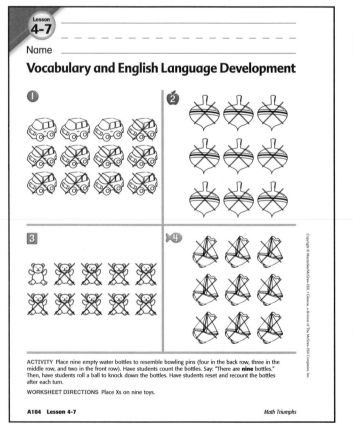

Answer Key (Lesson 4-7 and 5-1)

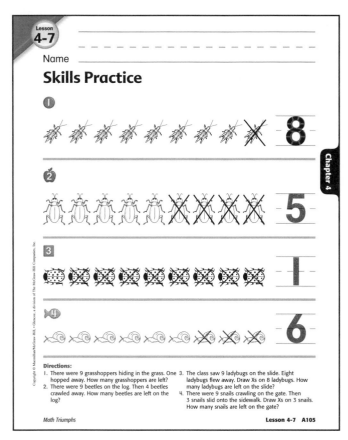

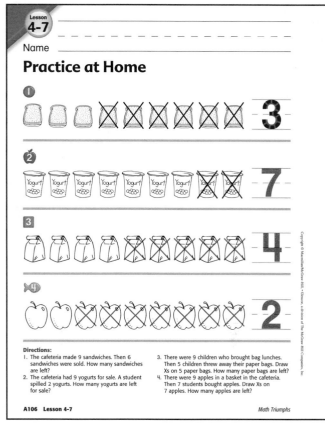

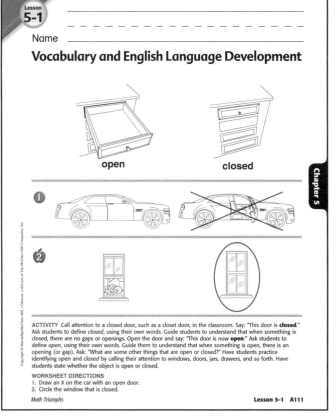

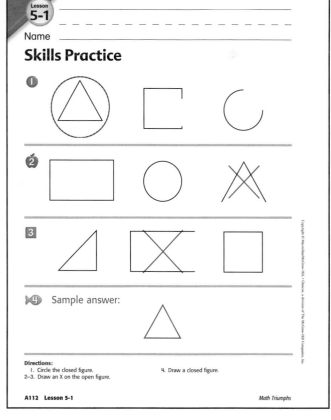

Answer Key (Lesson 5-1 and 5-2)

Practice at Home

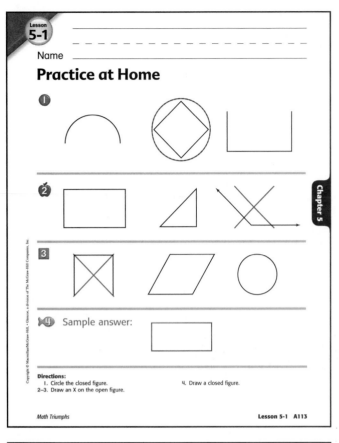

Directions:
1. Circle the closed figure.
2–3. Draw an X on the open figure.

4. Draw a closed figure.

Vocabulary and English Language Development

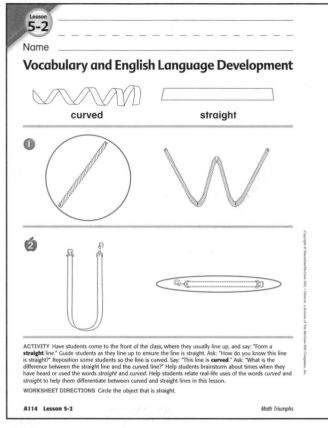

curved   straight

ACTIVITY Have students come to the front of the class, where they usually line up, and say: "Form a **straight** line." Guide students as they line up to ensure the line is straight. Ask: "How do you know this line is straight?" Reposition some students so the line is curved. Say: "This line is **curved**." Ask: "What is the difference between the straight line and the curved line?" Help students brainstorm about times when they have heard or used the words *straight* and *curved*. Help students relate real-life uses of the words *curved* and *straight* to help them differentiate between curved and straight lines in this lesson.

WORKSHEET DIRECTIONS Circle the object that is straight.

Skills Practice

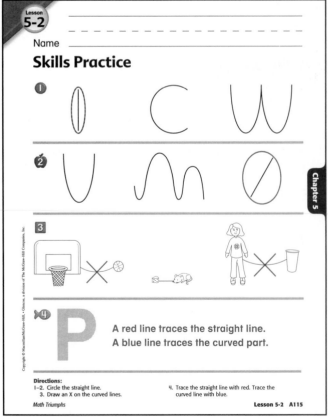

A red line traces the straight line.
A blue line traces the curved part.

Directions:
1–2. Circle the straight line.
3. Draw an X on the curved lines.

4. Trace the straight line with red. Trace the curved line with blue.

Practice at Home

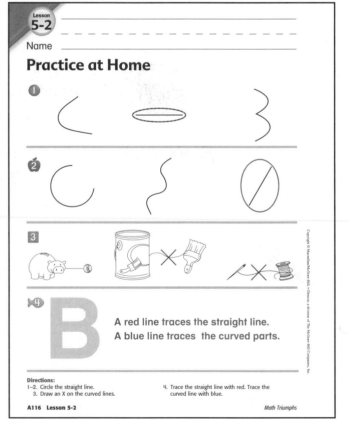

A red line traces the straight line.
A blue line traces the curved parts.

Directions:
1–2. Circle the straight line.
3. Draw an X on the curved lines.

4. Trace the straight line with red. Trace the curved line with blue.

Answer Key (Lesson 5-3 and 5-4)

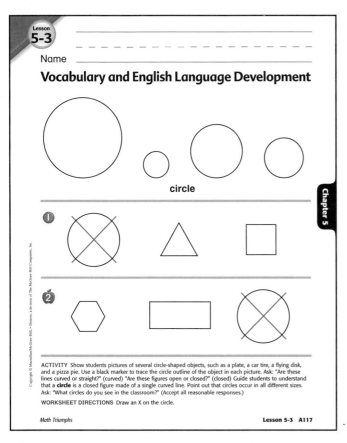

Lesson 5-3

Name

Vocabulary and English Language Development

circle

ACTIVITY Show students pictures of several circle-shaped objects, such as a plate, a car tire, a flying disk, and a pizza pie. Use a black marker to trace the circle outline of the object in each picture. Ask: "Are these lines curved or straight?" (curved) "Are these figures open or closed?" (closed) Guide students to understand that a **circle** is a closed figure made of a single curved line. Point out that circles occur in all different sizes. Ask: "What circles do you see in the classroom?" (Accept all reasonable responses.)

WORKSHEET DIRECTIONS Draw an X on the circle.

Math Triumphs   **Lesson 5-3   A117**

Chapter 5

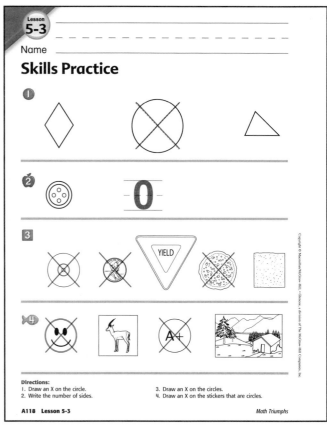

Lesson 5-3

Name

Skills Practice

1.

2. **0**

3. YIELD

4. A+

Directions:
1. Draw an X on the circle.   3. Draw an X on the circles.
2. Write the number of sides.   4. Draw an X on the stickers that are circles.

A118   Lesson 5-3   *Math Triumphs*

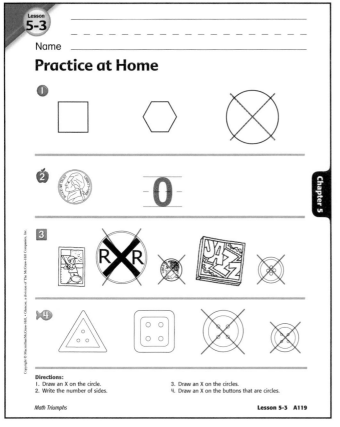

Lesson 5-3

Name

Practice at Home

1.

2. **0**

3. R×R   JAZZ

4.

Directions:
1. Draw an X on the circle.   3. Draw an X on the circles.
2. Write the number of sides.   4. Draw an X on the buttons that are circles.

Math Triumphs   **Lesson 5-3   A119**

Chapter 5

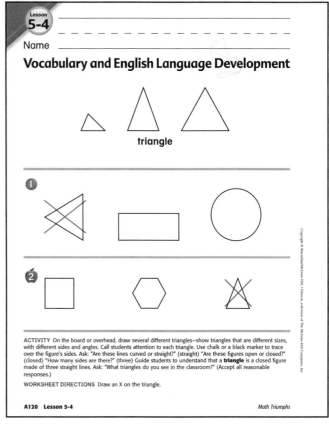

Lesson 5-4

Name

Vocabulary and English Language Development

triangle

1.

2.

ACTIVITY On the board or overhead, draw several different triangles—show triangles that are different sizes, with different sides and angles. Call students attention to each triangle. Use chalk or a black marker to trace over the figure's sides. Ask: "Are these lines curved or straight?" (straight) "Are these figures open or closed?" (closed) "How many sides are there?" (three) Guide students to understand that a **triangle** is a closed figure made of three straight lines. Ask: "What triangles do you see in the classroom?" (Accept all reasonable responses.)

WORKSHEET DIRECTIONS Draw an X on the triangle.

A120   Lesson 5-4   *Math Triumphs*

Answer Key (Lesson 5-4 and 5-5)

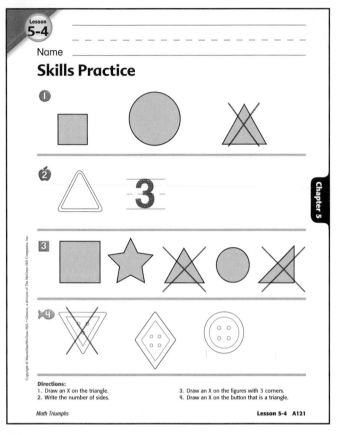

Chapter 5

Directions:
1. Draw an X on the triangle.
2. Write the number of sides.
3. Draw an X on the figures with 3 corners.
4. Draw an X on the button that is a triangle.

Math Triumphs   **Lesson 5-4 A121**

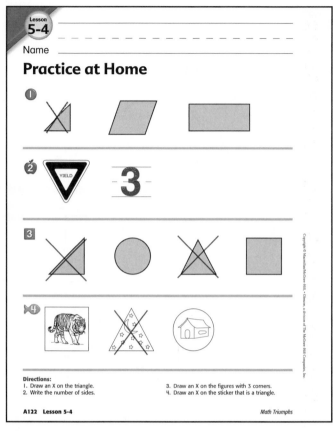

Directions:
1. Draw an X on the triangle.
2. Write the number of sides.
3. Draw an X on the figures with 3 corners.
4. Draw an X on the sticker that is a triangle.

A122 Lesson 5-4   *Math Triumphs*

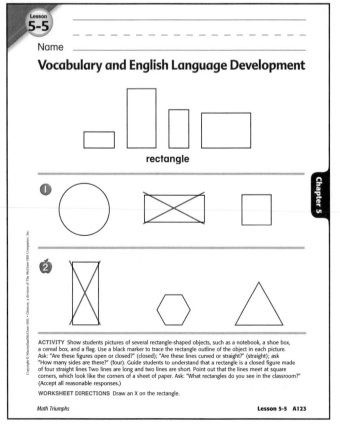

Chapter 5

ACTIVITY Show students pictures of several rectangle-shaped objects, such as a notebook, a shoe box, a cereal box, and a flag. Use a black marker to trace the rectangle outline of the object in each picture. Ask: "Are these figures open or closed?" (closed); "Are these lines curved or straight?" (straight); ask "How many sides are there?" (four). Guide students to understand that a rectangle is a closed figure made of four straight lines Two lines are long and two lines are short. Point out that the lines meet at square corners, which look like the corners of a sheet of paper. Ask: "What rectangles do you see in the classroom?" (Accept all reasonable responses.)

WORKSHEET DIRECTIONS Draw an X on the rectangle.

Math Triumphs   **Lesson 5-5 A123**

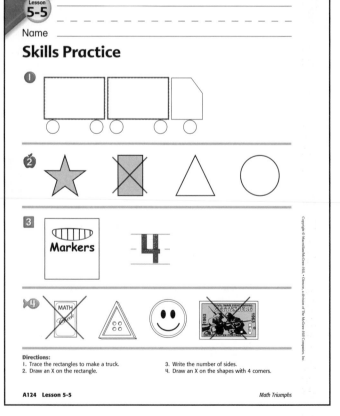

Directions:
1. Trace the rectangles to make a truck.
2. Draw an X on the rectangle.
3. Write the number of sides.
4. Draw an X on the shapes with 4 corners.

A124 Lesson 5-5   *Math Triumphs*

Answer Key (Lesson 5-5 and 5-6)

Lesson 5-5

Name

Practice at Home

Directions:
1. Trace the rectangle to make a school bus.
2. Draw an X on the rectangle.
3. Write the number of sides.
4. Draw an X on the shapes with 4 corners.

Math Triumphs   **Lesson 5-5 A125**

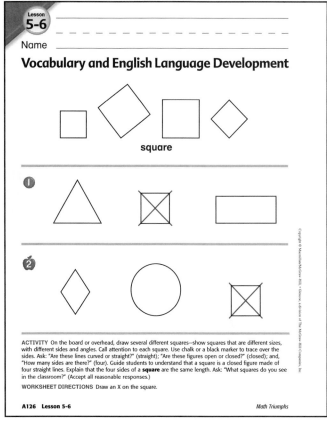

Lesson 5-6

Name

Vocabulary and English Language Development

square

ACTIVITY On the board or overhead, draw several different squares—show squares that are different sizes, with different sides and angles. Call attention to each square. Use chalk or a black marker to trace over the sides. Ask: "Are these lines curved or straight?" (straight); "Are these figures open or closed?" (closed); and, "How many sides are there?" (four). Guide students to understand that a square is a closed figure made of four straight lines. Explain that the four sides of a **square** are the same length. Ask: "What squares do you see in the classroom?" (Accept all reasonable responses.)
WORKSHEET DIRECTIONS Draw an X on the square.

A126 Lesson 5-6   *Math Triumphs*

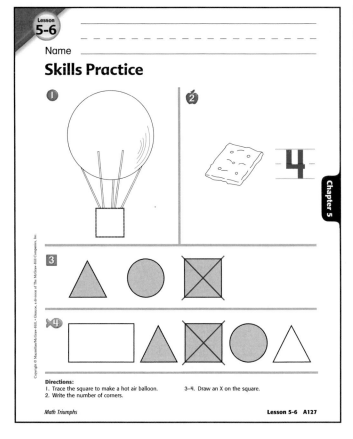

Lesson 5-6

Name

Skills Practice

Directions:
1. Trace the square to make a hot air balloon.
2. Write the number of corners.
3–4. Draw an X on the square.

Math Triumphs   **Lesson 5-6 A127**

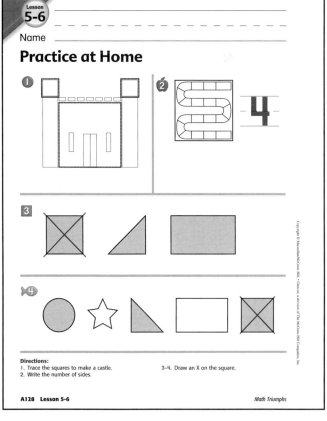

Lesson 5-6

Name

Practice at Home

Directions:
1. Trace the squares to make a castle.
2. Write the number of sides.
3–4. Draw an X on the square.

A128 Lesson 5-6   *Math Triumphs*

Answer Key (Lesson 5-7 and 6-1)

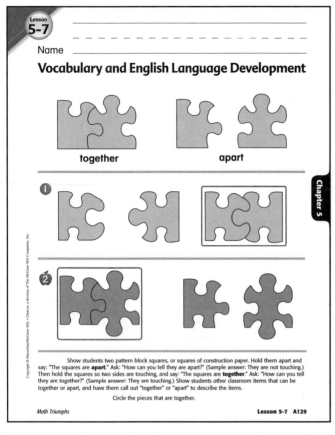

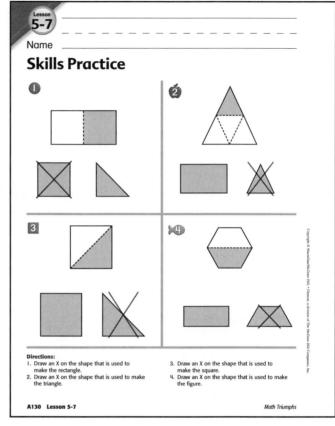

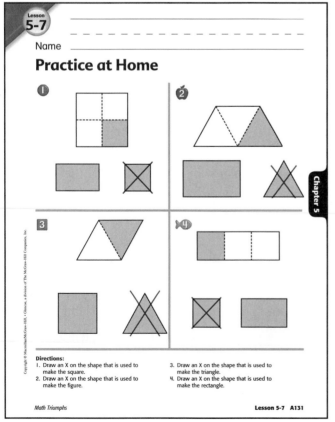

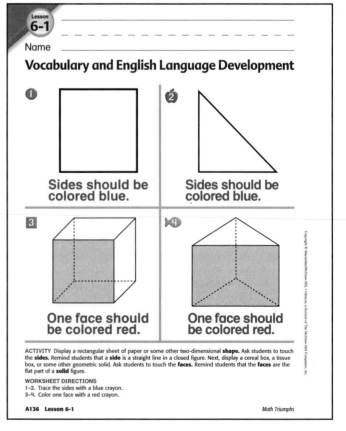

Answer Key (Lesson 6-1 and 6-2)

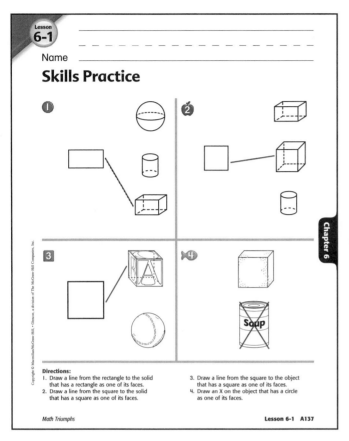

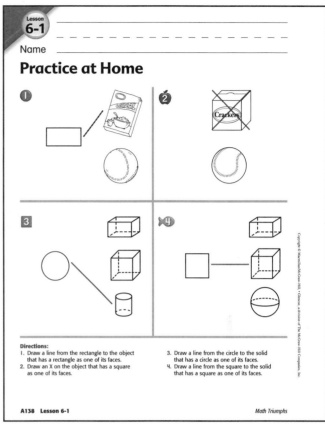

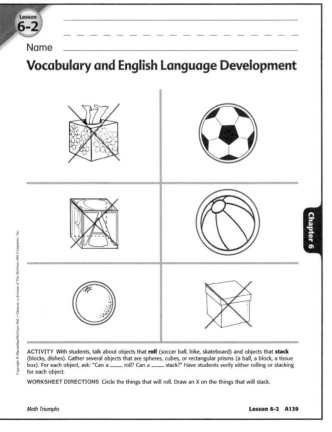

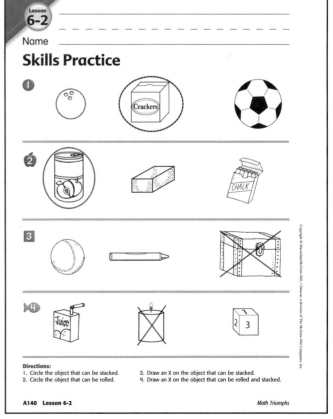

Answer Key (Lesson 6-2 and 6-3)

Lesson 6-2

Name

Practice at Home

Directions:
1. Draw an X on the object that can be rolled.
2. Draw an X on the object that can be stacked.
3. Circle the object that can be rolled.
4. Circle the object that can be rolled and stacked.

Math Triumphs   **Lesson 6-2   A141**

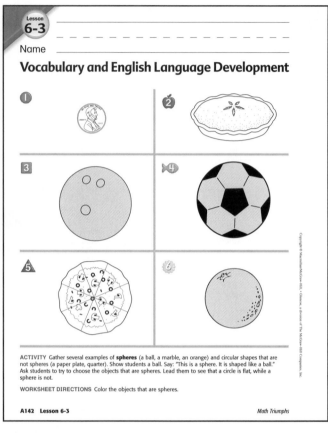

Lesson 6-3

Name

Vocabulary and English Language Development

ACTIVITY Gather several examples of **spheres** (a ball, a marble, an orange) and circular shapes that are not spheres (a paper plate, quarter). Show students a ball. Say: "This is a sphere. It is shaped like a ball." Ask students to try to choose the objects that are spheres. Lead them to see that a circle is flat, while a sphere is not.

WORKSHEET DIRECTIONS Color the objects that are spheres.

A142   Lesson 6-3   *Math Triumphs*

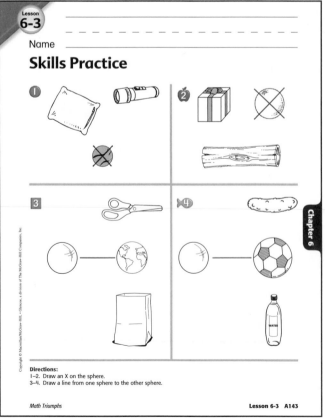

Lesson 6-3

Name

Skills Practice

Directions:
1–2. Draw an X on the sphere.
3–4. Draw a line from one sphere to the other sphere.

Math Triumphs   **Lesson 6-3   A143**

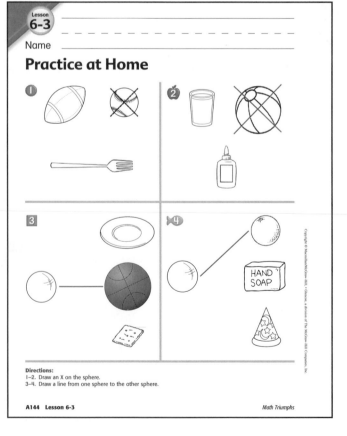

Lesson 6-3

Name

Practice at Home

Directions:
1–2. Draw an X on the sphere.
3–4. Draw a line from one sphere to the other sphere.

A144   Lesson 6-3   *Math Triumphs*

Answer Key (Lesson 6-4 and 6-5)

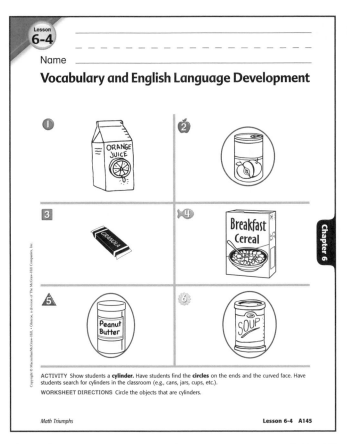

Lesson 6-4

Name

Vocabulary and English Language Development

Chapter 6

ACTIVITY Show students a **cylinder**. Have students find the **circles** on the ends and the curved face. Have students search for cylinders in the classroom (e.g., cans, jars, cups, etc.).

WORKSHEET DIRECTIONS Circle the objects that are cylinders.

Math Triumphs   **Lesson 6-4   A145**

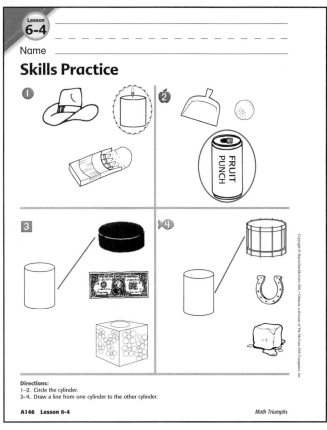

Lesson 6-4

Name

Skills Practice

Directions:
1–2. Circle the cylinder.
3–4. Draw a line from one cylinder to the other cylinder.

A146   Lesson 6-4   *Math Triumphs*

Lesson 6-4

Name

Practice at Home

Chapter 6

Directions:
1–2. Draw a line from one cylinder to the other cylinder.
3–4. Circle the cylinder.

Math Triumphs   **Lesson 6-4   A147**

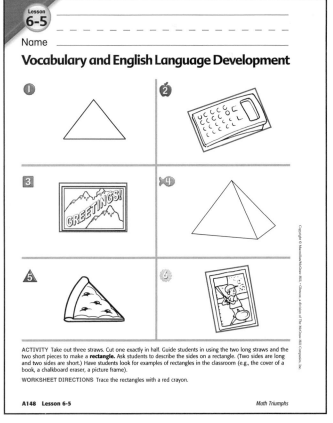

Lesson 6-5

Name

Vocabulary and English Language Development

ACTIVITY Take out three straws. Cut one exactly in half. Guide students in using the two long straws and the two short pieces to make a **rectangle**. Ask students to describe the sides on a rectangle. (Two sides are long and two sides are short.) Have students look for examples of rectangles in the classroom (e.g., the cover of a book, a chalkboard eraser, a picture frame).

WORKSHEET DIRECTIONS Trace the rectangles with a red crayon.

A148   Lesson 6-5   *Math Triumphs*

Math Triumphs   **Lesson 6-4 and 6-5   A285**

Answer Key (Lesson 6-5 and 6-6)

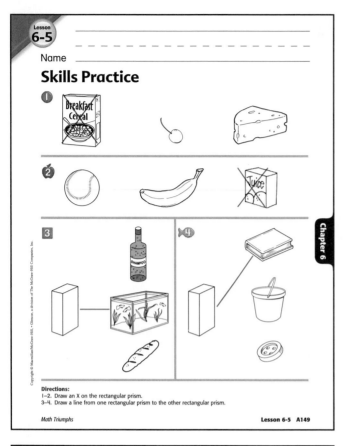

Directions:
1–2. Draw an X on the rectangular prism.
3–4. Draw a line from one rectangular prism to the other rectangular prism.

Math Triumphs

Lesson 6-5 A149

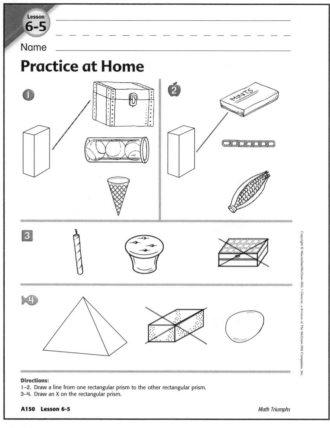

Directions:
1–2. Draw a line from one rectangular prism to the other rectangular prism.
3–4. Draw an X on the rectangular prism.

A150 Lesson 6-5

Math Triumphs

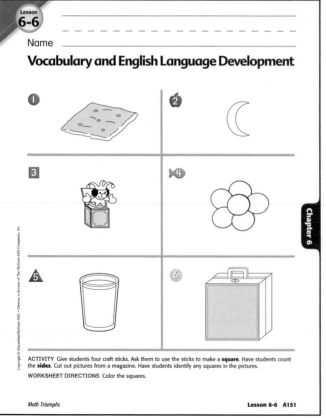

ACTIVITY Give students four craft sticks. Ask them to use the sticks to make a **square**. Have students count the **sides**. Cut out pictures from a magazine. Have students identify any squares in the pictures.
WORKSHEET DIRECTIONS Color the squares.

Math Triumphs

Lesson 6-6 A151

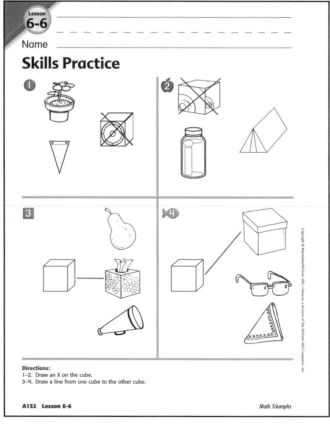

Directions:
1–2. Draw an X on the cube.
3–4. Draw a line from one cube to the other cube.

A152 Lesson 6-6

Math Triumphs

A286 Lesson 6-5 and 6-6

Math Triumphs

Answer Key (Lesson 6-6 and 6-7)

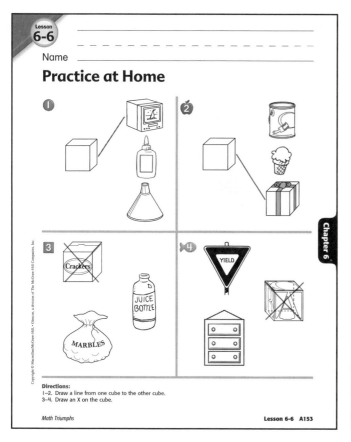

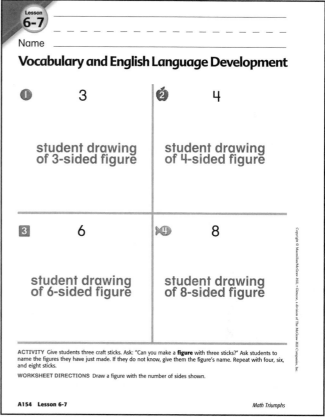

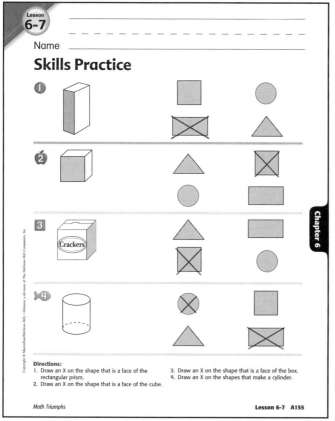

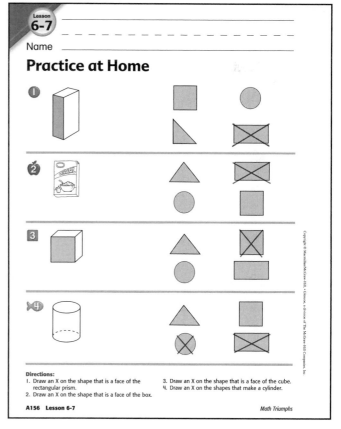

Answer Key (Lesson 7-1 and 7-2)

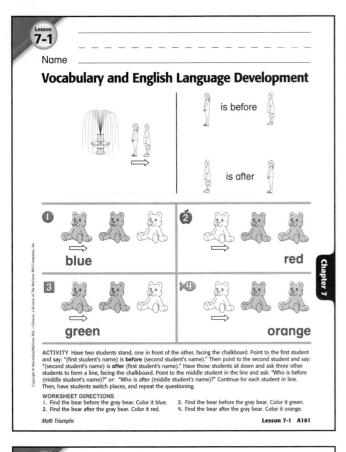

Lesson 7-1

Name

Vocabulary and English Language Development

is before

is after

1 blue

2 red

3 green

4 orange

ACTIVITY Have two students stand, one in front of the other, facing the chalkboard. Point to the first student and say: "(first student's name) is **before** (second student's name)." Then point to the second student and say: "(second student's name) is **after** (first student's name)." Have those students sit down and ask three other students to form a line, facing the chalkboard. Point to the middle student in the line and ask: "Who is before (middle student's name)?" or: "Who is after (middle student's name)?" Continue for each student in line. Then, have students switch places, and repeat the questioning.

WORKSHEET DIRECTIONS
1. Find the bear before the gray bear. Color it blue.
2. Find the bear after the gray bear. Color it red.
3. Find the bear before the gray bear. Color it green.
4. Find the bear after the gray bear. Color it orange.

Math Triumphs **Lesson 7-1 A161**

Chapter 7

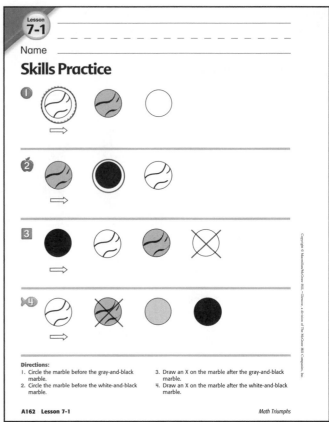

Lesson 7-1

Name

Skills Practice

1

2

3

4

Directions:
1. Circle the marble before the gray-and-black marble.
2. Circle the marble before the white-and-black marble.
3. Draw an X on the marble after the gray-and-black marble.
4. Draw an X on the marble after the white-and-black marble.

A162 Lesson 7-1 *Math Triumphs*

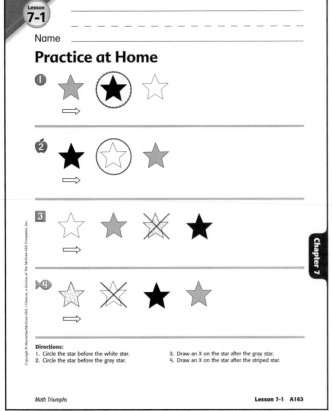

Lesson 7-1

Name

Practice at Home

1

2

3

4

Chapter 7

Directions:
1. Circle the star before the white star.
2. Circle the star before the gray star.
3. Draw an X on the star after the gray star.
4. Draw an X on the star after the striped star.

Math Triumphs **Lesson 7-1 A163**

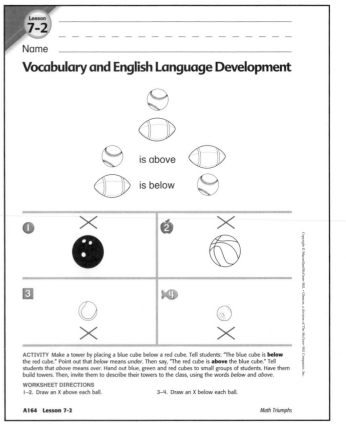

Lesson 7-2

Name

Vocabulary and English Language Development

is above

is below

1

2

3

4

ACTIVITY Make a tower by placing a blue cube below a red cube. Tell students: "The blue cube is **below** the red cube." Point out that *below* means *under*. Then say, "The red cube is **above** the blue cube." Tell students that *above* means *over*. Hand out blue, green and red cubes to small groups of students. Have them build towers. Then, invite them to describe their towers to the class, using the words *below* and *above*.

WORKSHEET DIRECTIONS
1–2. Draw an X above each ball.
3–4. Draw an X below each ball.

A164 Lesson 7-2 *Math Triumphs*

Answer Key (Lesson 7-2 and 7-3)

Lesson 7-2

Name

Skills Practice

Directions:
1. Draw an X below the boat.
2. Draw an X above the airplane.
3. Circle the object below the helicopter.
4. Circle the object above the wagon.

Math Triumphs

Lesson 7-2 A165

Chapter 7

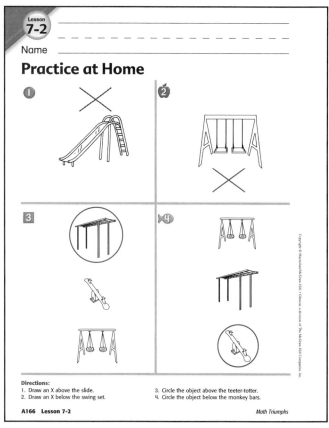

Lesson 7-2

Name

Practice at Home

Directions:
1. Draw an X above the slide.
2. Draw an X below the swing set.
3. Circle the object above the teeter-totter.
4. Circle the object below the monkey bars.

A166 Lesson 7-2

Math Triumphs

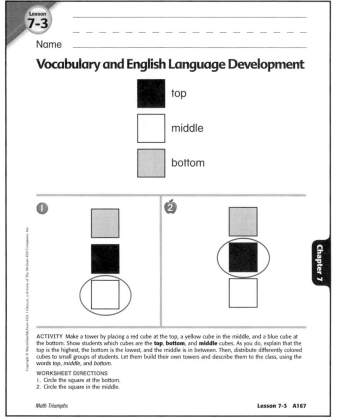

Lesson 7-3

Name

Vocabulary and English Language Development

■ top

□ middle

▨ bottom

ACTIVITY Make a tower by placing a red cube at the top, a yellow cube in the middle, and a blue cube at the bottom. Show students which cubes are the **top**, **bottom**, and **middle** cubes. As you do, explain that the top is the highest, the bottom is the lowest, and the middle is in between. Then, distribute differently colored cubes to small groups of students. Let them build their own towers and describe them to the class, using the words *top*, *middle*, and *bottom*.

WORKSHEET DIRECTIONS
1. Circle the square at the bottom.
2. Circle the square in the middle.

Math Triumphs

Lesson 7-3 A167

Chapter 7

Lesson 7-3

Name

Skills Practice

Directions:
1. Circle the object in the middle.
2. Circle the object at the top.
3. Circle the object at the bottom.
4. Draw a circle at the top. Draw an X at the bottom.

A168 Lesson 7-3

Math Triumphs

Answer Key (Lesson 7-3 and 7-4)

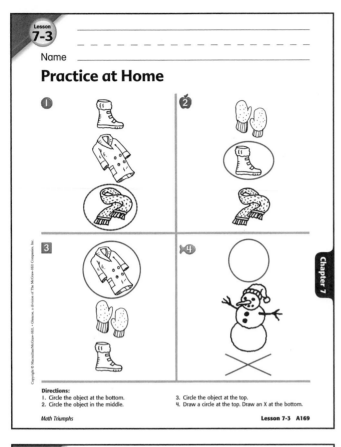

Lesson 7-3

Practice at Home

Directions:
1. Circle the object at the bottom.
2. Circle the object in the middle.

3. Circle the object at the top.
4. Draw a circle at the top. Draw an X at the bottom.

Math Triumphs

Lesson 7-3   A169

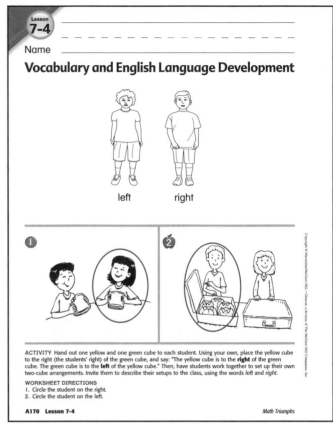

Lesson 7-4

Vocabulary and English Language Development

left   right

ACTIVITY Hand out one yellow and one green cube to each student. Using your own, place the yellow cube to the right (the students' right) of the green cube, and say: "The yellow cube is to the **right** of the green cube. The green cube is to the **left** of the yellow cube." Then, have students work together to set up their own two-cube arrangements. Invite them to describe their setups to the class, using the words *left* and *right*.

WORKSHEET DIRECTIONS
1. Circle the student on the right.
2. Circle the student on the left.

A170   Lesson 7-4

Math Triumphs

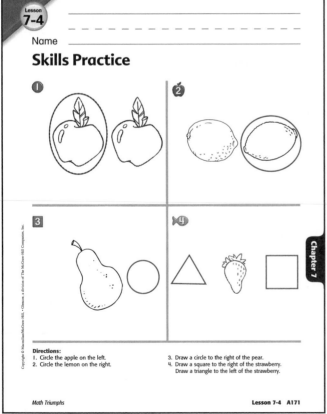

Lesson 7-4

Skills Practice

Directions:
1. Circle the apple on the left.
2. Circle the lemon on the right.

3. Draw a circle to the right of the pear.
4. Draw a square to the right of the strawberry.
   Draw a triangle to the left of the strawberry.

Math Triumphs

Lesson 7-4   A171

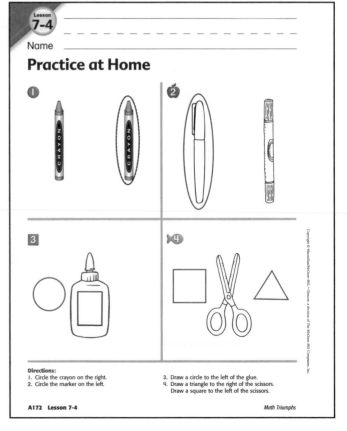

Lesson 7-4

Practice at Home

Directions:
1. Circle the crayon on the right.
2. Circle the marker on the left.

3. Draw a circle to the left of the glue.
4. Draw a triangle to the right of the scissors.
   Draw a square to the left of the scissors.

A172   Lesson 7-4

Math Triumphs

Answer Key (Lesson 7-5 and 7-6)

Lesson 7-5

Name

Vocabulary and English Language Development

front   back

ACTIVITY Show students the front of a stuffed animal. Ask: "What do you see on the **front**?" (eyes, a face, a belly, etc.) Show students the **back**. Ask: "What do you see on the back?" (a tail, etc.) Discuss with students how the front and back of the stuffed animal are alike and different. Then, show students the front and back of other objects, such as a cereal box or a book. Have them determine if you are showing the front or the back of the object. Ask students to explain their choices.

WORKSHEET DIRECTIONS
1. Circle the picture of the front of the bear.
2. Circle the picture of the back of the bunny.

Math Triumphs   **Lesson 7-5   A173**

Lesson 7-5

Name

Skills Practice

Directions:
1. Circle the picture of the front of the bunny.
2. Circle the picture of the back of the dog.
3. Draw an X on the back of the frog.
4. Draw an X on the front of the gerbil.
5. Circle the pictures that show the back of a bear.

A174   Lesson 7-5   *Math Triumphs*

Lesson 7-5

Name

Practice at Home

Directions:
1. Circle the picture of the back of the kitten.
2. Circle the picture of the front of the lion.
3. Draw an X on the front of the squirrel.
4. Draw an X on the back of the bear.
5. Circle the pictures that show the back of a bunny.

Math Triumphs   **Lesson 7-5   A175**

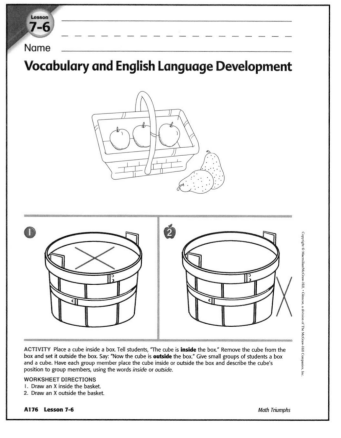

Lesson 7-6

Name

Vocabulary and English Language Development

ACTIVITY Place a cube inside a box. Tell students, "The cube is **inside** the box." Remove the cube from the box and set it outside the box. Say: "Now the cube is **outside** the box." Give small groups of students a box and a cube. Have each group member place the cube inside or outside the box and describe the cube's position to group members, using the words *inside* or *outside*.

WORKSHEET DIRECTIONS
1. Draw an X inside the basket.
2. Draw an X outside the basket.

A176   Lesson 7-6   *Math Triumphs*

Answer Key (Lesson 7-6 and 7-7)

Name

Skills Practice

Directions:
1. Draw an X outside the birdcage.
2. Draw an X inside the bathtub.
3. Draw an X on the ball that is inside the circle.
4. Draw an X on the book that is outside the circle.

Math Triumphs

Lesson 7-6 A177

Name

Practice at Home

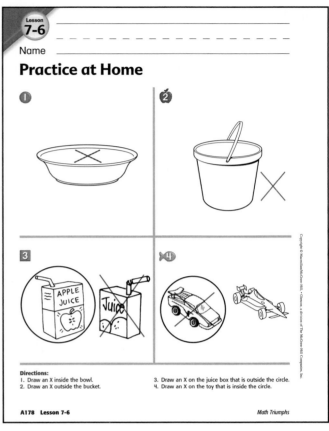

Directions:
1. Draw an X inside the bowl.
2. Draw an X outside the bucket.
3. Draw an X on the juice box that is outside the circle.
4. Draw an X on the toy that is inside the circle.

A178 Lesson 7-6

Math Triumphs

Name

Vocabulary and English Language Development

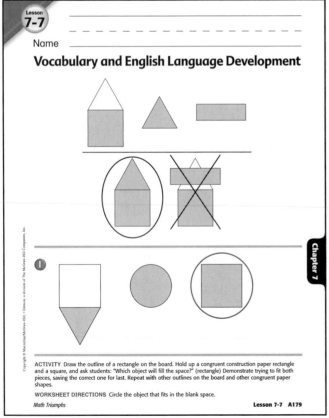

ACTIVITY Draw the outline of a rectangle on the board. Hold up a congruent construction paper rectangle and a square, and ask students: "Which object will fill the space?" (rectangle) Demonstrate trying to fit both pieces, saving the correct one for last. Repeat with other outlines on the board and other congruent paper shapes.

WORKSHEET DIRECTIONS Circle the object that fits in the blank space.

Math Triumphs

Lesson 7-7 A179

Name

Skills Practice

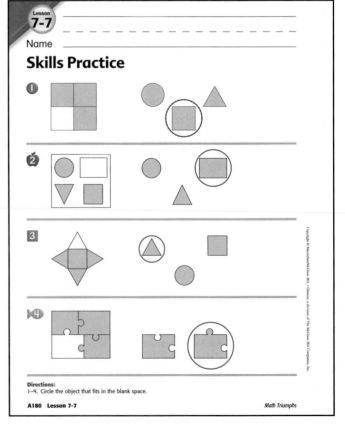

Directions:
1–4. Circle the object that fits in the blank space.

A180 Lesson 7-7

Math Triumphs

Math Triumphs

Answer Key (Lesson 7-7 and 8-1)

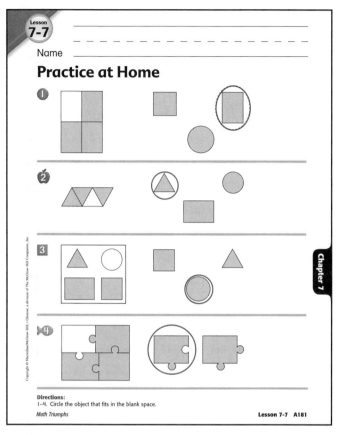

Lesson 7-7 — Practice at Home

Directions:
1–4. Circle the object that fits in the blank space.

Math Triumphs

Lesson 7-7   A181

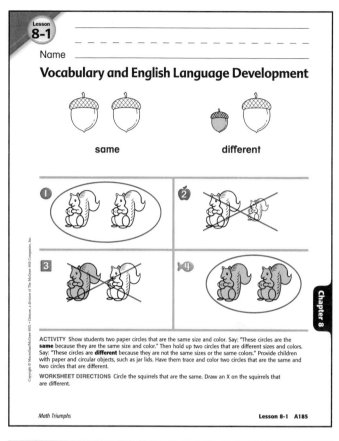

Lesson 8-1 — Vocabulary and English Language Development

same   different

ACTIVITY Show students two paper circles that are the same size and color. Say: "These circles are the **same** because they are the same size and color." Then hold up two circles that are different sizes and colors. Say: "These circles are **different** because they are not the same sizes or the same colors." Provide children with paper and circular objects, such as jar lids. Have them trace and color two circles that are the same and two circles that are different.

WORKSHEET DIRECTIONS Circle the squirrels that are the same. Draw an X on the squirrels that are different.

Math Triumphs

Lesson 8-1   A185

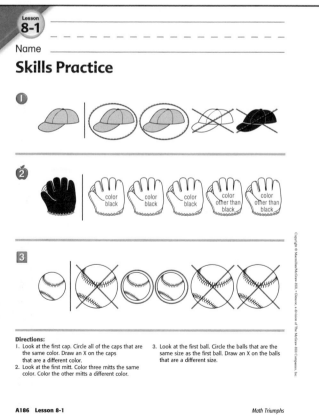

Lesson 8-1 — Skills Practice

color black | color black | color black | color other than black | color other than black

Directions:
1. Look at the first cap. Circle all of the caps that are the same color. Draw an X on the caps that are a different color.
2. Look at the first mitt. Color three mitts the same color. Color the other mitts a different color.
3. Look at the first ball. Circle the balls that are the same size as the first ball. Draw an X on the balls that are a different size.

A186   Lesson 8-1

Math Triumphs

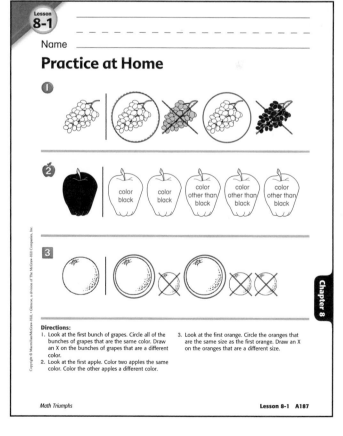

Lesson 8-1 — Practice at Home

color black | color black | color other than black | color other than black | color other than black

Directions:
1. Look at the first bunch of grapes. Circle all of the bunches of grapes that are the same color. Draw an X on the bunches of grapes that are a different color.
2. Look at the first apple. Color two apples the same color. Color the other apples a different color.
3. Look at the first orange. Circle the oranges that are the same size as the first orange. Draw an X on the oranges that are a different size.

Math Triumphs

Lesson 8-1   A187

Math Triumphs

Answer Key (Lesson 8-2 and 8-3)

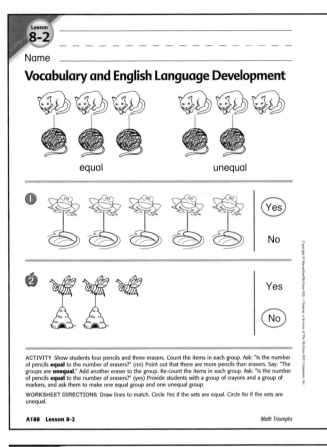

Vocabulary and English Language Development

equal   unequal

1. Yes / No

2. Yes / No

ACTIVITY Show students four pencils and three erasers. Count the items in each group. Ask: "Is the number of pencils **equal** to the number of erasers?" (no) Point out that there are more pencils than erasers. Say: "The groups are **unequal**." Add another eraser to the group. Re-count the items in each group. Ask: "Is the number of pencils **equal** to the number of erasers?" (yes) Provide students with a group of crayons and a group of markers, and ask them to make one equal group and one unequal group.

WORKSHEET DIRECTIONS Draw lines to match. Circle *Yes* if the sets are equal. Circle *No* if the sets are unequal.

A188 Lesson 8-2   *Math Triumphs*

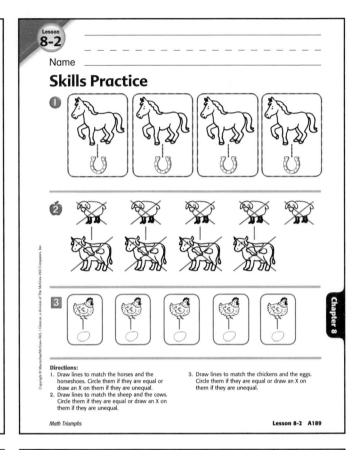

Lesson 8-2 — Name

Skills Practice

1.

2.

3.

Directions:
1. Draw lines to match the horses and the horseshoes. Circle them if they are equal or draw an X on them if they are unequal.
2. Draw lines to match the sheep and the cows. Circle them if they are equal or draw an X on them if they are unequal.
3. Draw lines to match the chickens and the eggs. Circle them if they are equal or draw an X on them if they are unequal.

Math Triumphs   Lesson 8-2   A189

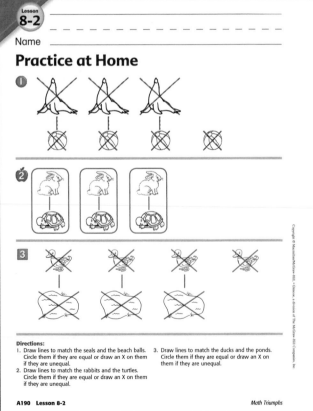

Lesson 8-2 — Name

Practice at Home

1.

2.

3.

Directions:
1. Draw lines to match the seals and the beach balls. Circle them if they are equal or draw an X on them if they are unequal.
2. Draw lines to match the rabbits and the turtles. Circle them if they are equal or draw an X on them if they are unequal.
3. Draw lines to match the ducks and the ponds. Circle them if they are equal or draw an X on them if they are unequal.

A190 Lesson 8-2   *Math Triumphs*

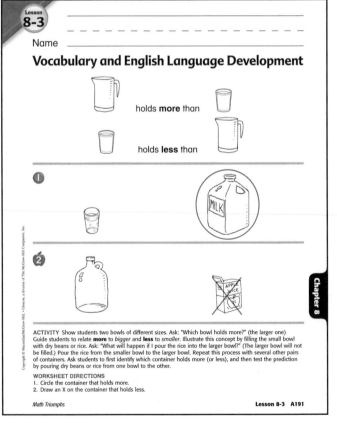

Lesson 8-3 — Name

Vocabulary and English Language Development

holds **more** than

holds **less** than

1.

2.

ACTIVITY Show students two bowls of different sizes. Ask: "Which bowl holds more?" (the larger one) Guide students to relate *more* to *bigger* and *less* to *smaller*. Illustrate this concept by filling the small bowl with dry beans or rice. Ask: "What will happen if I pour the rice into the larger bowl?" (The larger bowl will not be filled.) Pour the rice from the smaller bowl to the larger bowl. Repeat this process with several other pairs of containers. Ask students to first identify which container holds more (or less), and then test the prediction by pouring dry beans or rice from one bowl to the other.

WORKSHEET DIRECTIONS
1. Circle the container that holds more.
2. Draw an X on the container that holds less.

Math Triumphs   Lesson 8-3   A191

A294   Lesson 8-2 and 8-3   *Math Triumphs*

Answer Key (Lesson 8-3 and 8-4)

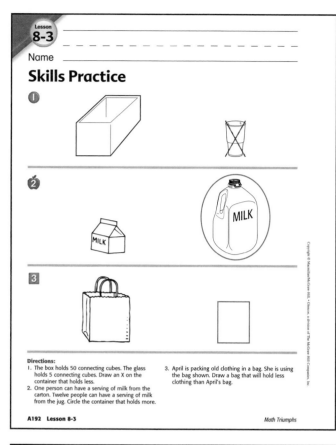

Lesson 8-3

Name

Skills Practice

Directions:

1. The box holds 50 connecting cubes. The glass holds 5 connecting cubes. Draw an X on the container that holds less.
2. One person can have a serving of milk from the carton. Twelve people can have a serving of milk from the jug. Circle the container that holds more.
3. April is packing old clothing in a bag. She is using the bag shown. Draw a bag that will hold less clothing than April's bag.

A192 Lesson 8-3

Math Triumphs

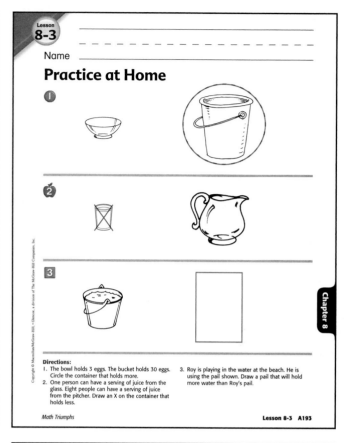

Lesson 8-3

Name

Practice at Home

Directions:

1. The bowl holds 3 eggs. The bucket holds 30 eggs. Circle the container that holds more.
2. One person can have a serving of juice from the glass. Eight people can have a serving of juice from the pitcher. Draw an X on the container that holds less.
3. Roy is playing in the water at the beach. He is using the pail shown. Draw a pail that will hold more water than Roy's pail.

Math Triumphs

Lesson 8-3 A193

Chapter 8

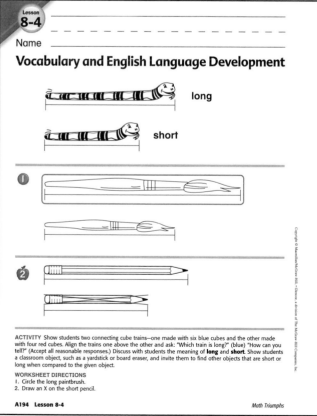

Lesson 8-4

Name

Vocabulary and English Language Development

long

short

ACTIVITY Show students two connecting cube trains—one made with six blue cubes and the other made with four red cubes. Align the trains one above the other and ask: "Which train is long?" (blue) "How can you tell?" (Accept all reasonable responses.) Discuss with students the meaning of **long** and **short**. Show students a classroom object, such as a yardstick or board eraser, and invite them to find other objects that are short or long when compared to the given object.

WORKSHEET DIRECTIONS

1. Circle the long paintbrush.
2. Draw an X on the short pencil.

A194 Lesson 8-4

Math Triumphs

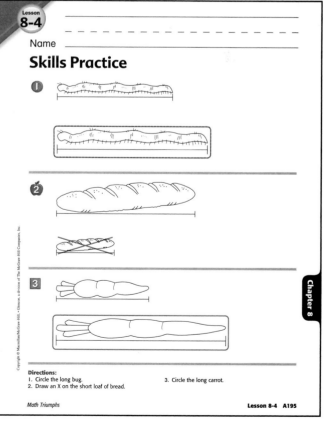

Lesson 8-4

Name

Skills Practice

Directions:

1. Circle the long bug.
2. Draw an X on the short loaf of bread.
3. Circle the long carrot.

Math Triumphs

Lesson 8-4 A195

Chapter 8

Math Triumphs

Lesson 8-3 and 8-4 A295

Answer Key (Lesson 8-4 and 8-5)

Lesson 8-4

Name _____

Practice at Home

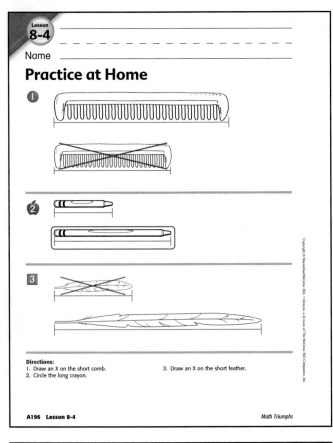

Directions:
1. Draw an X on the short comb.
2. Circle the long crayon.
3. Draw an X on the short feather.

Lesson 8-5

Name _____

Vocabulary and English Language Development

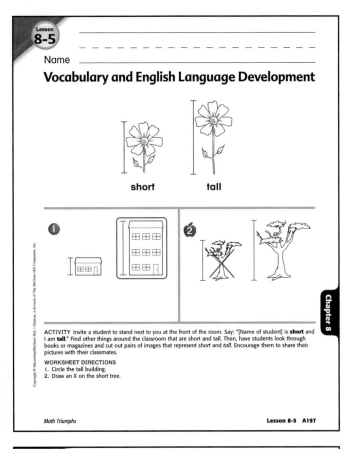

short   tall

ACTIVITY Invite a student to stand next to you at the front of the room. Say: "[Name of student] is **short** and I am **tall**." Find other things around the classroom that are short and tall. Then, have students look through books or magazines and cut out pairs of images that represent *short* and *tall*. Encourage them to share their pictures with their classmates.

WORKSHEET DIRECTIONS
1. Circle the tall building.
2. Draw an X on the short tree.

Lesson 8-5

Name _____

Skills Practice

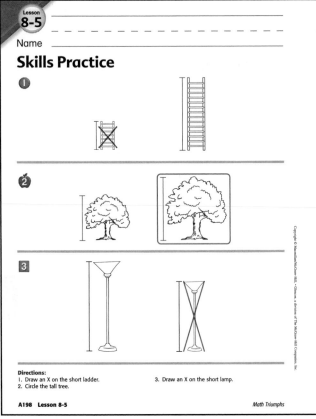

Directions:
1. Draw an X on the short ladder.
2. Circle the tall tree.
3. Draw an X on the short lamp.

Lesson 8-5

Name _____

Practice at Home

Directions:
1. Circle the tall flower.
2. Draw an X on the short flagpole.
3. Circle the tall giraffe.

Answer Key (Lesson 8-6 and 8-7)

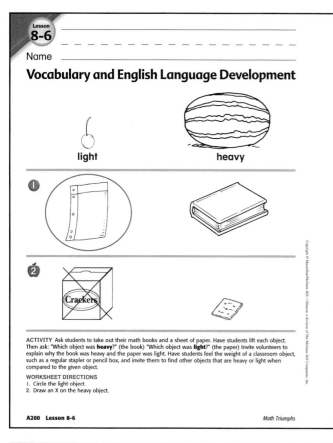

Lesson 8-6

Name

Vocabulary and English Language Development

light   heavy

❶

❷ Crackers

ACTIVITY Ask students to take out their math books and a sheet of paper. Have students lift each object. Then ask: "Which object was **heavy**?" (the book) "Which object was **light**?" (the paper) Invite volunteers to explain why the book was heavy and the paper was light. Have students feel the weight of a classroom object, such as a regular stapler or pencil box, and invite them to find other objects that are heavy or light when compared to the given object.

WORKSHEET DIRECTIONS
1. Circle the light object.
2. Draw an X on the heavy object.

A200   Lesson 8-6   Math Triumphs

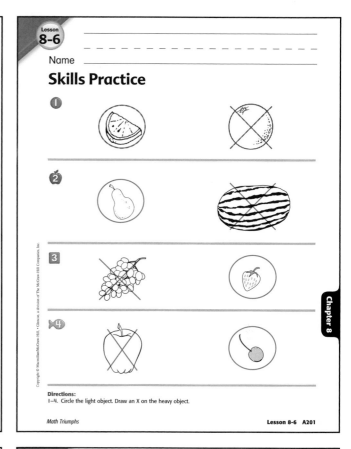

Lesson 8-6

Name

Skills Practice

❶

❷

❸

❹

Directions:
1–4. Circle the light object. Draw an X on the heavy object.

Math Triumphs   Lesson 8-6   A201

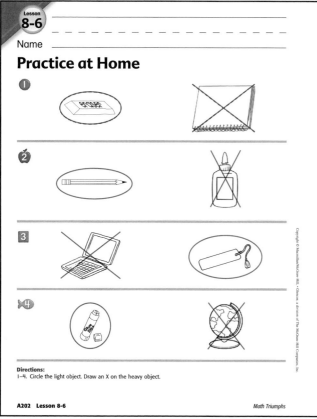

Lesson 8-6

Name

Practice at Home

❶ eraser

❷

❸

❹

Directions:
1–4. Circle the light object. Draw an X on the heavy object.

A202   Lesson 8-6   Math Triumphs

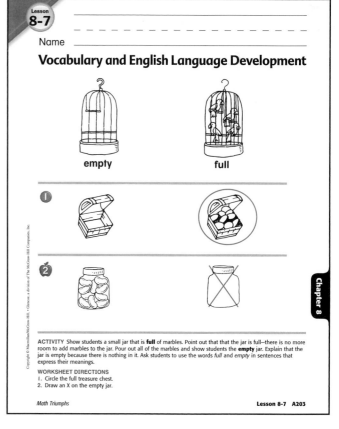

Lesson 8-7

Name

Vocabulary and English Language Development

empty   full

❶

❷

ACTIVITY Show students a small jar that is **full** of marbles. Point out that that the jar is full–there is no more room to add marbles to the jar. Pour out all of the marbles and show students the **empty** jar. Explain that the jar is empty because there is nothing in it. Ask students to use the words *full* and *empty* in sentences that express their meanings.

WORKSHEET DIRECTIONS
1. Circle the full treasure chest.
2. Draw an X on the empty jar.

Math Triumphs   Lesson 8-7   A203

Answer Key (Lesson 8-7 and 9-1)

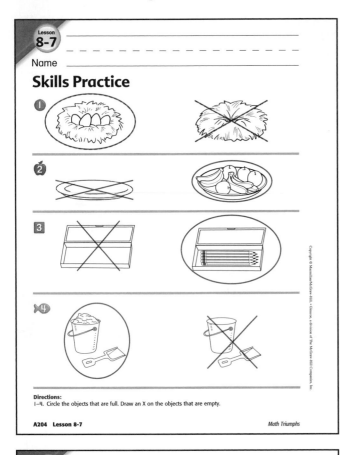

Directions:
1–4. Circle the objects that are full. Draw an X on the objects that are empty.

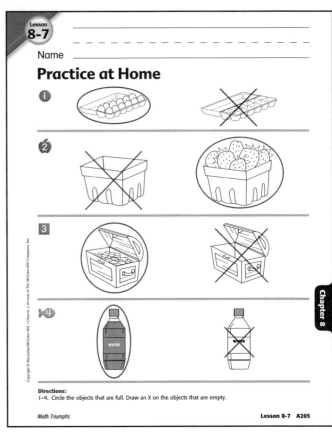

Directions:
1–4. Circle the objects that are full. Draw an X on the objects that are empty.

ACTIVITY Cut three strings of different lengths. Invite students to order the strings by increasing length, pointing to each string and saying: **"long, longer, longest."**

WORKSHEET DIRECTIONS
1–2. Draw a string that is longer.
  3. Draw a string that is the longest.

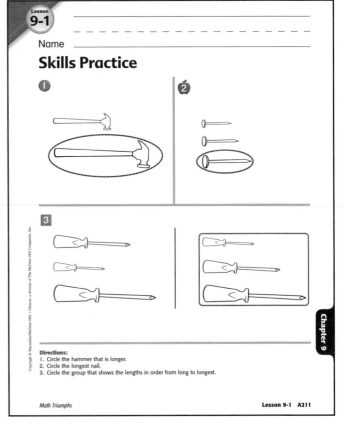

Directions:
1. Circle the hammer that is longer.
2. Circle the longest nail.
3. Circle the group that shows the lengths in order from long to longest.

Answer Key (Lesson 9-1 and 9-2)

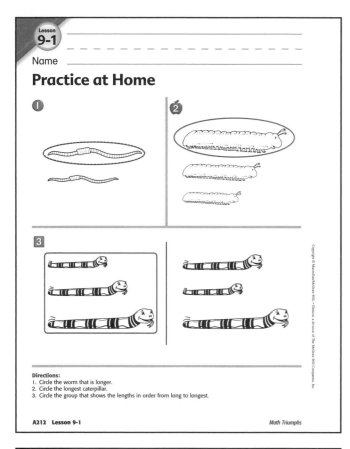

Lesson 9-1

Name _____

Practice at Home

Directions:
1. Circle the worm that is longer.
2. Circle the longest caterpillar.
3. Circle the group that shows the lengths in order from long to longest.

Math Triumphs

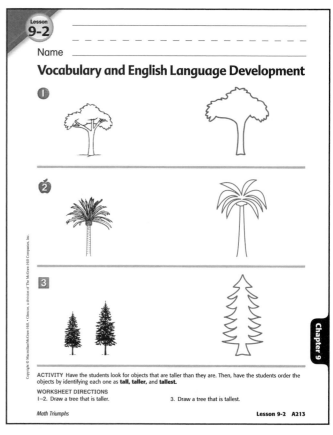

Lesson 9-2

Name _____

Vocabulary and English Language Development

ACTIVITY Have the students look for objects that are taller than they are. Then, have the students order the objects by identifying each one as **tall, taller,** and **tallest.**

WORKSHEET DIRECTIONS
1–2. Draw a tree that is taller.   3. Draw a tree that is tallest.

Math Triumphs

Chapter 9

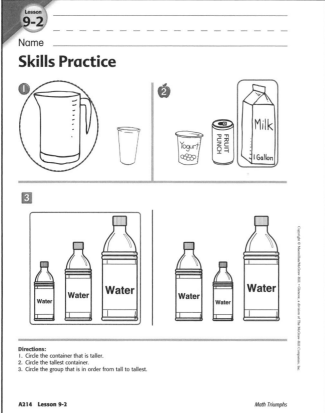

Lesson 9-2

Name _____

Skills Practice

Directions:
1. Circle the container that is taller.
2. Circle the tallest container.
3. Circle the group that is in order from tall to tallest.

Math Triumphs

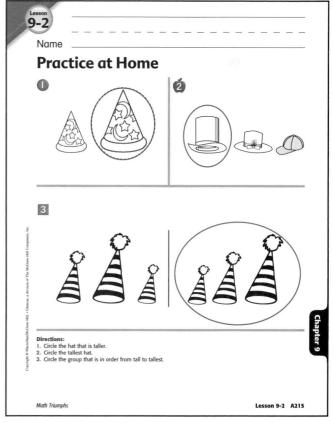

Lesson 9-2

Name _____

Practice at Home

Directions:
1. Circle the hat that is taller.
2. Circle the tallest hat.
3. Circle the group that is in order from tall to tallest.

Math Triumphs

Chapter 9

Answer Key (Lesson 9-3 and 9-4)

Lesson 9-3

Name

Vocabulary and English Language Development

ACTIVITY Gather magazine pictures of haircuts to demonstrate *short, shorter, shortest.* Show the students pictures of two haircuts. Ask: "Which is the shorter haircut?" Then add the third picture and ask: "Which is the shortest haircut?" Have the students point to each picture and say, **"short, shorter,** and **shortest."**

WORKSHEET DIRECTIONS Draw short hair on the first picture. Draw shorter hair on the second picture. Draw the shortest hair on the third picture.

A216 Lesson 9-3

Math Triumphs

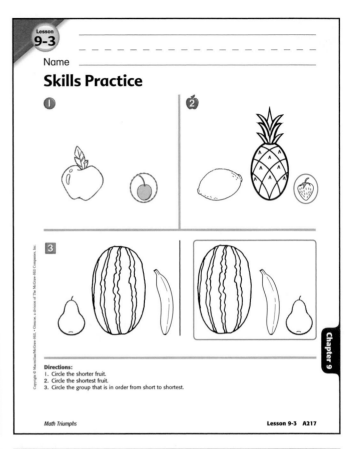

Lesson 9-3

Name

Skills Practice

Directions:
1. Circle the shorter fruit.
2. Circle the shortest fruit.
3. Circle the group that is in order from short to shortest.

Math Triumphs

Lesson 9-3 A217

Chapter 9

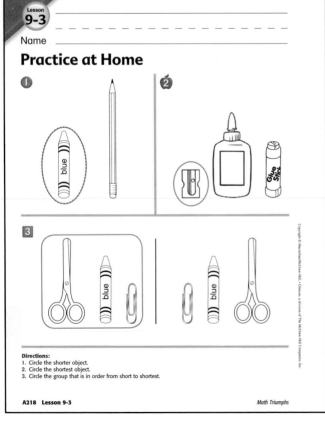

Lesson 9-3

Name

Practice at Home

Directions:
1. Circle the shorter object.
2. Circle the shortest object.
3. Circle the group that is in order from short to shortest.

A218 Lesson 9-3

Math Triumphs

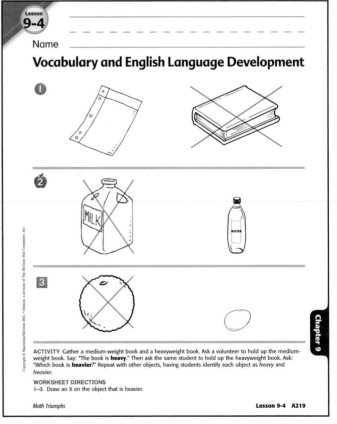

Lesson 9-4

Name

Vocabulary and English Language Development

ACTIVITY Gather a medium-weight book and a heavyweight book. Ask a volunteer to hold up the medium-weight book. Say: "The book is **heavy**." Then ask the same student to hold up the heavyweight book. Ask: "Which book is **heavier**?" Repeat with other objects, having students identify each object as *heavy* and *heavier.*

WORKSHEET DIRECTIONS
1–3. Draw an X on the object that is heavier.

Math Triumphs

Lesson 9-4 A219

Chapter 9

Answer Key (Lesson 9-4 and 9-5)

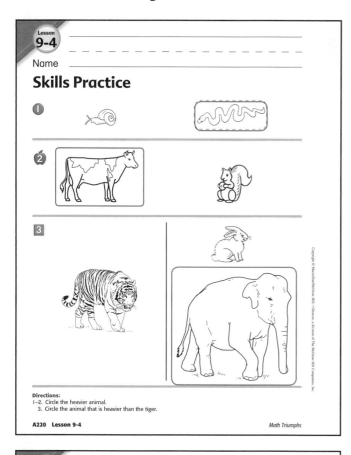

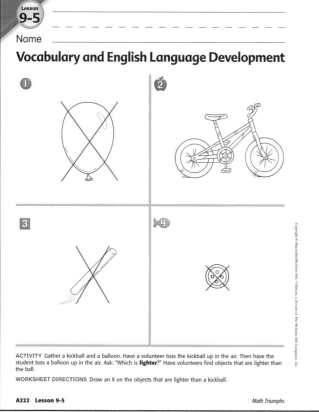

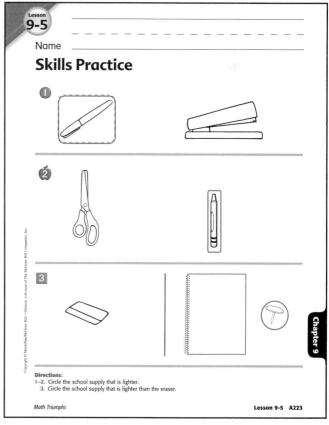

Answer Key (Lesson 9-5 and 9-6)

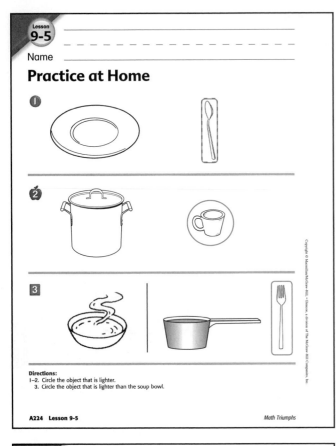

Lesson 9-5

Name

Practice at Home

Directions:
1–2. Circle the object that is lighter.
3. Circle the object that is lighter than the soup bowl.

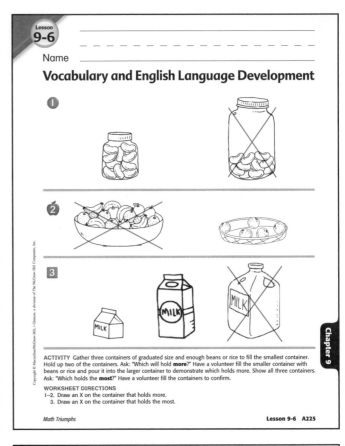

Lesson 9-6

Name

Vocabulary and English Language Development

ACTIVITY Gather three containers of graduated size and enough beans or rice to fill the smallest container. Hold up two of the containers. Ask: "Which will hold **more**?" Have a volunteer fill the smaller container with beans or rice and pour it into the larger container to demonstrate which holds more. Show all three containers. Ask: "Which holds the **most**?" Have a volunteer fill the containers to confirm.

WORKSHEET DIRECTIONS
1–2. Draw an X on the container that holds more.
3. Draw an X on the container that holds the most.

Chapter 9

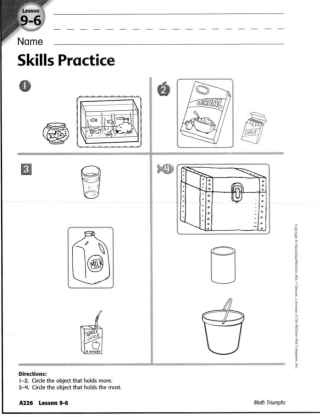

Lesson 9-6

Name

Skills Practice

Directions:
1–2. Circle the object that holds more.
3–4. Circle the object that holds the most.

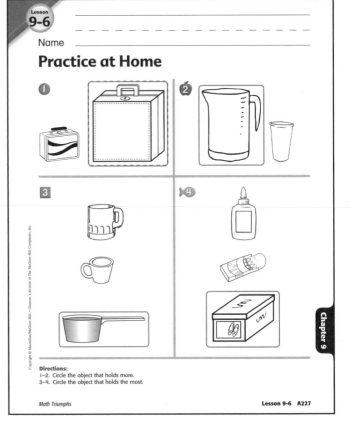

Lesson 9-6

Name

Practice at Home

Directions:
1–2. Circle the object that holds more.
3–4. Circle the object that holds the most.

Chapter 9

Answer Key (Lesson 9-7 and 10-1)

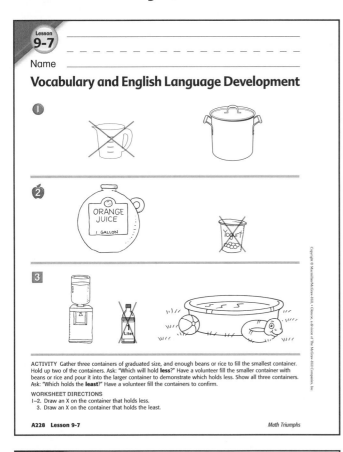

Lesson 9-7

Name

Vocabulary and English Language Development

ACTIVITY Gather three containers of graduated size, and enough beans or rice to fill the smallest container. Hold up two of the containers. Ask: "Which will hold **less**?" Have a volunteer fill the smaller container with beans or rice and pour it into the larger container to demonstrate which holds less. Show all three containers. Ask: "Which holds the **least**?" Have a volunteer fill the containers to confirm.

WORKSHEET DIRECTIONS
1–2. Draw an X on the container that holds less.
3. Draw an X on the container that holds the least.

A228 **Lesson 9-7** *Math Triumphs*

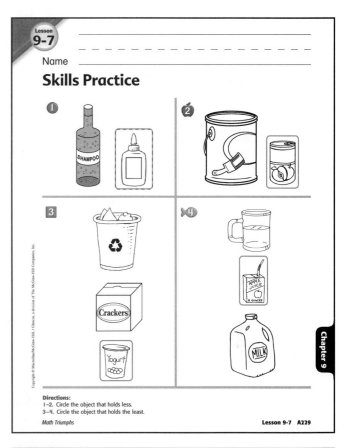

Lesson 9-7

Name

Skills Practice

Directions:
1–2. Circle the object that holds less.
3–4. Circle the object that holds the least.

Math Triumphs **Lesson 9-7 A229**

Chapter 9

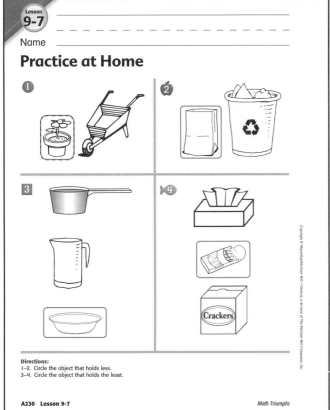

Lesson 9-7

Name

Practice at Home

Directions:
1–2. Circle the object that holds less.
3–4. Circle the object that holds the least.

A230 **Lesson 9-7** *Math Triumphs*

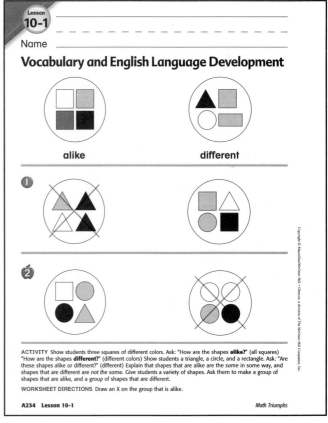

Lesson 10-1

Name

Vocabulary and English Language Development

alike   different

ACTIVITY Show students three squares of different colors. Ask: "How are the shapes **alike**?" (all squares) "How are the shapes **different**?" (different colors) Show students a triangle, a circle, and a rectangle. Ask: "Are these shapes alike or different?" (different) Explain that shapes that are alike are the *same* in some way, and shapes that are different are *not the same*. Give students a variety of shapes. Ask them to make a group of shapes that are alike, and a group of shapes that are different.

WORKSHEET DIRECTIONS Draw an X on the group that is alike.

A234 **Lesson 10-1** *Math Triumphs*

Math Triumphs   **Lesson 9-7 and 10-1   A303**

Answer Key (Lesson 10-1 and 10-2)

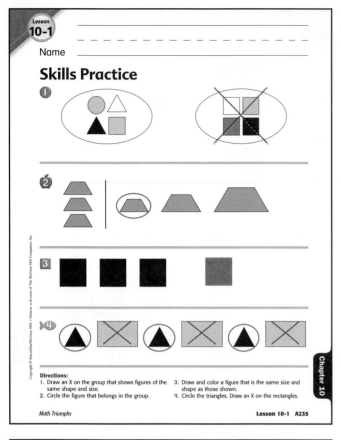

Lesson 10-1

Skills Practice

Directions:
1. Draw an X on the group that shows figures of the same shape and size.
2. Circle the figure that belongs in the group.
3. Draw and color a figure that is the same size and shape as those shown.
4. Circle the triangles. Draw an X on the rectangles.

Math Triumphs   **Lesson 10-1 A235**

Chapter 10

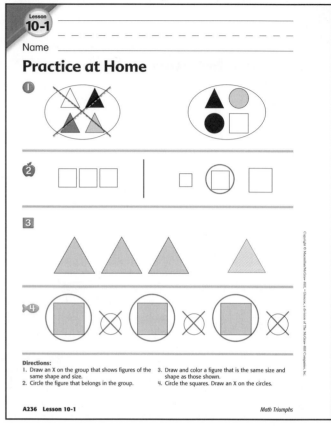

Lesson 10-1

Practice at Home

Directions:
1. Draw an X on the group that shows figures of the same shape and size.
2. Circle the figure that belongs in the group.
3. Draw and color a figure that is the same size and shape as those shown.
4. Circle the squares. Draw an X on the circles.

A236 Lesson 10-1   *Math Triumphs*

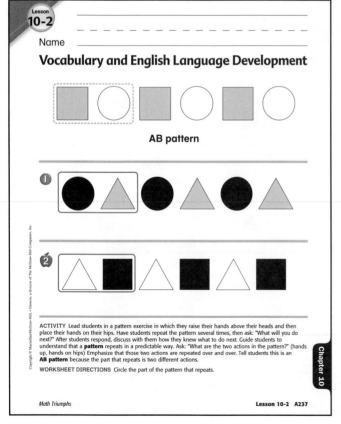

Lesson 10-2

Vocabulary and English Language Development

AB pattern

ACTIVITY Lead students in a pattern exercise in which they raise their hands above their heads and then place their hands on their hips. Have students repeat the pattern several times, then ask: "What will you do next?" After students respond, discuss with them how they knew what to do next. Guide students to understand that a **pattern** repeats in a predictable way. Ask: "What are the two actions in the pattern?" (hands up, hands on hips) Emphasize that those two actions are repeated over and over. Tell students this is an **AB pattern** because the part that repeats is two different actions.

WORKSHEET DIRECTIONS Circle the part of the pattern that repeats.

Math Triumphs   **Lesson 10-2 A237**

Chapter 10

Lesson 10-2

Skills Practice

Directions:
1. Circle the insect that comes next in the pattern.
2. Draw an X on the animal that does not belong.
3. Circle the butterfly that comes next in the pattern.
4. Draw and color the caterpillar that comes next.

A238 Lesson 10-2   *Math Triumphs*

Answer Key (Lesson 10-2 and 10-3)

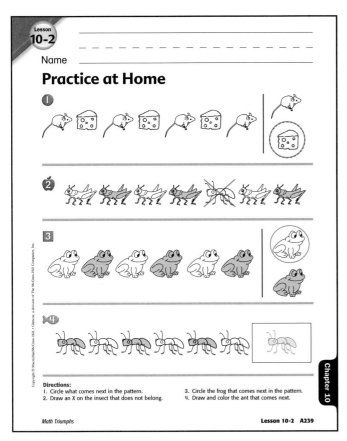

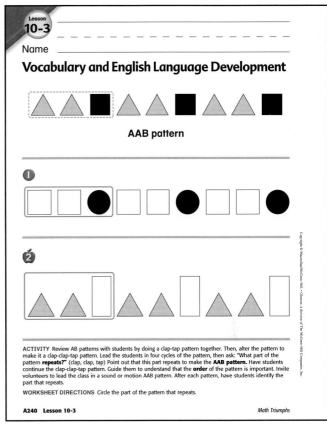

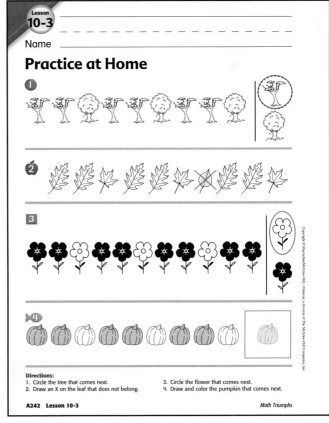

Answer Key (Lesson 10-4 and 10-5)

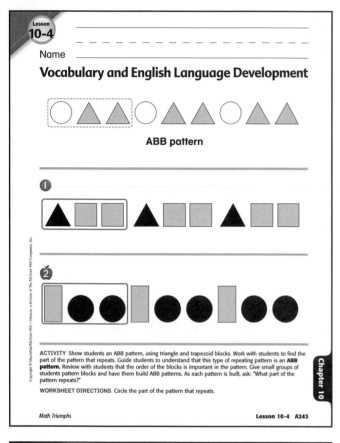

Name

Vocabulary and English Language Development

ABB pattern

ACTIVITY Show students an ABB pattern, using triangle and trapezoid blocks. Work with students to find the part of the pattern that repeats. Guide students to understand that this type of repeating pattern is an **ABB pattern.** Review with students that the order of the blocks is important in the pattern. Give small groups of students pattern blocks and have them build ABB patterns. As each pattern is built, ask: "What part of the pattern repeats?"

WORKSHEET DIRECTIONS Circle the part of the pattern that repeats.

Math Triumphs   **Lesson 10-4   A243**

Name

Skills Practice

Directions:
1. Circle the object that comes next.
2. Draw an X on the drink that does not belong.
3. Circle the object that comes next.
4. Draw the object that comes next.

A244   Lesson 10-4   *Math Triumphs*

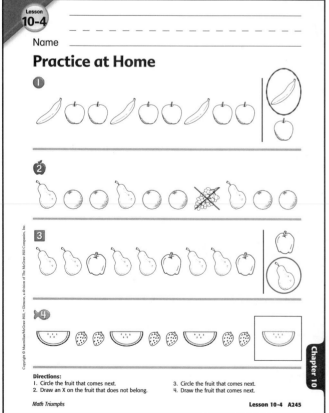

Name

Practice at Home

Directions:
1. Circle the fruit that comes next.
2. Draw an X on the fruit that does not belong.
3. Circle the fruit that comes next.
4. Draw the fruit that comes next.

Math Triumphs   **Lesson 10-4   A245**

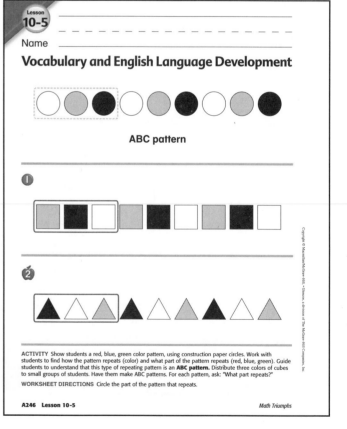

Name

Vocabulary and English Language Development

ABC pattern

ACTIVITY Show students a red, blue, green color pattern, using construction paper circles. Work with students to find how the pattern repeats (color) and what part of the pattern repeats (red, blue, green). Guide students to understand that this type of repeating pattern is an **ABC pattern.** Distribute three colors of cubes to small groups of students. Have them make ABC patterns. For each pattern, ask: "What part repeats?"

WORKSHEET DIRECTIONS Circle the part of the pattern that repeats.

A246   Lesson 10-5   *Math Triumphs*

Answer Key (Lesson 10-5 and 10-6)

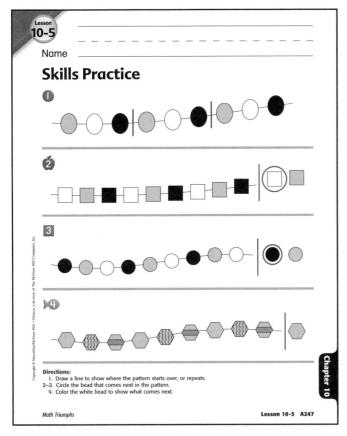

Lesson 10-5

Name

Skills Practice

Directions:
1. Draw a line to show where the pattern starts over, or repeats.
2–3. Circle the bead that comes next in the pattern.
4. Color the white bead to show what comes next.

Math Triumphs **Lesson 10-5   A247**

Chapter 10

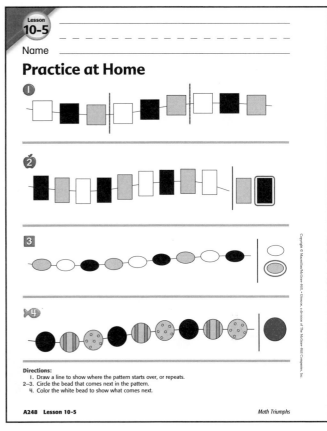

Lesson 10-5

Name

Practice at Home

Directions:
1. Draw a line to show where the pattern starts over, or repeats.
2–3. Circle the bead that comes next in the pattern.
4. Color the white bead to show what comes next.

A248   Lesson 10-5   *Math Triumphs*

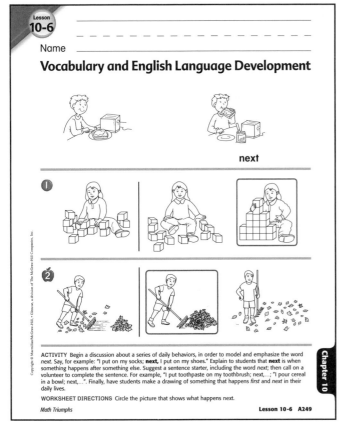

Lesson 10-6

Name

Vocabulary and English Language Development

next

ACTIVITY Begin a discussion about a series of daily behaviors, in order to model and emphasize the word *next*. Say, for example: "I put on my socks; **next,** I put on my shoes." Explain to students that **next** is when something happens after something else. Suggest a sentence starter, including the word *next*; then call on a volunteer to complete the sentence. For example, "I put toothpaste on my toothbrush; next,…; "I pour cereal in a bowl; next,…". Finally, have students make a drawing of something that happens *first* and *next* in their daily lives.

WORKSHEET DIRECTIONS Circle the picture that shows what happens next.

Math Triumphs **Lesson 10-6   A249**

Chapter 10

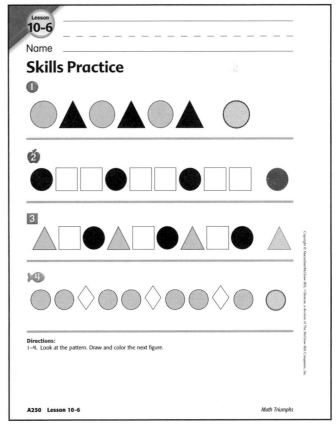

Lesson 10-6

Name

Skills Practice

Directions:
1–4. Look at the pattern. Draw and color the next figure.

A250   Lesson 10-6   *Math Triumphs*

Answer Key (Lesson 10-6 and 10-7)

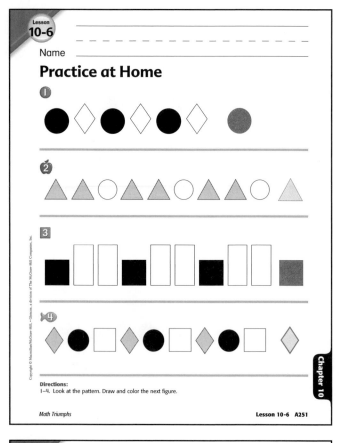

Name

Practice at Home

Directions:
1–4. Look at the pattern. Draw and color the next figure.

Math Triumphs — Lesson 10-6   A251

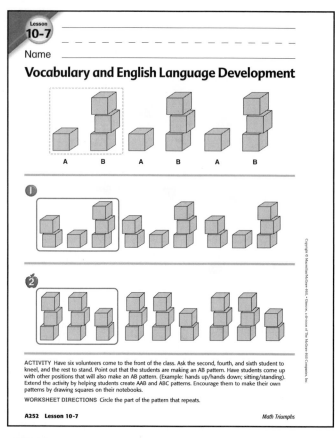

Lesson 10-7

Name

Vocabulary and English Language Development

A   B   A   B   A   B

ACTIVITY Have six volunteers come to the front of the class. Ask the second, fourth, and sixth student to kneel, and the rest to stand. Point out that the students are making an AB pattern. Have students come up with other positions that will also make an AB pattern. (Example: hands up/hands down; sitting/standing). Extend the activity by helping students create AAB and ABC patterns. Encourage them to make their own patterns by drawing squares on their notebooks.

WORKSHEET DIRECTIONS Circle the part of the pattern that repeats.

A252   Lesson 10-7   *Math Triumphs*

Lesson 10-7

Name

Skills Practice

1 Sample answer:

| P | Q | P | Q | P | Q | P | Q |

2 Sample answer:

| 1 | 2 | 2 | 1 | 2 | 2 | 1 | 2 | 2 |

3 Sample answer:

| △ | □ | ○ | △ | □ | ○ | △ | □ | ○ |

4 Sample answer:

| Z | 4 | △ | Z | 4 | △ | Z | 4 | △ |

Directions:
1. Use the letters P and Q to make a pattern.
2. Choose two numbers. Make an ABB pattern.
3. Choose three figures. Make an ABC pattern.
4. Choose a letter, a number, and a figure. Draw a pattern in the boxes. Use one letter, number, or figure in each box.

Math Triumphs — Lesson 10-7   A253

Lesson 10-7

Name

Skills Practice

1 Sample answer:

| D | E | D | E | D | E | D | E |

2 Sample answer:

| 3 | 4 | 4 | 3 | 4 | 4 | 3 | 4 | 4 |

3 Sample answer:

| ◇ | ○ | △ | ◇ | ○ | △ | ◇ | ○ | △ |

4 Sample answer:

| M | I | □ | M | I | □ | M | I | □ |

Directions:
1. Use the letters D and E to make a pattern.
2. Choose two numbers. Make an ABB pattern.
3. Choose three figures. Make an ABC pattern.
4. Choose a letter, a number, and a figure. Draw a pattern in the boxes. Use one letter, number, or figure in each box.

A254   Lesson 10-7   *Math Triumphs*